JOURNEYS THROUGH BOOKLAND

Lucille Richmond Lambourn
1913

The Retreat of Cortes

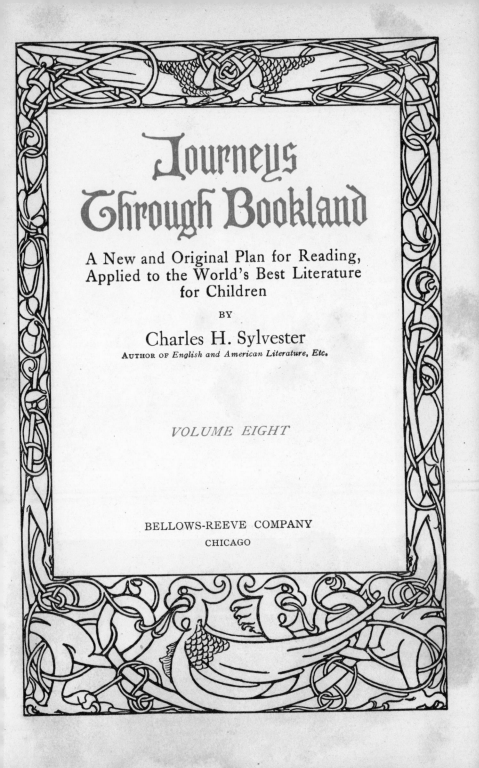

Journeys Through Bookland

A New and Original Plan for Reading, Applied to the World's Best Literature for Children

BY

Charles H. Sylvester

AUTHOR OF *English and American Literature, Etc.*

VOLUME EIGHT

BELLOWS-REEVE COMPANY

CHICAGO

CONTENTS

For classification of selections, see the index at the end of Volume X.

ILLUSTRATIONS

Title-page and halftone decorations by Mrs. Thomas Wood Stevens. Initial letters, tailpieces and other decorations by Mrs. Thomas Wood Stevens, Frederick Grant and Miss Edith Virden.

THE FORSAKEN MERMAN

MATTHEW ARNOLD

COME, dear children, let us away;
Down and away below!
Now my brothers call from the
bay,
Now the great winds shoreward
blow,
Now the salt tides seaward flow;
Now the wild white horses play,
Champ and chafe and toss in the spray.
Children dear, let us away!
This way, this way!

Call her once before you go—
Call once yet!
In a voice that she will know
"Margaret! Margaret!"
Children's voices should be dear
(Call once more) to a mother's ear;
Children's voices, wild with pain—
Surely she will come again!
Call her once and come away;
This way, this way!
"Mother dear, we cannot stay!
The wild white horses foam and fret."
Margaret! Margaret!

Come, dear children, come away down;
Call no more!
One last look at the white-wall'd town,

And the little gray church on the windy shore;
Then come down!
She will not come though you call all day;
Come away, come away!

Children dear, was it yesterday
We heard the sweet bells over the bay?
In the caverns where we lay,
Through the surf and through the swell,
The far-off sound of a silver bell?
Sand-strewn caverns, cool and deep,
Where the winds are all asleep;
Where the spent lights quiver and gleam,
Where the salt weed sways in the stream,
Where the sea beasts, ranged all round,
Feed in the ooze of their pasture ground;
Where the sea snakes coil and twine,
Dry their mail and bask in the brine;
Where great whales come sailing by,
Sail and sail, with unshut eye,
Round the world for ever and aye?
When did music come this way?
Children dear, was it yesterday?

Children dear, was it yesterday
(Call yet once) that she went away?
Once she sate with you and me,
On a red gold throne in the heart of the sea,
And the youngest sate on her knee.
She comb'd its bright hair, and she tended it well,
When down swung the sound of a far-off bell.
She sigh'd, she look'd up through the clear green
      sea;

She said: "I must go, for my kinsfolk pray
In the little gray church on the shore to-day.
'Twill be Easter-time in the world—ah me!
And I lose my poor soul, Merman! here with
    thee."
I said: "Go up, dear heart, through the waves;
Say thy prayer, and come back to the kind sea
    caves!"
She smil'd, she went up through the surf in the
    bay.
Children dear, was it yesterday?

Children dear, were we long alone?
"The sea grows stormy, the little ones moan;
Long prayers," I said, "in the world they say;
Come!" I said; and we rose through the surf in
    the bay.
We went up the beach, by the sandy down
Where the sea stocks bloom, to the white-wall'd
    town;
Through the narrow, pav'd streets, where all
    was still,
To the little gray church on the windy hill.
From the church came a murmur of folk at their
    prayers,
But we stood without in the cold blowing airs.
We climb'd on the graves, on the stones worn
    with rains,
And we gaz'd up the aisle through the small
    leaded panes.
She sate by the pillar; we saw her clear;
"Margaret, hist! come quick, we are here!
Dear heart," I said, "we are long alone;

THE LITTLE GRAY CHURCH ON THE WINDY HILL

The sea grows stormy, the little ones moan."
But, ah, she gave me never a look,
For her eyes were seal'd to the holy book!
Loud prays the priest: shut stands the door.
Come away, children, call no more!
Come away, come down, call no more!

Down, down, down!
Down to the depths of the sea!
She sits at her wheel in the humming town,
Singing most joyfully.
Hark what she sings: "O joy, O joy,
For the humming street, and the child with its
    toy!
For the priest, and the bell, and the holy well;
For the wheel where I spun,
And the blessed light of the sun!"
And so she sings her fill,
Singing most joyfully,
Till the spindle drops from her hand,
And the whizzing wheel stands still.
She steals to the window, and looks at the sand,
And over the sand at the sea;
And her eyes are set in a stare;
And anon there breaks a sigh,
And anon there drops a tear,
From a sorrow-clouded eye,
And a heart sorrow-laden,
A long, long sigh,
For the cold, strange eyes of a little Mermaiden
And the gleam of her golden hair.

    Come away, away, children;
    Come, children, come down!
    The hoarse wind blows colder;
    Lights shine in the town.
    She will start from her slumber
    When gusts shake the door;
    She will hear the winds howling,
    Will hear the waves roar.

We shall see, while above us
The waves roar and whirl,
A ceiling of amber,
A pavement of pearl.
Singing: "Here came a mortal,
But faithless was she!
And alone dwell for ever
The kings of the sea."

But, children, at midnight,
When soft the winds blow,
When clear falls the moonlight,
When spring-tides are low;
When sweet airs come seaward
From heaths starr'd with broom,
And high rocks throw mildly
On the blanch'd sands a gloom;
Up the still, glistening beaches,
Up the creeks we will hie,
Over banks of bright seaweed
The ebb-tide leaves dry.
We will gaze, from the sand hills,
At the white, sleeping town;
At the church on the hillside—
And then come back down.
Singing: "There dwells a lov'd one,
But cruel is she!
She left lonely forever
The kings of the sea."

TOM AND MAGGIE TULLIVER

NOTE,—This account of Tom and Maggie Tulliver is taken from the early chapters of George Eliot's *The Mill on the Floss.* The book follows the fortunes of Tom and Maggie, whom at the opening of the story we find living with their parents at the old mill house on the Floss River, until they meet their death, in their early manhood and womanhood. We give here, however, only a part of the story of their childhood.

I

IT was a heavy disappointment to Maggie that she was not allowed to go with her father in the gig when he went to fetch Tom home from the academy; but the morning was too wet, Mrs. Tulliver said, for a little girl to go out in her best bonnet. Maggie took the opposite view very strongly, and it was a direct consequence of this difference of opinion that when her mother was in the act of brushing out the reluctant black crop Maggie suddenly rushed from under her hands and dipped her head in a basin of water standing near, in the vindictive determination that there should be no more chance of curls that day.

"Maggie, Maggie!" exclaimed Mrs. Tulliver,

sitting stout and helpless with the brushes on her lap, "what is to become of you if you're so naughty? I'll tell your aunt Glegg and your aunt Pullet when they come next week, and they'll never love you any more. Oh dear, oh dear! look at your clean pinafore, wet from top to bottom. Folks 'ull think it's a judgment on me as I've got such a child,—they'll think I've done summat wicked."

Before this remonstrance was finished, Maggie was already out of hearing, making her way toward the great attic that run under the old high-pitched roof, shaking the water from her black locks as she ran, like a Skye terrier escaped from his bath. This attic was Maggie's favorite retreat on a wet day, when the weather was not too cold; here she fretted out all her ill humors, and talked aloud to the worm-eaten floors and the worm-eaten shelves, and the dark rafters festooned with cobwebs; and here she kept a Fetish which she punished for all her misfortunes. This was the trunk of a large wooden doll, which once stared with the roundest of eyes above the reddest of cheeks; but was now entirely defaced by a long career of vicarious suffering. Three nails driven into the head commemorated as many crises in Maggie's nine years of earthly struggle; that luxury of vengeance having been suggested to her by the picture of Jael destroying Sisera in the old Bible. The last nail had been driven in with a fiercer stroke than usual, for the Fetish on that occasion represented aunt Glegg. But immediately afterward Maggie had reflected

that if she drove many nails in she would not be
so well able to fancy that the head was hurt when
she knocked it against the wall, nor to comfort
it, and make believe to poultice it, when her fury
was abated; for even aunt Glegg would be pitiable when she had been hurt very much, and
thoroughly humiliated, so as to beg her niece's
pardon. Since then she had driven no more
nails in, but had soothed herself by alternately
grinding and beating the wooden head against
the rough brick of the great chimneys that made
two square pillars supporting the roof. That
was what she did this morning on reaching the
attic, sobbing all the while with a passion that
expelled every other form of consciousness,—
even the memory of the grievance that had
caused it.

As at last the sobs were getting quieter, and
the grinding less fierce, a sudden beam of sunshine, falling through the wire lattice across the
worm-eaten shelves, made her throw away the
Fetish and run to the window. The sun was
really breaking out; the sound of the mill seemed
cheerful again; the granary doors were open; and
there was Yap, the queer white-and-brown
terrier, with one ear turned back, trotting about
and sniffing vaguely, as if he were in search of a
companion. It was irresistible. Maggie tossed
her hair back and ran downstairs, seized her
bonnet without putting it on, peeped, and then
dashed along the passage lest she should encounter her mother, and was quickly out in the yard,
whirling around like a Pythoness, and singing as

"TOM'S COMING HOME!"

she whirled, "Yap, Yap, Tom's coming home!"
while Yap danced and barked round her, as
much as to say, if there was any noise wanted
he was the dog for it.

"Hegh, hegh, Miss! you'll make yourself
giddy, an' tumble down i' the dirt," said Luke,

the head miller, a tall, broad-shouldered man of forty, black-eyed and black-haired, subdued by a general mealiness, like an auricula.

Maggie paused in her whirling and said, staggering a little, "Oh no, it doesn't make me giddy, Luke; may I go into the mill with you?"

Maggie loved to linger in the great spaces of the mill, and often came out with her black hair powdered to a soft whiteness that made her dark eyes flash out with new fire. The resolute din, the unresting motion of the great stones, giving her a dim, delicious awe as at the presence of an uncontrollable force; the meal forever pouring, pouring; the fine white powder softening all surfaces, and making the very spider-nets look like a faery lace-work; the sweet, pure scent of the meal,—all helped to make Maggie feel that the mill was a little world apart from her outside everyday life. She was in the habit of taking this recreation as she conversed with Luke, to whom she was very communicative, wishing him to think well of her understanding, as her father did.

Perhaps she felt it necessary to recover her position with him on the present occasion, for, as she sat sliding on the heap of grain near which he was busying himself, she said, at that shrill pitch which was requisite in mill-society,—

"I think you never read any book but the Bible, did you, Luke?"

"Nay, Miss, an' not much o' that," said Luke, with great frankness. "I'm no reader, I aren't."

"But if I lent you one of my books, Luke?

I've not got any *very* pretty books that would be
easy for you to read; but there's 'Pug's Tour of
Europe,'—that would tell you all about the different sorts of people in the world, and if you didn't
understand the reading, the pictures would help
you; they show the looks and ways of the people
and what they do. There are the Dutchmen,
very fat, and smoking, you know, and one sitting
on a barrel."

"Nay, Miss, I'n no opinion o' Dutchmen. There ben't much good i' knowin' about
them."

"But they're our fellow-creatures, Luke; we
ought to know about our fellow-creatures."

"Not much o' fellow-creatures, I think, Miss;
all I know—my old master, as war a knowin'
man, used to say, says he, 'If e'er I sow my wheat
wi'out brinin', I'm a Dutchman,' says he; an'
that war as much as to say as a Dutchman war
a fool, or next door. Nay, nay, I aren't goin' to
bother mysen about Dutchmen. There's fools
enoo, an' rogues enoo, wi'out lookin' i' books
for 'em."

"Oh, well," said Maggie, rather foiled by
Luke's unexpectedly decided views about Dutchmen, "perhaps you would like 'Animated
Nature' better; that's not Dutchmen, you know,
but elephants and kangaroos, and the civet cat,
and the sunfish, and a bird sitting on its tail,—
I forget its name. There are countries full of
those creatures, instead of horses and cows, you
know. Shouldn't you like to know about them,
Luke?"

"Nay, Miss, I'n got to keep count o' the flour an' corn; I can't do wi' knowin' so many things beside my work. That's what brings folks to the gallows,—knowin' everything but what they'n got to get their bread by. An' they're mostly lies, I think, what's printed i' the books: them printed sheets are, anyhow, as the men cry i' the streets."

"Why, you're like my brother Tom, Luke," said Maggie, wishing to turn the conversation agreeably; "Tom's not fond of reading. I love Tom so dearly, Luke,—better than anybody else in the world. When he grows up I shall keep his house, and we shall always live together. I can tell him everything he doesn't know. But I think Tom's clever, for all he doesn't like books; he makes beautiful whipcord and rabbit pens."

"Ah," said Luke, "but he'll be fine an' vexed, as the rabbits are all dead."

"Dead!" screamed Maggie, jumping up from her sliding seat on the corn. "Oh dear, Luke! What! the lop-eared one, and the spotted doe that Tom spent all his money to buy?"

"As dead as moles," said Luke, fetching his comparison from the unmistakable corpses nailed to the stable wall.

"Oh, Luke," said Maggie in a piteous tone, "Tom told me to be sure and remember the rabbits every day; but how could I, when they didn't come into my head, you know? Oh, he will be so angry with me, I know he will, and so sorry about his rabbits, and so am I sorry. Oh, what *shall* I do?"

"Don't you fret, Miss," said Luke, soothingly; "they're nash things, them lop-eared
rabbits; they'd happen ha' died, if they'd been
fed. Things out o' natur niver thrive: God
A'mighty doesn't like 'em. He made the rabbits' ears to lie back, an' it's nothin' but con-
trairiness to make 'em hing down like a mastiff
dog's. Master Tom 'ull know better nor buy
such things another time. Don't you fret, Miss.
Will you come along home wi' me, and see my
wife? I'm a-goin' this minute."

The invitation offered an agreeable distraction
to Maggie's grief, and her tears gradually subsided as she trotted along by Luke's side to his
pleasant cottage, which stood with its apple and
pear trees, and with the added dignity of a lean-
to pigsty, at the other end of the Mill fields.

II

TOM was to arrive early in the
afternoon, and there was another
fluttering heart besides Maggie's
when it was late enough for the
sound of the gig wheels to be expected; for if Mrs. Tulliver had a
strong feeling, it was fondness
for her boy. At last the sound came,—that
quick light bowling of the gig wheels,—and in
spite of the wind, which was blowing the clouds
about, and was not likely to respect Mrs. Tulliver's curls and cap-strings, she came outside
the door and even held her hand on Maggie's

offending head, forgetting all the griefs of the
morning.

"There he is, my sweet lad! But, Lord ha'
mercy! he's got never a collar on; it's been lost
on the road, I'll be bound, and spoilt the set."

Mrs. Tulliver stood with her arms open;
Maggie jumped first on one leg and then on the
other; while Tom descended from the gig, and
said, with masculine reticence as to the tender
emotions, "Hallo! Yap—what! are you there?"

Nevertheless he submitted to be kissed willingly enough, though Maggie hung on his neck
in rather a strangling fashion, while his blue-
gray eyes wandered toward the croft and the
lambs and the river, where he promised himself
that he would begin to fish the first thing to-
morrow morning. He was one of those lads
that grow everywhere in England, and at twelve
or thirteen years of age look as much alike as
goslings,—a lad with light-brown hair, cheeks
of cream and roses, full lips, indeterminate nose
and eyebrows,—face in which it seems impossible
to see anything but boyhood; as different as
possible from poor Maggie's phiz, which Nature
seemed to have moulded and colored with the
most decided intention. But that same Nature
has the deep cunning which hides itself under
the appearance of openness, so that simple people
think they can see through her quite well, and
all the while she is secretly preparing a refutation
of their confident prophecies. Under these
average boyish physiognomies that she seems
to turn off by the gross, she conceals some of her

most rigid, inflexible purposes, some of her most
unmodified characters; and the dark-eyed, de-
monstrative, rebellious girl may after all turn out
to be a passive being compared with this pink-
and-white bit of masculinity with the indeterminate features.

"Maggie," said Tom, confidentially, taking
her into a corner, as soon as his mother was gone
out to examine his box, and the warm parlor had
taken off the chill he had felt from the long drive,
"you don't know what I've got in *my* pockets,"
nodding his head up and down as a means of
rousing her sense of mystery.

"No," said Maggie. "How stodgy they look,
Tom! Is it marls (marbles) or cobnuts?"
Maggie's heart sank a little, because Tom always
said it was "no good" playing with *her* at those
games, she played so badly.

"Marls! no; I've swopped all my marls with
the little fellows, and cobnuts are no fun, you
silly, only when the nuts are green. But see
here!" He drew something half out of his right-
hand pocket.

"What is it?" said Maggie, in a whisper.
"I can see nothing but a bit of yellow."

"Why, it's—a—new—guess, Maggie!"

"Oh, I *can't* guess, Tom," said Maggie, im-
patiently.

"Don't be a spitfire, else I won't tell you,"
said Tom, thrusting his hand back into his
pocket and looking determined.

"No, Tom," said Maggie, imploringly, laying
hold of the arm that was held stiffly in the pocket.

"I'm not cross, Tom; it was only because I can't bear guessing. *Please* be good to me."

Tom's arm slowly relaxed, and he said, "Well, then, it's a new fish line—two new uns,—one for you, Maggie, all to yourself. And here's hooks; see here—I say, *won't* we go and fish to-morrow down by the Round Pool? And you shall catch your own fish, Maggie, and put the worms on, and everything; won't it be fun?"

Maggie's answer was to throw her arms round Tom's neck and hug him, and hold her cheek against his without speaking, while he slowly unwound some of the line, saying, after a pause,—

"Wasn't I a good brother, now, to buy you a line all to yourself? You know, I needn't have bought it, if I hadn't liked."

"Yes, very, very good—I *do* love you, Tom." Tom had put the line back in his pocket, and was looking at the hooks one by one, before he spoke again.

"And the fellows fought me, because I wouldn't give in about the toffee."

"Oh, dear! I wish they wouldn't fight at your school, Tom. Didn't it hurt you?"

"Hurt me? no," said Tom, putting up the hooks again, taking out a large pocketknife, and slowly opening the largest blade, which he looked at meditatively as he rubbed his finger along it. Then he added,—

"I gave Spouncer a black eye, I know; that's what he got by wanting to leather *me;* I wasn't going to go halves because anybody leathered me."

"Oh, how brave you are, Tom! I think you're like Samson. If there came a lion roaring at me, I think you'd fight him, wouldn't you, Tom?"

"How can a lion come roaring at you, you silly thing? There's no lions, only in the shows."

"No, but if we were in the lion countries—I mean in Africa, where it's very hot; the lions eat people there. I can show it you in the book where I read it."

"Well, I should get a gun and shoot him."

"But if you hadn't got a gun,—we might have gone out, you know, not thinking, just as we go fishing; and then a great lion might run toward us roaring, and we couldn't get away from him. What should you do, Tom?"

Tom paused, and at last turned away contemptuously, saying, "But the lion *isn't* coming. What's the use of talking?"

"But I like to fancy how it would be," said Maggie, following him. "Just think what you would do, Tom."

"Oh, don't bother, Maggie! you're such a silly. I shall go and see my rabbits."

Maggie's heart began to flutter with fear. She dared not tell the sad truth at once, but she walked after Tom in trembling silence as he went out, thinking how she could tell him the news so as to soften at once his sorrow and his anger; for Maggie dreaded Tom's anger of all things; it was quite different anger from her own.

"Tom," she said, timidly, when they were out

of doors, "how much money did you give for
your rabbits?"

"Two half-crowns and a sixpence," said Tom,
promptly.

"I think I've got a great deal more than that
in my steel purse upstairs. I'll ask mother to
give it you."

"What for?" said Tom. "I don't want *your*
money, you silly thing. I've got a great deal
more money than you, because I'm a boy. I
always have half-sovereigns and sovereigns for
my Christmas boxes because I shall be a man,
and you have only five-shilling pieces, because
you're only a girl."

"Well, but, Tom—if mother would let me
give you two half-crowns and a sixpence out of
my purse to put into your pocket and spend, you
know, and buy some more rabbits with it?"

"More rabbits? I don't want any more."

"Oh, but, Tom, they're all dead."

Tom stopped immediately in his walk and
turned round toward Maggie. "You forgot to
feed 'em, then?" he said, his color heightening
for a moment, but soon subsiding. I don't love
you, Maggie. You shan't go fishing with me
to-morrow. I told you to go and see the rabbits
every day." He walked on again.

"Yes, but I forgot—and I couldn't help it,
indeed, Tom. I'm so very sorry," said Maggie,
while the tears rushed fast.

"You're a naughty girl," said Tom, severely,
"and I'm sorry I bought you the fish line. I
don't love you."

"Oh, Tom, it's very cruel," sobbed Maggie. "I'd forgive you, if *you* forgot anything—I wouldn't mind what you did—I'd forgive you and love you."

"Yes, you're a silly; but I never *do* forget things, *I* don't."

"Oh, please forgive me, Tom; my heart will break," said Maggie, shaking with sobs, clinging to Tom's arm, and laying her wet cheek on his shoulder.

Tom shook her off, and stopped again, saying in a peremptory tone, "Now, Maggie, you just listen. Aren't I a good brother to you?"

"Ye-ye-es," sobbed Maggie, her chin rising and falling convulsedly.

"Didn't I think about your fish line all this quarter, and mean to buy it, and saved my money o' purpose, and wouldn't go halves in the toffee, and Spouncer fought me because I wouldn't?"

"Ye-ye-es—and I—lo-lo-love you so, Tom."

"But you're a naughty girl. Last holidays you licked the paint off my lozenge box, and the holidays before that you let the boat drag my fish line down when I'd set you to watch it, and you pushed your head through my kite, all for nothing."

"But I didn't mean," said Maggie; "I couldn't help it."

"Yes, you could," said Tom, "if you'd minded what you were doing. And you're a naughty girl, and you sha'n't go fishing with me to-morrow."

With this terrible conclusion, Tom ran away
from Maggie toward the mill. Maggie stood
motionless, except from her sobs, for a minute
or two; then she turned round and ran into the
house, and up to her attic, where she sat on the
floor and laid her head against the worm-eaten
shelf, with a crushing sense of misery. Tom
was come home, and she had thought how happy
she should be; and now he was cruel to her.
What use was anything if Tom didn't love her?
Oh, he was very cruel! Hadn't she wanted to
give him the money, and said how very sorry she
was? She knew she was naughty to her mother,
but she had never been naughty to Tom—had
never *meant* to be naughty to him.

"Oh, he is cruel!" Maggie sobbed aloud,
finding a wretched pleasure in the hollow
resonance that came through the long empty
space of the attic. She never thought of beating
or grinding her Fetish; she was too miserable to
be angry.

These bitter sorrows of childhood! when
sorrow is all new and strange, when hope has
not yet got wings to fly beyond the days and
weeks, and the space from summer to summer
seems measureless.

Maggie soon thought she had been hours in
the attic, and it must be tea time, and they were
all having their tea, and not thinking of her.
Well, then, she would stay up there and starve
herself,—hide herself behind the tub, and stay
there all night,—and then they would all be
frightened, and Tom would be sorry. Thus

Maggie thought in the pride of her heart, as she crept behind the tub; but presently she began to cry again at the idea that they didn't mind her being there. If she went down again to Tom now—would he forgive her ?   Perhaps her father would be there, and he would take her part. But then she wanted Tom to forgive her because he loved her, not because his father told him.   No, she would never go down if Tom didn't come to fetch her   This resolution lasted in great intensity for five dark minutes behind the tub; but then the need of being loved—the strongest need in poor Maggie's nature—began to wrestle with her pride, and soon threw it. She crept from behind the tub into the twilight of the long attic, but just then she heard a quick footstep on the stairs.

Tom had been too much interested in his talk with Luke, in going the round of the premises, walking in and out where he pleased, and whittling sticks without any particular reason,—except that he didn't whittle sticks at school,—to think of Maggie and the effect his anger had produced on her. He meant to punish her, and that business having been performed, he occupied himself with other matters, like a practical person. But when he had been called in to tea, his father said, "Why, where's the little wench ?" and Mrs. Tulliver, almost at the same moment, said, "Where's your little sister ?"—both of them having supposed that Maggie and Tom had been together all the afternoon.

"I don't know," said Tom. He didn't want

to "tell" of Maggie, though he was angry with
her; for Tom Tulliver was a lad of honor.

"What! hasn't she been playing with you all
this while?" said the father. "She'd been
thinking o' nothing but your coming home."

"I haven't seen her this two hours," says Tom,
commencing on the plumcake.

"Goodness heart! she's got drownded!" exclaimed Mrs. Tulliver, rising from her seat and
running to the window. "How could you let
her do so?" she added, as became a fearful
woman, accusing she didn't know whom of she
didn't know what.

"Nay, nay, she's none drownded," said Mr.
Tulliver. "You've been naughty to her, I
doubt, Tom?"

"I'm sure I haven't, father," said Tom in-
dignantly. "I think she's in the house."

"Perhaps up in that attic," said Mrs. Tulliver,
"a-singing and talking to herself, and forgetting
all about meal times."

"You go and fetch her down, Tom," said Mr.
Tulliver, rather sharply,—his perspicacity or his
fatherly fondness for Maggie making him suspect
that the lad had been hard upon "the little un,"
else she would never have left his side. "And
be good to her, do you hear? Else I'll let you
know better."

Tom never disobeyed his father, for Mr.
Tulliver was a peremptory man, and, as he said,
would never let anybody get hold of his whip
hand; but he went out rather sullenly, carrying
his piece of plumcake, and not intending to

reprieve Maggie's punishment, which was no
more than she deserved. Tom was only thirteen,
and had no decided views in grammar and
arithmetic, regarding them for the most part as
open questions, but he was particularly clear and
positive on one point,—namely, that he would
punish everybody who deserved it. Why, he
wouldn't have minded being punished himself
if he deserved it; but, then, he never *did* deserve
it.

It was Tom's step, then, that Maggie heard
on the stairs, when her need of love had tri-
umphed over her pride, and she was going down
with her swollen eyes and dishevelled hair to beg
for pity. At least her father would stroke her
head and say, "Never mind, my wench." It is
a wonderful subduer, this need of love,—this
hunger of the heart,—as peremptory as that
other hunger by which Nature forces us to
submit to the yoke, and change the face of the
world.

But she knew Tom's step, and her heart began
to beat violently with the sudden shock of hope.
He only stood still at the top of the stairs and
said, "Maggie, you're to come down." But she
rushed to him and clung round his neck, sobbing,
"Oh, Tom, please forgive me—I can't bear it—I
will always be good—always remember things
—do love me—please, dear Tom!"

We learn to restrain ourselves as we get older.
We keep apart when we have quarrelled, express
ourselves in well-bred phrases, and in this way
preserve a dignified alienation, showing much

firmness on one side, and swallowing much grief
on the other. We no longer approximate in our
behavior to the mere impulsiveness of the lower
animals, but conduct ourselves in every respect
like members of a highly civilized society.
Maggie and Tom were still very much like young
animals, and so she could rub her cheek against
his, and kiss his ear in a random sobbing way;
and there were tender fibres in the lad that had
been used to answer to Maggie's fondling, so
that he behaved with a weakness quite incon-
sistent with his resolution to punish her as much
as she deservd. He actually began to kiss her
in return, and say,—

"Don't cry, then, Magsie; here, eat a bit o'
cake."

Maggie's sobs began to subside, and she put
out her mouth for the cake and bit a piece; and
then Tom bit a piece, just for company, and they
ate together and rubbed each other's cheeks and
brows and noses together, while they ate, with a
humiliating resemblance to two friendly ponies.

"Come along, Magsie, and have tea," said
Tom at last, when there was no more cake except
what was downstairs.

So ended the sorrows of this day, and the next
morning Maggie was trotting with her own
fishing rod in one hand and a handle of the basket
in the other, stepping always, by a peculiar gift,
in the muddiest places, and looking darkly
radiant from under her beaver-bonnet because
Tom was good to her. She had told Tom,
however, that she should like him to put the

worms on the hook for her, although she accepted his word when he assured her that worms
couldn't feel (it was Tom's private opinion that
it didn't much matter if they did). He knew
all about worms, and fish, and those things; and
what birds were mischievous, and how padlocks
opened, and which way the handles of the gates
were to be lifted. Maggie thought this sort of
knowledge was very wonderful,—much more
difficult than remembering what was in the
books; and she was rather in awe of Tom's
superiority, for he was the only person who
called her knowledge "stuff," and did not feel
surprised at her cleverness. Tom, indeed, was
of opinion that Maggie was a silly little thing;
all girls were silly,—they couldn't throw a stone
so as to hit anything, couldn't do anything
with a pocketknife, and were frightened at
frogs. Still, he was very fond of his sister, and
meant always to take care of her, make her
his housekeeper, and punish her when she did
wrong.

They were on their way to the Round Pool,—
that wonderful pool, which the floods had made
a long while ago. No one knew how deep it
was; and it was mysterious, too, that it should be
almost a perfect round, framed in with willows
and tall reeds, so that the water was only to
be seen when you got close to the brink. The
sight of the old favorite spot always heightened
Tom's good humor, and he spoke to Maggie in
the most amicable whispers, as he opened the
precious basket and prepared their tackle. He

SHE LIKED FISHING VERY MUCH

threw her line for her, and put the rod into her
hand. Maggie thought it probable that the
small fish would come to her hook, and the large
ones to Tom's. But she had forgotten all about
the fish, and was looking dreamily at the glassy
water, when Tom said, in a loud whisper, "Look,

look, Maggie!" and came running to prevent her
from snatching her line away.

Maggie was frightened lest she had been doing
something wrong, as usual, but presently Tom
drew out her line and brought a large tench
bouncing on the grass.

Tom was excited.

"O Magsie, you little duck! Empty the
basket."

Maggie was not conscious of unusual merit,
but it was enough that Tom called her Magsie,
and was pleased with her. There was nothing
to mar her delight in the whispers and the
dreamy silences, when she listened to the light
dipping sounds of the rising fish, and the gentle
rustling, as if the willows and the reeds and the
water had their happy whisperings also. Maggie
thought it would make a very nice heaven to sit
by the pool in that way, and never be scolded.
She never knew she had a bite till Tom told her;
but she liked fishing very much.

III

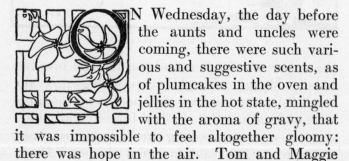N Wednesday, the day before
the aunts and uncles were
coming, there were such various and suggestive scents, as
of plumcakes in the oven and
jellies in the hot state, mingled
with the aroma of gravy, that
it was impossible to feel altogether gloomy:
there was hope in the air. Tom and Maggie

made several inroads into the kitchen, and, like
other marauders, were induced to keep aloof for
a time only by being allowed to carry away a
sufficient load of booty.

"Tom," said Maggie, as they sat on the boughs
of the elder-tree, eating their jam-puffs, "shall
you run away to-morrow?"

"No," said Tom, slowly, when he had finished
his puff, and was eying the third, which was to
be divided between them,—"no, I sha'n't."

"Why, Tom? Because Lucy's coming?"

"No," said Tom, opening his pocketknife and
holding it over the puff, with his head on one
side in a dubitative manner. (It was a difficult
problem to divide that very irregular polygon
into two equal parts.) "What do *I* care about
Lucy? She's only a girl,—*she* can't play at
bandy."

"Is it the tipsy-cake, then?" said Maggie,
exerting her hypothetic powers, while she leaned
forward toward Tom with her eyes fixed on the
hovering knife.

"No, you silly, that'll be good the day after.
It's the pudden. I know what the pudden's to
be,—apricot roll-up—O my buttons!"

With this interjection, the knife descended
on the puff, and it was in two, but the result
was not satisfactory to Tom, for he still eyed the
halves doubtfully. At last he said,—

"Shut your eyes, Maggie."

"What for?"

"You never mind what for. Shut 'em when
I tell you."

Maggie obeyed.

"Now, which'll you have, Maggie,—right hand or left?"

"I'll have that with the jam run out," said Maggie, keeping her eyes shut to please Tom.

"Why, you don't like that, you silly. You may have it if it comes to you fair, but I sha'n't give it you without. Right or left,—you choose, now. Ha-a-a!" said Tom, in a tone of exasperation, as Maggie peeped. "You keep your eyes shut, now, else you sha'n't have any."

Maggie's power of sacrifice did not extend so far; indeed, I fear she cared less that Tom should enjoy the utmost possible amount of puff, than that he should be pleased with her for giving him the best bit. So she shut her eyes quite close, till Tom told her to "say which," and then she said, "Left hand."

"You've got it," said Tom, in rather a bitter tone.

"What! the bit with the jam run out?"

"No; here, take it," said Tom, firmly, handing decidedly the best piece to Maggie.

"Oh, please, Tom, have it; I don't mind—I like the other; please take this."

"No, I sha'n't," said Tom, almost crossly, beginning on his own inferior piece.

Maggie, thinking it was no use to contend further, began too, and ate up her half puff with considerable relish as well as rapidity. But Tom had finished first, and had to look on while Maggie ate her last morsel or two, feeling in himself a capacity for more. Maggie

THE KNIFE DESCENDED ON THE PUFF

didn't know Tom was looking at her; she was
see-sawing on the elder bough, lost to almost
everything but a vague sense of jam and idle-
ness.

"Oh, you greedy thing!" said Tom, when she
had swallowed the last morsel. He was conscious of having acted very fairly, and thought
she ought to have considered this, and made up
to him for it. He would have refused a bit of
hers beforehand, but one is naturally at a different point of view before and after one's own
share of puff is swallowed.

Maggie turned quite pale. "Oh, Tom, why
didn't you ask me?"

"I wasn't going to ask you for a bit, you
greedy. You might have thought of it without,
when you knew I gave you the best bit."

"But I wanted you to have it; you know I
did," said Maggie, in an injured tone.

"Yes, but I wasn't going to do what wasn't
fair. If I go halves, I'll go 'em fair; only I
wouldn't be a greedy."

With this cutting innuendo, Tom jumped
down from his bough, and threw a stone with a
"hoigh!" as a friendly attention to Yap, who
had also been looking on while the eatables
vanished, with an agitation of his ears and
feelings which could hardly have been without
bitterness. Yet the excellent dog accepted
Tom's attention with as much alacrity as if he
had been treated quite generously.

But Maggie, gifted with that superior power
of misery which distinguishes the human being,

and places him at a proud distance from the
most melancholy chimpanzee, sat still on her
bough, and gave herself up to the keen sense of
unmerited reproach. She would have given the
world not to have eaten all her puff, and to have
saved some of it for Tom. Not but that the puff
was very nice, for Maggie's palate was not at
all obtuse, but she would have gone without it
many times over, sooner than Tom should call
her greedy and be cross with her. And he. had
said he wouldn't have it, and she ate it without
thinking; how could she help it? The tears
flowed so plentifully that Maggie saw nothing
around her for the next ten minutes; but by that
time resentment began to give way to the desire
of reconciliation, and she jumped from her bough
to look for Tom. He was no longer in the
paddock behind the rickyard; where was he
likely to be gone, and Yap with him? Maggie
ran to the high bank against the great holly tree,
where she could see far away toward the Floss.
There was Tom; but her heart sank again as she
saw how far off he was on his way to the great
river, and that he had another companion besides
Yap,—naughty Bob Jakin, whose official, if not
natural, function of frightening the birds was
just now at a standstill.

Well! there was no hope for it; he was gone
now, and Maggie could think of no comfort but
to sit down by the hollow, or wander by the
hedgerow, and fancy it was all different, re-
fashioning her little world into just what she
should like it to be.

IV

AGGIE had thrown her bonnet off very carelessly, and coming in with her hair rough as well as out of curl, rushed at once to Lucy, who was standing by her mother's knee. Certainly the contrast between the cousins was conspicuous. It was like the contrast between a rough, dark, overgrown puppy and a white kitten. Lucy put up the neatest little rosebud mouth to be kissed; everything about her was neat—her little round neck, with the row of coral beads; her little straight nose, not at all snubby; her little clear eyebrows, rather darker than her curls, to match her hazel eyes, which looked up with shy pleasure at Maggie, taller by the head, though scarcely a year older. Maggie always looked at Lucy with delight. She was fond of fancying a world where the people never got any larger than children of their own age, and she made the queen of it just like Lucy, with a little crown on her head, and a little sceptre in her hand—only the queen was Maggie herself in Lucy's form.

"Oh, Lucy," she burst out, after kissing her, "you'll stay with Tom and me, won't you? Oh, kiss her, Tom."

Tom, too, had come up to Lucy, but he was not going to kiss her—no; he came up to her with Maggie, because it seemed easier, on the whole, than saying, "How do you do?" to all those

aunts and uncles. He stood looking at nothing
in particular, with the blushing, awkward air
and semi-smile which are common to shy boys
when in company,—very much as if they had
come into the world by mistake, and found it in
a degree of undress that was quite embarrassing.

"Maggie," said Mrs. Tulliver, beckoning
Maggie to her, and whispering in her ear, as soon
as this point of Lucy's staying was settled, "go
and get your hair brushed, do, for shame. I told
you not to come in without going to Martha first;
you know I did."

"Tom, come out with me," whispered Maggie,
pulling his sleeve as she passed him; and Tom
followed willingly enough.

"Come upstairs with me, Tom," she whispered, when they were outside the door. "There's
something I want to do before dinner."

"There's no time to play at anything before
dinner," said Tom, whose imagination was impatient of any intermediate prospect.

"Oh yes, there is time for this; *do* come, Tom."

Tom followed Maggie upstairs into her mother's room, and saw her go at once to a drawer,
from which she took out a large pair of scissors.

"What are they for, Maggie?" said Tom,
feeling his curiosity awakened.

Maggie answered by seizing her front locks
and cutting them straight across the middle of
her forehead.

"Oh, my buttons! Maggie, you'll catch it!"
exclaimed Tom; "you'd better not cut any more
off."

THE LOCKS FELL ON THE FLOOR.

Snip! went the great scissors again while Tom
was speaking, and he couldn't help feeling it was
rather good fun; Maggie would look so queer.

"Here, Tom, cut it behind for me," said
Maggie, excited by her own daring, and anxious
to finish the deed.

"You'll catch it, you know," said Tom, nodding his head in an admonitory manner, and
hesitating a little as he took the scissors.

"Never mind, make haste!" said Maggie, giving a little stamp with her foot. Her cheeks were quite flushed.

The black locks were so thick, nothing could be more tempting to a lad who had already tasted the forbidden pleasure of cutting the pony's mane. I speak to those who know the satisfaction of making a pair of shears meet through a duly resisting mass of hair. One delicious grinding snip, and then another and another, and the hinder locks fell heavily on the floor, and Maggie stood cropped in a jagged, uneven manner, but with a sense of clearness and freedom, as if she had emerged from a wood into the open plain.

"Oh, Maggie," said Tom, jumping round her, and slapping his knees as he laughed, "Oh, my buttons! what a queer thing you look! Look at yourself in the glass; you look like the idiot we throw out nutshells to at shcool."

Maggie felt an unexpected pang. She had thought beforehand chiefly of her own deliverance from her teasing hair and teasing remarks about it, and something also of the triumph she should have over her mother and her aunts by this very decided course of action; she didn't want her hair to look pretty,—that was out of the question,—she only wanted people to think her a clever little girl, and not to find fault with her. But now, when Tom began to laugh at her, and say she was like the idiot, the affair had quite a new aspect. She looked in the glass, and still Tom laughed and clapped his hands, and Maggie's flushed cheeks began to pale, and her lips to tremble a little.

"Oh, Maggie, you'll have to go down to dinner directly," said Tom. "Oh, my!"

"Don't laugh at me, Tom," said Maggie, in a passionate tone, with an outburst of angry tears, stamping, and giving him a push.

"Now, then, spitfire!" said Tom. "What did you cut it off for, then? I shall go down: I can smell the dinner going in."

He hurried downstairs and left poor Maggie to that bitter sense of the irrevocable which was almost an everyday experience of her small soul. She could see clearly enough, now the thing was done, that it was very foolish, and that she should have to hear and think more about her hair than ever; for Maggie rushed to her deeds with passionate impulse, and then saw not only their consequences, but what would have happened if they had not been done, with all the detail and exaggerated circumstanse of an active imagination.

"Miss Maggie, you're to come down this minute," said Kezia, entering the room hurriedly. "Lawks! what have you been a-doing? I niver *see* such a fright!"

"Don't, Kezia," said Maggie, angrily. "Go away!"

"But I tell you you're to come down, Miss, this minute; your mother says so," said Kezia, going up to Maggie and taking her by the hand to raise her from the floor.

"Get away, Kezia; I don't want any dinner,"

said Maggie, resisting Kezia's arm. "I sha'n't come."

"Oh, well, I can't stay. I've got to wait at dinner," said Kezia, going out again.

"Maggie, you little silly," said Tom, peeping into the room ten minutes after, "why don't you come and have your dinner? There's lots o' goodies, and mother says you're to come. What are you crying for, you little spooney?"

Oh, it was dreadful! Tom was so hard and unconcerned; if *he* had been crying on the floor, Maggie would have cried too. And there was the dinner, so nice; and she was *so* hungry. It was very bitter.

But Tom was not altogether hard. He was not inclined to cry, and did not feel that Maggie's grief spoiled his prospect of the sweets; but he went and put his head near her, and said in a lower, comforting tone,—

"Won't you come, then, Magsie? Shall I bring you a bit o' pudding when I've had mine, and a custard and things?"

"Ye-e-es," said Maggie, beginning to feel life a little more tolerable.

"Very well," said Tom, going away. But he turned again at the door and said, "But you'd better come, you know. There's the dessert,— nuts, you know, and cowslip wine."

Maggie's tears had ceased, and she looked reflective as Tom left her. His good nature had taken off the keenest edge of her sufferings, and nuts with cowslip wine began to assert their legitimate influence.

Slowly she rose from amongst her scattered locks, and slowly she made her way downstairs. Then she stood leaning with one shoulder against the frame of the dining-parlor door, peeping in when it was ajar. She saw Tom and Lucy with an empty chair between them, and there were the custards on a side table; it was too much. She slipped in and went toward the empty chair. But she had no sooner sat down than she repented and wished herself back again.

Mrs. Tulliver gave a little scream as she saw her, and felt such a "turn" that she dropped the large gravy-spoon into the dish, with the most serious results to the tablecloth. For Kezia had not betrayed the reason of Maggie's refusal to come down, not liking to give her mistress a shock in the moment of carving, and Mrs. Tulliver thought there was nothing worse in question than a fit of perverseness, which was inflicting its own punishment by depriving Maggie of half her dinner.

Mrs. Tulliver's scream made all eyes turn toward the same point as her own, and Maggie's cheeks and ears began to burn, while uncle Glegg, a kind-looking, white-haired old gentleman, said,—

"Heyday! what little gell's this? Why, I don't know her. Is it some little gell you've picked up in the road, Kezia?"

"Why, she's gone and cut her hair herself," said Mr. Tulliver in an undertone to Mr. Deane, laughing with much enjoyment. "Did you ever know such a little hussy as it is?"

"Why, little miss, you've made yourself look very funny," said uncle Pullet, and perhaps he never in his life made an observation which was felt to be so lacerating.

"Fie, for shame!" said aunt Glegg, in her loudest, severest tone of reproof. "Little gells as cut their own hair should be whipped and fed on bread and water,—not come and sit down with their aunts and uncles."

"Ay, ay," said uncle Glegg, meaning to give a playful turn to this denunciation, "she must be sent to jail, I think, and they'll cut the rest of her hair off there, and make it all even."

"She's more like a gypsy nor ever," said aunt Pullet, in a pitying tone; "it's very bad luck, sister, as the gell should be so brown; the boy's fair enough. I doubt it'll stand in her way i' life to be so brown."

"She's a naughty child, as'll break her mother's heart," said Mrs. Tulliver, with the tears in her eyes.

Maggie seemed to be listening to a chorus of reproach and derision. Her first flush came from anger, which gave her a transient power of defiance, and Tom thought she was braving it out, supported by the recent appearance of the pudding and custard. Under this impression, he whispered, "Oh, my! Maggie, I told you you'd catch it." He meant to be friendly, but Maggie felt convinced that Tom was rejoicing in her ignominy. Her feeble power of defiance left her in an instant, her heart swelled, and getting up from her chair, she ran to her father, hid her face on his shoulder, and burst out into loud sobbing.

"Come, come, my wench," said her father, soothingly, putting his arm round her, "never mind; you was i' the right to cut it off if it plagued you; give over crying; father'll take your part."

Delicious words of tenderness! Maggie never forgot any of these moments when her father "took her part"; she kept them in her heart, and thought of them long years after, when every one else said that her father had done very ill by his children.

With the dessert there came entire deliverance for Maggie, for the children were told they might have their nuts and wine in the summerhouse, since the day was so mild; and they scampered out among the budding bushes of the garden with the alacrity of small animals getting from under a burning glass.

V

WHILE the possible troubles of Maggie's future were occupying her father's mind, she herself was tasting only the bitterness of the present. Childhood has not forebodings; but then, it is soothed by no memories of out-lived sorrow. The fact was, the day had begun ill with Maggie. The pleasure of having Lucy to look at, and the prospect of the afternoon visit to

Garum Firs, where she would hear uncle Pullet's musical box, had been marred as early as eleven o'clock by the advent of the hairdresser from Saint Ogg's, who had spoken in the severest terms of the condition in which he had found her hair, holding up one jagged lock after another and saying, "See here! tut, tut, tut!" in a tone of mingled disgust and pity, which to Maggie's imagination was equivalent to the strongest expression of public opinion. Mr. Rappit, the hairdresser, with his well-anointed coronal locks tending wavily upward, like the simulated pyramid of flame on a monumental urn, seemed to her at that moment the most formidable of her contemporaries, into whose street at Saint Ogg's she would carefully refrain from entering through the rest of her life.

Already, at twelve o'clock, Mrs. Tulliver had on her visiting costume, with a protective apparatus of brown holland, as if she had been a piece of satin furniture in danger of flies; Maggie was frowning and twisting her shoulders, that she might if possible shrink away from the prickliest of tuckers, while her mother was remonstrating, "Don't, Maggie, my dear; don't make yourself so ugly!" and Tom's cheeks were looking particularly brilliant as a relief to his best blue suit, which he wore with becoming calmness, having, after a little wrangling, effected what was always the one point of interest to him in his toilet: he had transferred all the contents of his everyday pockets to those actually in wear.

As for Lucy, she was just as pretty and neat as she had been yesterday; no accidents ever happened to her clothes, and she was never uncomfortable in them, so that she looked with wondering pity at Maggie, pouting and writhing under the exasperating tucker. Maggie would certainly have torn it off, if she had not been checked by the remembrance of her recent

BUILDING CARD HOUSES

humiliation about her hair; as it was, she confined herself to fretting and twisting, and behaving peevishly about the card houses which they were allowed to build till dinner, as a suitable amusement for boys and girls in their best clothes. Tom could build perfect pyramids of houses; but Maggie's would never bear the laying on the roof. It was always so with the things that Maggie made; and Tom had deduced the con-

clusion that no girls could ever make anything.
But it happened that Lucy proved wonderfully
clever at building; she handled the cards so
lightly, and moved so gently, that Tom con-
descended to admire her houses as well as his
own, the more readily because she had asked
him to teach her. Maggie, too, would have
admired Lucy's houses, and would have given
up her own unsuccessful building to contemplate
them, without ill temper, if her tucker had not
made her peevish, and if Tom had not incon-
siderately laughed when her houses fell, and
told her she was "a stupid."

"Don't laugh at me, Tom!" she burst out
angrily; "I'm not a stupid. I know a great many
things you don't."

"Oh, I dare say, Miss Spitfire! I'd never be
such a cross thing as you, making faces like that.
Lucy doesn't do so. I like Lucy better than
you; *I* wish Lucy was *my* sister."

"Then it's very wicked and cruel of you to
wish so," said Maggie, starting up hurriedly
from her place on the floor, and upsetting Tom's
wonderful pagoda. She really did not mean it,
but the circumstantial evidence was against her,
and Tom turned white with anger, but said
nothing; he would have struck her, only he knew
it was cowardly to strike a girl, and Tom Tulliver
was quite determined he would never do anything cowardly.

Maggie stood in dismay and terror, while Tom
got up from the floor and walked away, pale,
from the scattered ruins of his pagoda, and Lucy

looked on mutely, like a kitten pausing from its
lapping.

"Oh, Tom," said Maggie, at last, going halfway toward him, "I didn't mean to knock it
down,—indeed, indeed I didn't."

Tom took no notice of her, but took, instead,
two or three hard peas out of his pocket, and shot
them with his thumb-nail against the window,
vaguely at first, but presently with the distinct
aim of hitting a superannuated blue bottle which
was exposing its imbecility in the spring sunshine, clearly against the views of Nature, who
had provided Tom and the peas for the speedy
destruction of this weak individual.

Thus the morning had been made heavy to
Maggie, and Tom's persistent coldness to her
all through their walk spoiled the fresh air and
sunshine for her. He called Lucy to look at
the half-built bird's nest without caring to show
it Maggie, and peeled a willow switch for Lucy
and himself, without offering one to Maggie.
Lucy had said, "Maggie, shouldn't *you* like
one?" but Tom was deaf.

Still, the sight of the peacock opportunely
spreading his tail on the stackyard wall, just as
they reached Garum Firs, was enough to divert
the mind temporarily from personal grievances.
And this was only the beginning of beautiful
sights at Garum Firs. All the farmyard life
was wonderful there,—bantams, speckled and
topknotted; Friesland hens, with their feathers
all turned the wrong way; Guinea fowls that
flew and screamed and dropped their pretty

spotted feathers; pouter pigeons and a tame magpie; nay, a goat, and a wonderful brindled dog, half mastiff, half bulldog, as large as a lion. Then there were white railings and white gates all about, and glittering weathercocks of various design, and garden walks paved with pebbles in beautiful patterns,—nothing was quite common at Garum Firs; and Tom thought that the unusual size of the toads there was simply due to the general unusualness which characterized uncle Pullet's possessions as a gentleman farmer. Toads who paid rent were naturally leaner. As for the house, it was not less remarkable; it had a receding centre, and two wings with battle-mented turrets, and was covered with glittering white stucco.

The small demons who had taken possession of Maggie's soul at an earlier period of the day had returned in all the greater force after a temporary absence. All the disagreeable recol-lections of the morning were thick upon her, when Tom said, "Here, Lucy, you come along with me," and walked off to the area where the toads were, as if there were no Maggie in ex-istence. Seeing this, Maggie lingered at a distance, looking like a small Medusa with her snakes cropped. Lucy was naturally pleased that cousin Tom was so good to her, and it was very amusing to see him tickling a fat toad with a piece of string when the toad was safe down the area, with an iron grating over him. Still Lucy wished Maggie to enjoy the spectacle also, especially as she would doubtless find a name for the toad, and say what had been his past history; for Lucy had a delighted semi-belief in Maggie's stories about the live things they came upon by accident,—how Mrs. Earwig had a wash at home, and one of her children had fallen into the hot copper, for which reason she was running so fast to fetch the doctor. Tom had a profound contempt for this nonsense of Maggie's, smashing the earwig at once as a superfluous yet easy means of proving the entire unreality of such a story; but Lucy, for the life of her, could not help fancying there was something in it, and at all events thought it was very pretty make-believe. So now the desire to know the history of a very portly toad, added to her habitual affectionateness, made her run back to Maggie and say, "Oh, there is such a big, funny toad, Maggie! Do come and see!"

Maggie said nothing, but turned away from her with a deeper frown. As long as Tom seemed to prefer Lucy to her, Lucy made part of his unkindness. Maggie would have thought a little while ago that she could never be cross with pretty little Lucy, any more than she could be cruel to a little white mouse; but then, Tom had always been quite indifferent to Lucy before, and it had been left to Maggie to pet and make much of her. As it was, she was actually beginning to think that she should like to make Lucy cry by slapping or pinching her, especially as it might vex Tom, whom it was of no use to slap, even if she dared, because he didn't mind it. And if Lucy hadn't been there, Maggie was sure he would have got friends with her sooner.

Tickling a fat toad who is not highly sensitive is an amusement that it is possible to exhaust, and Tom by and by began to look round for some other mode of passing the time. But in so prim a garden, where they were not to go off the paved walks, there was not a great choice of sport. The only great pleasure such a restriction suggested was the pleasure of breaking it, and Tom began to meditate an insurrectionary visit to the pond, about a field's length beyond the garden.

"I say, Lucy," he began, nodding his head up and down with great significance, as he coiled up his string again, "what do you think I mean to do?"

"What, Tom?" said Lucy, with curiosity.

"I mean to go to the pond and look at the pike. You may go with me if you like," said the young sultan.

"Oh, Tom, *dare* you?" said Lucy. "Aunt said we mustn't go out of the garden."

"Oh, I shall go out at the other end of the garden," said Tom. "Nobody 'ull see us. Besides, I don't care if they do,—I'll run off home."

"But *I* couldn't run," said Lucy, who had never before been exposed to such severe temptation.

"Oh, never mind; they won't be cross with *you*," said Tom. "You say I took you."

Tom walked along, and Lucy trotted by his

side, timidly enjoying the rare treat of doing
something naughty,—excited also by the mention
of that celebrity, the pike, about which she was
quite uncertain whether it was a fish or a fowl.
Maggie saw them leaving the garden, and could
not resist the impulse to follow. Anger and
jealousy can no more bear to lose sight of their
objects than love, and that Tom and Lucy should
do or see anything of which she was ignorant
would have been an intolerable idea to Maggie.
So she kept a few yards behind them, unobserved
by Tom, who was presently absorbed in watching
for the pike,—a highly interesting monster; he
was said to be so very old, so very large, and to
have such a remarkable appetite. The pike,
like other celebrities, did not show when he was
watched for, but Tom caught sight of something
in rapid movement in the water, which attracted
him to another spot on the brink of the pond.

"Here, Lucy!" he said in a loud whisper,
"come here! take care! keep on the grass!—don't
step where the cows have been!" he added,
pointing to a peninsula of dry grass, with trodden
mud on each side of it; for Tom's contemptuous
conception of a girl included the attribute of
being unfit to walk in dirty places.

Lucy came carefully as she was bidden, and
bent down to look at what seemed a golden
arrowhead darting through the water. It was
a water snake, Tom told her; and Lucy at last
could see the serpentine wave of its body, very
much wondering that a snake could swim.
Maggie had drawn nearer and nearer; she *must*

see it too, though it was bitter to her, like everything else, since Tom did not care about her seeing it. At last she was close by Lucy; and Tom, who had been aware of her approach, but would not notice it till he was obliged, turned round and said,—

"Now, get away, Maggie; there's no room for you on the grass here. Nobody asked *you* to come."

There were passions at war in Maggie at that moment to have made a tragedy, if tragedies were made by passion only; the utmost Maggie could do, with a fierce thrust of her small brown arm, was to push poor little pink-and-white Lucy into the cow-trodden mud.

Then Tom could not restrain himself, and gave Maggie two smart slaps on the arm as he ran to pick up Lucy, who lay crying helplessly. Maggie retreated to the roots of a tree a few yards off, and looked on impenitently. Usually her repentance came quickly after one rash deed, but now Tom and Lucy had made her so miserable, she was glad to spoil their happiness,—glad to make everybody uncomfortable. Why should she be sorry? Tom was very slow to forgive *her*, however sorry she might have been.

"I shall tell mother, you know, Miss Mag," said Tom, loudly and emphatically, as soon as Lucy was up and ready to walk away. Lucy was too entirely absorbed by the evil that had befallen her,—the spoiling of her pretty best clothes, and the discomfort of being wet and dirty,—to think much of the cause, which was entirely mysterious to her. She could never have guessed what she had done to make Maggie angry with her; but she felt that Maggie was very unkind and disagreeable, and made no magnanimous entreaties to Tom that he would not "tell," only running along by his side and crying piteously, while Maggie sat on the roots of the tree and looked after them with her small Medusa face.

"Sally," said Tom, when they reached the kitchen door, and Sally looked at them in speechless amaze, with a piece of bread-and-butter in her mouth and a toasting-fork in her hand,— "Sally, tell mother it was Maggie pushed Lucy into the mud."

"But Lors ha' massy, how did you get near such mud as that?" said Sally, making a wry face, as she stooped down and examined the *corpus delicti.*

Tom's imagination had not been rapid and capacious enough to include this question among the foreseen consequences, but it was no sooner put than he foresaw whither it tended, and that Maggie would not be considered the only culprit in the case. He walked quietly away from the kitchen door, leaving Sally to that pleasure of guessing which active minds notoriously prefer to ready-made knowledge.

Sally lost no time in presenting Lucy at the parlor door, for to have so dirty an object introduced into the house at Garum Firs was too great a weight to be sustained by a single mind.

"Goodness gracious!" aunt Pullet exclaimed, after preluding by an inarticulate scream; "keep her at the door, Sally! Don't bring her off the oilcloth, whatever you do."

"Why, she's tumbled into some nasty mud," said Mrs. Tulliver, going up to Lucy to examine into the amount of damage to clothes for which she felt herself responsible to her sister Deane.

"If you please, 'um, it was Miss Maggie as pushed her in," said Sally; "Master Tom's been and said so, and they must ha' been to the pond, for it's only there they could ha' got into such dirt."

"There it is, Bessy; it's what I've been telling you," said Mrs. Pullet, in a tone of prophetic sadness; "it's your children,—there's no knowing what they'll come to."

Mrs. Tulliver was mute, feeling herself a truly wretched mother. As usual, the thought pressed upon her that people would think she had done something wicked to deserve her maternal troubles, while Mrs. Pullet began to give elaborate directions to Sally how to guard the premises from serious injury in the course of removing the dirt. Meantime tea was to be brought in by the cook, and the two naughty children were to have theirs in an ignominious manner in the kitchen. Mrs. Tulliver went out to speak to these naughty children, supposing them to be close at hand; but it was not until after some search that she found Tom leaning with rather a hardened, careless air against the white paling of the poultry yard, and lowering his piece of string on the other side as a means of exasperating the turkey cock.

"Tom, you naughty boy, where's your sister?" said Mrs. Tulliver, in a distressed voice.

"I don't know," said Tom; his eagerness for justice on Maggie had diminished since he had seen clearly that it could hardly be brought about without the injustice of some blame on his own conduct.

"Why, where did you leave her?" said the mother, looking round.

"Sitting under the tree, against the pond," said Tom, apparently indifferent to everything but the string and the turkey cock.

"Then go and fetch her in this minute, you naughty boy. And how could you think o' going to the pond, and taking your sister where there was dirt? You know she'll do mischief if there's mischief to be done."

It was Mrs. Tulliver's way, if she blamed Tom, to refer his misdemeanor, somehow or other, to Maggie.

The idea of Maggie sitting alone by the pond roused an habitual fear in Mrs. Tulliver's mind, and she mounted the horse block to satisfy herself by a sight of that fatal child, while Tom walked—not very quickly—on his way toward her.

"They're such children for the water, mine are," she said aloud, without reflecting that there was no one to hear her; "they'll be brought in dead and drownded some day. I wish that river was far enough."

But when she not only failed to discern Maggie, but presently saw Tom returning from the pool alone, this hovering fear entered and took complete possession of her, and she hurried to meet him.

"Maggie's nowhere about the pond, mother," said Tom; "she's gone away."

You may conceive the terrified search for Maggie, and the difficulty of convincing her mother that she was not in the pond. Mrs. Pullet observed that the child might come to a worse end if she lived, there was no knowing; and Mr. Pullet reached down a key to the goose-pen as a likely place for Maggie to lie concealed in.

Tom, after a while, started the idea that Maggie was gone home (without thinking it necessary to state that it was what he should have done himself under the circumstances), and the suggestion was seized as a comfort by his mother.

"Sister, for goodness' sake let 'em put the horse in the carriage and take me home; we shall perhaps find her on the road. Lucy can't walk in her dirty clothes," she said, looking at that innocent victim, who was wrapped up in a shawl, and sitting with naked feet on the sofa.

Aunt Pullet was quite willing to take the shortest means of restoring her premises to order and quiet, and it was not long before Mrs. Tulliver was in the chaise, looking anxiously at the most distant point before her. What the father would say if Maggie was lost, was a question that predominated over every other.

VI

AGGIE'S intentions, as usual, were on a larger scale than Tom had imagined. The resolution that gathered in her mind, after Tom and Lucy had walked away, was not so simple as that of going home. No! she would run away and go to the gypsies, and Tom should never see her any more. That was by no means a new idea to Maggie; she had been so often told she was like a gypsy, and "half wild," that when she was miserable it seemed to her the only way of escaping opprobrium, and being entirely in harmony with circumstances, would be to live in a little brown tent on the commons; the gypsies, she considered, would gladly receive her and pay her much respect on account of her superior knowledge. She had once mentioned her views on this point to Tom, and suggested that he should stain his face brown, and they should run away together; but Tom rejected the scheme with contempt, observing that gypsies were thieves, and hardly got anything to eat, and had nothing to drive but a donkey. To-day, however, Maggie thought her misery had reached a pitch at which gypsydom was her only refuge, and she rose from her seat on the roots of the tree with the sense that this was a great crisis in her life; she would run straight away till she came to Dunlow Common, where there would certainly be gypsies; and cruel Tom, and the

rest of her relations who found fault with her, should never see her any more. She thought of her father as she ran along, but she reconciled herself to the idea of parting with him, by determining that she would secretly send him a letter by a small gypsy, who would run away without telling where she was, and just let him know that she was well and happy, and always loved him very much.

Maggie soon got out of breath with running, but by the time Tom got to the pond again she was at the distance of three long fields, and was on the edge of the lane leading to the highroad. She stopped to pant a little, reflecting that running away was not a pleasant thing until one had got quite to the common where the gypsies were, but her resolution had not abated; she presently passed through the gate into the lane, not knowing where it would lead her; for it was not this way that they came from Dorlcote Mill to Garum Firs, and she felt all the safer for that, because there was no chance of her being overtaken. But she was soon aware, not without trembling, that there were two men coming along the lane in front of her; she had not thought of meeting strangers, she had been too much occupied with the idea of her friends coming after her. The formidable strangers were two shabby-looking men with flushed faces, one of them carrying a bundle on a stick over his shoulder; but to her surprise, while she was dreading their disapprobation as a runaway, the man with the bundle stopped, and in a half-whining, half-coaxing tone asked her if she had a copper to give a poor man. Maggie had a sixpence in her pocket, which she immediately drew out and gave this poor man with a polite smile, hoping that he would feel very kindly toward her as a generous person. "That's the only money I've got," she said apologetically. "Thank you, little miss," said the man, in a less respectful and grateful tone than Maggie anticipated, and she even observed that he smiled and winked at his companion. She walked on hurriedly, but was aware that the two men were standing still, probably to look after her, and she presently heard them laughing loudly. Suddenly it occurred to her that they might think she was an idiot; Tom had said that her cropped hair made her look like an idiot, and it was too painful an idea to be readily forgotten. Besides, she had no sleeves on—only a cape and a bonnet. It was clear that she was not likely to make a favorable impression on passengers, and she thought she would turn into the fields again.

She turned through the first gate that was not locked, and felt a delightful sense of privacy in creeping along by the hedgerows, after her recent humiliating encounter. She was used to wandering about the fields by herself, and was less timid there than on the highroad. Sometimes she had to climb over high gates, but that was a small evil; she was getting out of reach very fast, and she would probably soon come within sight of Dunlow Common, or at least of some other common, for she had heard her father say that

she couldn't go very far without coming to a
common. She hoped so, for she was getting
rather tired and hungry, and until she reached
the gypsies there was no definite prospect of
bread and butter. It was still broad daylight;
so, though it was nearly an hour since Maggie
started, there was no gathering gloom on the
fields to remind her that the night would come.
Still, it seemed to her that she had been walking
a very great distance indeed, and it was really
surprising that the common did not come within
sight.

At last, however, the green fields came to an
end, and Maggie found herself looking through
the bars of a gate into a lane with a wide margin
of grass on each side of it. She had never seen
such a wide lane before, and, without her knowing
why, it gave her the impression that the common
could not be far off; perhaps it was because she
saw a donkey with a log to his foot feeding on
the grassy margin, for she had seen a donkey
with that pitiable encumbrance on Dunlow
Common when she had been across it in her
father's gig. She crept through the bars of the
gate and walked on with new spirit, though not
without haunting images of Apollyon, and a
highwayman with a pistol, and a blinking dwarf
in yellow with a mouth from ear to ear, and
other miscellaneous dangers. For poor little
Maggie had at once the timidity of an active
imagination, and the daring that comes from
over-mastering impulse. She had rushed into
the adventure of seeking her unknown kindred,

the gypsies; and now she was in this strange
lane, she hardly dared look on one side of her,
lest she should see the diabolical blacksmith in
his leathern apron grinning at her with arms
akimbo. It was not without a leaping of the
heart that she caught sight of a small pair of
bare legs sticking up, feet uppermost, by the side
of a hillock; they seemed something hideously
preternatural,—a diabolical kind of fungus; for
she was too much agitated at the first glance to
see the ragged clothes and the dark shaggy head
attached to them. It was a boy asleep, and
Maggie trotted along faster and more lightly,
lest she should wake him; it did not occur to her
that he was one of her friends the gypsies, who
in all probability would have very genial manners. But the fact was so, for at the next bend
in the lane Maggie actually saw the little semi-
circular black tent with the blue smoke rising
before it, which was to be her refuge from all the
blighting obloquy that had pursued her in
civilized life. She even saw a tall female figure
by the column of smoke, doubtless the gypsy-
mother, who provided the tea and other groceries; it was astonishing to herself that she did
not feel more delight. But it was startling to
find the gypsies in a lane, after all, and not on a
common; indeed, it was rather disappointing;
for a mysterious illimitable common, where
there were sand pits to hide in, and one was out
of everybody's reach, had always made part of
Maggie's picture of gypsy life. She went on,
however, and thought with some comfort that

gypsies most likely knew nothing about idiots, so there was no danger of their falling into the mistake of setting her down at the first glance as an idiot. It was plain she had attracted attention; for the tall figure, who proved to be a young woman with a baby on her arm, walked slowly to meet her. Maggie looked up in the new face rather tremblingly as it approached, and was reassured by the thought that her aunt Pullet and the rest were right when they called her a gypsy; for this face, with the bright dark eyes and the long hair, was really something like what she used to see in the glass before she cut her hair off.

"My little lady, where are you going to?" the gypsy said, in a tone of coaxing deference.

It was delightful, and just what Maggie expected; the gypsies saw at once that she was a little lady, and were prepared to treat her accordingly.

"Not any farther," said Maggie, feeling as if she were saying what she had rehearsed in a dream. "I'm come to stay with *you*, please."

"That's pretty; come, then. Why, what a nice little lady you are, to be sure!" said the gypsy, taking her by the hand. Maggie thought her very agreeable, but wished she had not been so dirty.

There was quite a group round the fire when they reached it. An old gypsy woman was seated on the ground nursing her knees, and occasionally poking a skewer into the round kettle that sent forth an odorous steam; two

small shock-headed children were lying prone
and resting on their elbows something like small
sphinxes; and a placid donkey was bending his
head over a tall girl, who, lying on her back, was
scratching his nose and indulging him with a
bite of excellent stolen hay. The slanting sun-
light fell kindly upon them, and the scene was
really very pretty and comfortable, Maggie
thought, only she hoped they would soon set out
the teacups. Everything would be quite charm-
ing when she had taught the gypsies to use a
washing basin, and to feel an interest in books.
It was a little confusing, though, that the young
woman began to speak to the old one in a language which Maggie did not understand, while
the tall girl, who was feeding the donkey, sat up
and stared at her without offering any salutation.
At last the old woman said,—

"What! my pretty lady, are you come to stay
with us? Sit ye down and tell us where you
come from."

It was just like a story; Maggie liked to be
called pretty lady and treated in this way. She
sat down and said,—

"I'm come from home because I'm unhappy,
and I mean to be a gypsy. I'll live with you if
you like, and I can teach you a great many
things."

"Such a clever little lady," said the woman
with the baby, sitting down by Maggie, and
allowing baby to crawl; "and such a pretty
bonnet and frock," she added, taking off Maggie's bonnet and looking at it while she made an

observation to the old woman, in the unknown language. The tall girl snatched the bonnet and put it on her own head hind-foremost with a grin; but Maggie was determined not to show any weakness on this subject, as if she were susceptible about her bonnet.

"I don't want to wear a bonnet," she said; "I'd rather wear a red handkerchief, like yours" (looking at her friend by her side). "My hair was quite long till yesterday, when I cut it off; but I dare say it will grow again very soon," she added apologetically, thinking it probable the gypsies had a strong prejudice in favor of long hair. And Maggie had forgotten even her hunger at that moment in the desire to conciliate gypsy opinion.

"Oh, what a nice little lady!—and rich, I'm sure," said the old woman. "Didn't you live in a beautiful house at home?"

"Yes, my home is pretty, and I'm very fond of the river, where we go fishing, but I'm often very unhappy. I should have liked to bring my books with me, but I came away in a hurry, you know. But I can tell you almost everything there is in my books, I've read them so many times, and that will amuse you. And I can tell you something about Geography too—that's about the world we live in—very useful and interesting. Did you ever hear about Columbus?"

Maggie's eyes had begun to sparkle and her cheeks to flush,—she was really beginning to instruct the gypsies, and gaining great influence over them. The gypsies themselves were not

without amazement at this talk, though their
attention was divided by the contents of Maggie's pocket, which the friend at her right hand
had by this time emptied without attracting her
notice.

"Is that where you live, my little lady?" said
the old woman, at the mention of Columbus.

"Oh, no!" said Maggie, with some pity;
"Columbus was a very wonderful man, who
found out half the world, and they put chains
on him and treated him very badly, you know;
it's in my Catechism of Geography, but perhaps
it's rather too long to tell before tea—*I want my
tea so.*"

The last words burst from Maggie, in spite
of herself, with a sudden drop from patronizing
instruction to simple peevishness.

"Why, she's hungry, poor little lady," said
the younger woman. "Give her some o' the
cold victual. You've been walking a good way,
I'll be bound, my dear. Where's your home?"

"It's Dorlcote Mill, a good way off," said
Maggie. "My father is Mr. Tulliver, but we
mustn't let him know where I am, else he'll fetch
me home again. Where does the queen of the
gypsies live?"

"What! do you want to go to her, my little
lady?" said the younger woman. The tall
girl meanwhile was constantly staring at Maggie
and grinning. Her manners were certainly not
agreeable.

"No," said Maggie, "I'm only thinking that
if she isn't a very good queen you might be glad

when she died, and you could choose another.
If I was a queen, I'd be a very good queen, and
kind to everybody."

"Here's a bit o' nice victual, then," said the
old woman, handing to Maggie a lump of dry
bread, which she had taken from a bag of scraps,
and a piece of cold bacon.

"Thank you," said Maggie, looking at the
food without taking it; "but will you give me
some bread-and-butter and tea instead? I don't
like bacon."

"We've got no tea nor butter," said the old
woman, with something like a scowl, as if she
were getting tired of coaxing.

"Oh, a little bread and treacle would do,"
said Maggie.

"We han't got no treacle," said the old woman,
crossly, whereupon there followed a sharp dia-
logue between the two women in their unknown
tongue, and one of the small sphinxes snatched
at the bread and bacon, and began to eat it. At
this moment the tall girl, who had gone a few
yards off, came back, and said something which
produced a strong effect. The old woman,
seeming to forget Maggie's hunger, poked the
skewer into the pot with new vigor, and the
younger crept under the tent, and reached out
some platters and spoons. Maggie trembled a
little, and was afraid the tears would come into
her eyes. Meanwhile the tall girl gave a shrill
cry, and presently came running up the boy
whom Maggie had passed as he was sleeping,—
a rough urchin about the age of Tom. He

stared at Maggie, and there ensued much incomprehensible chattering. She felt very lonely, and was quite sure she should begin to cry before long; the gypsies didn't seem to mind her at all, and she felt quite weak among them. But the springing tears were checked by new terror, when two men came up, whose approach had been the cause of the sudden excitement. The elder of the two carried a bag, which he flung down, addressing the women in a loud and scolding tone, which they answered by a shower of treble sauciness; while a black cur ran barking up to Maggie, and threw her into a tremor that only found a new cause in the curses with which the younger man called the dog off, and gave him a rap with a great stick he held in his hand.

Maggie felt that it was impossible she should ever be queen of these people, or ever communicate to them amusing and useful knowledge.

Both the men now seemed to be inquiring about Maggie, for they looked at her, and the tone of the conversation became of that pacific kind which implies curiosity on one side and the power of satisfying it on the other. At last the younger woman said in her previous deferential, coaxing tone,—

"This nice little lady's come to live with us; aren't you glad?"

"Ay, very glad," said the younger man, who was looking at Maggie's silver thimble and other small matters that had been taken from her pocket. He returned them all except the thimble

to the younger woman, with some observation,
and she immediately restored them to Maggie's
pocket, while the men seated themselves, and
began to attack the contents of the kettle,—a
stew of meat and potatoes,—which had been
taken off the fire and turned out into a yellow
platter.

Maggie began to think that Tom must be
right about the gypsies; they must certainly be
thieves, unless the man meant to return her
thimble by and by. She would willingly have
given it to him, for she was not at all attached to
her thimble; but the idea that she was among
thieves prevented her from feeling any comfort
in the revival of deference and attention toward
her; all thieves, except Robin Hood, were wicked
people. The women saw she was frightened.

"We've got nothing nice for a lady to eat,"
said the old woman, in her coaxing tone. "And
she's so hungry, sweet little lady."

"Here, my dear, try if you can eat a bit o'
this," said the younger woman, handing some
of the stew on a brown dish with an iron spoon
to Maggie, who, remembering that the old woman had seemed angry with her for not liking
the bread and bacon, dared not refuse the stew,
though fear had chased away her appetite. If
her father would but come by in the gig and take
her up! Or even if Jack the Giantkiller, or Mr.
Greatheart, or Saint George who slew the dragon
on the half-pennies, would happen to pass that
way! But Maggie thought with a sinking heart
that these heroes were never seen in the neigh-

borhood of Saint Ogg's; nothing very wonderful
ever came there.

Maggie Tulliver, you perceive, was by no
means that well-trained, well-informed young
person that a small female of eight or nine necessarily is in these days; she had only been to school
a year at Saint Ogg's, and had so few books that
she sometimes read the dictionary; so that in
traveling over her small mind you would have
found the most unexpected ignorance as well as
unexpected knowledge. She could have informed you that there was such a word as
"polygamy," and being also acquainted with
"polysyllable," she had deduced the conclusion
that "poly" meant "many"; but she had had
no idea that gypsies were not well supplied with
groceries, and her thoughts generally were the
oddest mixture of clear-eyed acumen and blind
dreams.

Her ideas about the gypsies had undergone a
rapid modification in the last five minutes. From
having considered them very respectful companions, amenable to instruction, she had begun
to think that they meant perhaps to kill her as
soon as it was dark, and cut up her body for
gradual cooking; the suspicion crossed her that
the fierce-eyed old man was in fact the Devil,
who might drop that transparent disguise at any
moment, and turn either into a grinning blacksmith, or else a fiery-eyed monster with dragon's
wings. It was no use trying to eat the stew, and
yet the thing she most dreaded was to offend the
gypsies, by betraying her extremely unfavorable

opinion of them; and she wondered, with a keenness of interest that no theologian could have exceeded, whether, if the Devil were really present, he would know her thoughts.

"What! you don't like the smell of it, my dear," said the young woman, observing that Maggie did not even take a spoonful of the stew. "Try a bit, come."

"No, thank you," said Maggie, summoning all her force for a desperate effort, and trying to smile in a friendly way. "I haven't time, I think; it seems getting darker. I think I must go home now, and come again another day, and then I can bring you a basket with some jam-tarts and things."

Maggie rose from her seat as she threw out this illusory prospect, devoutly hoping that Apollyon was gullible; but her hope sank when the old gypsy woman said, "Stop a bit, stop a bit, little lady; we'll take you home, all safe, when we've done supper; you shall ride home, like a lady."

Maggie sat down again, with little faith in this promise, though she presently saw the tall girl putting a bridle on the donkey, and throwing a couple of bags on his back.

"Now, then, little missis," said the younger man, rising, and leading the donkey forward, "tell us where you live; what's the name of the place?"

"Dorlcote Mill is my home," said Maggie, eagerly. "My father is Mr. Tulliver; he lives there."

"What! a big mill a little way this side o' Saint Ogg's?"

"Yes," said Maggie. "Is it far off? I think I should like to walk there, if you please."

"No, no, it'll be getting dark, we must make haste. And the donkey'll carry you as nice as can be; you'll see."

He lifted Maggie as he spoke, and set her on the donkey. She felt relieved that it was not the old man who seemed to be going with her, but she had only a trembling hope that she was really going home.

"Here's your pretty bonnet," said the younger woman, putting that recently despised but now welcome article of costume on Maggie's head; "and you'll say we've been very good to you, won't you? and what a nice little lady we said you was."

"Oh yes, thank you," said Maggie, "I'm very much obliged to you. But I wish you'd go with me too." She thought anything was better than going with one of the dreadful men alone; it would be more cheerful to be murdered by a larger party.

"Ah, you're fondest o' *me*, aren't you?" said the woman. "But I can't go; you'll go too fast for me."

It now appeared that the man also was to be seated on the donkey, holding Maggie before him, and she was as incapable of remonstrating against this arrangement as the donkey himself, though no nightmare had ever seemed to her more horrible. When the woman had patted

"TO SAINT OGG'S, TWO MILES."

her on the back, and said "Good-bye," the donkey, at a strong hint from the man's stick, set off
at a rapid walk along the lane toward the point
Maggie had come from an hour ago, while the
tall girl and the rough urchin, also furnished with
sticks, obligingly escorted them for the first hun-

dred yards, with much screaming and thwack-
ing.

Not Leonore, in that preternatural midnight
excursion with her phantom lover, was more
terrified than poor Maggie in this entirely natural
ride on a short-paced donkey, with a gypsy behind her, who considered that he was earning
half-a-crown. The red light of the setting sun
seemed to have a portentous meaning, with which
the alarming bray of the second donkey with the
log on its foot must surely have some connection.
Two low thatched cottages—the only houses
they passed in this lane—seemed to add to its
dreariness; they had no windows to speak of, and
the doors were closed; it was probable that they
were inhabited by witches, and it was a relief to
find that the donkey did not stop there.

At last—oh, sight of joy!—this lane, the longest in the world, was coming to an end, was opening on a broad highroad, where there was actually a coach passing! And there was a finger-
post at the corner,—she had surely seen that
finger-post before,—"To Saint Ogg's, 2 miles."
The gypsy really meant to take her home, then;
he was probably a good man, after all, and might
have been rather hurt at the thought that she
didn't like coming with him alone. This idea
became stronger as she felt more and more certain that she knew the road quite well, and she
was considering how she might open a conversation with the injured gypsy, and not only gratify
his feelings but efface the impression of her
cowardice, when, as they reached a crossroad,

Maggie caught sight of some one coming on a white-faced horse.

"Oh, stop, stop!" she cried out. "There's my father! Oh, father, father!"

The sudden joy was almost painful, and before her father reached her, she was sobbing. Great was Mr. Tulliver's wonder, for he had made a round from Basset, and had not yet been home.

"Why, what's the meaning o' this?" he said, checking his horse, while Maggie slipped from the donkey and ran to her father's stirrup.

"The little miss lost herself, I reckon," said the gypsy. "She'd come to our tent at the far end o' Dunlow Lane, and I was bringing her where she said her home was. It's a good way to come arter being on the tramp all day."

"Oh yes, father, he's been very good to bring me home," said Maggie,—"a very kind, good man!"

"Here, then, my man," said Mr. Tulliver, taking out five shillings. "It's the best day's work *you* ever did. I couldn't afford to lose the little wench; here, lift her up before me."

"Why, Maggie, how's this, how's this?" he said, as they rode along, while she laid her head against her father and sobbed. "How came you to be rambling about and lose yourself?"

"Oh, father," sobbed Maggie, "I ran away because I was so unhappy; Tom was so angry with me. I couldn't bear it."

"Pooh, pooh," said Mr. Tulliver, soothingly, "you mustn't think o' running away from father. What 'ud father do without his little wench?"

"Oh, no, I never will again, father—never."

Mr. Tulliver spoke his mind very strongly when he reached home that evening; and the effect was seen in the remarkable fact that Maggie never heard one reproach from her mother, or one taunt from Tom, about this foolish business of her running away to the gypsies. Maggie was rather awe-stricken by this unusual treatment, and sometimes thought that her conduct had been too wicked to be alluded to.

———

Of the three children who are presented to us in these chapters, Tom, Maggie and little Lucy, which is the most attractive to you?

Do you think the author meant us to receive this impression?

Is Maggie proud? Is she impetuous? Is she highly sensitive? Find as many passages as you can which prove your answers to these questions. Do these qualities usually make a person attractive?

What is the mainspring of Maggie's character —the motive for most of her actions? Does Tom seem to you worthy of the intense affection she bestows upon him? Do you think a person with Maggie's nature would be likely to live a happy or an unhappy life?

Few writers have ever been able to draw as distinct, lifelike a picture of a child as we have of Maggie Tulliver in *The Mill on the Floss*. This is to be in part accounted for by the fact that it is herself as a child that George Eliot is describing.

A GORILLA HUNT

PAUL DU CHAILLU

HAD not been at the village long before news came that gorillas had been recently seen in the neighborhood of a plantation only half a mile distant. Early in the morning of the twenty-fifth of June, I wended my way thither, accompanied by one of my boys, named Odanga. The plantation was a large one, and situated on very broken ground, surrounded by the virgin forest. It was a lovely morning; the sky was almost cloudless, and all around was still as death, except the slight rustling of the tree tops moved by the gentle land breeze. When I reached the place, I had first to pick my way through the maze of tree stumps and half-burnt logs by the side of a field of cassada. I was going quietly along the borders of this, when I heard, in the grove of plantain trees towards which I was walking, a great crashing noise, like the breaking of trees. I immediately hid myself behind a bush, and was soon gratified with the sight of a female gorilla; but before I had time to notice its movements, a second and third emerged from the masses of colossal foliage; at length no less than four came into view.

They were all busily engaged in tearing down the larger trees. One of the females had a young one following her. I had an excellent opportunity of watching the movements of the impish-looking band. The shaggy hides, the protuberant abdomens, the hideous features of these strange creatures, whose forms so nearly resemble man, made up a picture like a vision in some morbid dream. In destroying a tree, they first grasped the base of the stem with one of their feet, and then with their powerful arms pulled it down, a matter of not much difficulty with so loosely formed a stem as that of the plantain. They then set upon the juicy heart of the trees at the bases of the leaves, and devoured it with great voracity. While eating they made a kind of clucking noise, expressive of contentment. Many trees they destroyed apparently out of pure mischief. Now and then they stood still and looked around. Once or twice they seemed on the point of starting off in alarm, but recovered themselves and continued their work. Gradually they got nearer to the edge of the dark forest, and finally disappeared. I was so intent on watching them, that I let go the last chance of shooting one almost before I became aware of it.

The next day I went again with Odanga to the same spot. I had no expectation of seeing gorillas in the same plantation, and was carrying a light shot gun, having given my heavy double-barreled rifle to the boy to carry. The plantation extended over two hills, with a deep hollow between, planted with sugar cane. Before I had crossed the hollow I saw on the opposite slope a monstrous gorilla, standing erect and looking

directly towards me. Without turning my face
I beckoned to the boy to bring me my rifle, but
no rifle came,—the little coward had bolted, and
I lost my chance. The huge beast stared at me
for about two minutes, and then, without utter-
ing any cry, moved off to the shade of the forest,
running nimbly on his hands and feet.

As my readers may easily imagine, I had excellent opportunity of observing, during these
two days, the manner in which the gorillas
walked when in open ground. They move along
with great rapidity and on all fours, that is, with
the knuckles of their hands touching the ground.
Artists, in representing the gorilla walking, generally make the arms too much bowed outwards,
and the elbows too much bent; this gives the
figures an appearance of heaviness and awk-
wardness. When the gorillas that I watched
left their plantain trees, they moved off at a great
pace over the ground, with their arms extended
straight forwards towards the ground, and moving rapidly. I may mention also that having
now opened the stomachs of several freshly
killed gorillas, I have never found anything but
vegetable matter in them.

When I returned to Nkongon Mboumba I
found there my old friend Akondogo, chief of one
of the Commi villages, who had just returned
from the Ngobi country, a little further south.
To my great surprise and pleasure, he had brought
for me a living gorilla, a young one, but the largest I had ever seen captured alive Like Joe,
the young male whose habits in confinement I

described in 'Equatorial Africa,' this one showed the most violent and ungovernable disposition. He tried to bite every one who came near him, and was obliged to be secured by a forked stick closely applied to the back of his neck. This mode of imprisoning these animals is a very improper one if the object be to keep them alive and to tame them, but, unfortunately, in this barbarous country, we had not the materials requisite to build a strong cage. The injury caused to this one by the forked stick eventually caused his death. As I had some more hunting to do, I left the animal in charge of Akondogo until he should have an opportunity of sending it to me on the Fernand Vaz.

The natives of all the neighboring country were now so well aware that I wanted live gorillas, and was willing to give a high price for them, that many were stimulated to search with great perseverance; the good effects of this were soon made evident.

One day as I was quietly dining with Captain Holder, of the *Cambria* (a vessel just arrived from England), one of my men came in with the startling news that three live gorillas had been brought, one of them full grown. I had not long to wait; in they came. First, a very large adult female, bound hand and foot; then her female child, screaming terribly; and lastly, a vigorous young male, also tightly bound. The female had been ingeniously secured by the negroes to a strong stick, the wrists bound to the upper part and the ankles to the lower, so that she could not reach to tear the cords with her teeth. It was dark, and the scene was one so wild and strange that I shall never forget it. The fiendish countenances of the Calibanish trio, one of them distorted by pain, for the mother gorilla was severely wounded, were lit up by the ruddy glare of native torches. The thought struck me, what would I not give to have the group in London for a few days!

The young male I secured by a chain which I had in readiness, and gave him henceforth the name of Tom. We untied his hands and feet; to show his gratitude for this act of kindness he immediately made a rush at me, screaming with all his might; happily the chain was made fast, and I took care afterwards to keep out of his way. The old mother gorilla was in an unfortunate plight. She had an arm broken and a wound in the chest, besides being dreadfully beaten on the head. She groaned and roared many times during the night, probably from pain.

I noticed next day, and on many occasions, that the vigorous young male whenever he made a rush at any one and missed his aim, immediately ran back. This corresponds with what is known of the habits of the large males in their native woods; when attacked they make a furious rush at their enemy, break an arm or tear his bowels open, and then beat a retreat, leaving their victim to shift for himself.

The wounded female died in the course of the next day; her moanings were more frequent in the morning, and they gradually became weaker as her life ebbed out. Her death was like that of a human being, and afflicted me more than I could have thought possible. Her child clung to her to the last, and tried to obtain milk from her breast after she was dead. I photographed them both when the young one was resting in its dead mother's lap. I kept the young one alive for three days after its mother's death. It moaned at night most piteously. I fed it on goat's milk, for it was too young to eat berries. It died the fourth day, having taken an unconquerable dislike to the milk. It had, I think, begun to know me a little. As to the male, I made at least a dozen attempts to photograph the irascible little demon, but all in vain. The pointing of the camera towards him threw him into a perfect rage, and I was almost provoked to give him a sound thrashing. The day after, however, I succeeded with him, taking two views, not very perfect, but sufficient for my object.

I must now relate how these three animals were caught, premising that the capture of the female was the first instance that had come to my knowledge of an adult gorilla being taken alive. The place where they were found was on the left bank of the Fernand Vaz, about thirty miles above my village. At this part a narrow promontory projects into the river. It was the place where I had intended to take the distinguished traveler, Captain Burton, to show him a live gorilla, if he had paid me a visit, as I had expected, for I had written to invite him whilst

GORILLA WITH HER YOUNG

he was on a tour from his consulate at Fernando Po to several points on the West African coast. A woman, belonging to a neighboring village, had told her people that she had seen two squads of female gorillas, some of them accompanied by their young ones, in her plantain field. The men resolved to go in chase of them, so they armed themselves with guns, axes, and spears, and sallied forth. The situation was very favorable for the hunters; they formed a line across the narrow strip of land and pressed forward, driving the animals to the edge of the water. When they came in sight of them, they made all the noise in their power, and thus bewildered the gorillas, who were shot or beaten down in their endeavors to escape. There were eight adult females altogether, but not a single male. The negroes thought the males were in concealment in the adjoining woods, having probably been frightened away by the noise.

This incident led me to modify somewhat the opinions I had expressed, in 'Adventures in Equatorial Africa,' regarding some of the habits of the gorilla. I there said I believed it impossible to capture an adult female alive, but I ought to have added, unless wounded. I have also satisfied myself that the gorilla is more gregarious than I formerly considered it to be; at least it is now clear that, at certain times of the year, it goes in bands more numerous than those I saw in my former journey. Then I never saw more than five together. I have myself seen, on my present expedition, two of these bands of gorillas, numbering eight or ten, and have had authentic accounts from the natives of other similar bands. It is true that, when gorillas become aged, they seem to be more solitary, and to live in pairs, or, as in the case of old males, quite alone. I have been assured by the negroes that solitary and aged gorillas are sometimes

seen almost white; the hair becomes grizzled
with age, and I have no doubt that the statement
of their becoming occasionally white with extreme old age is quite correct.

The gorilla is of migratory habits at some
seasons of the year. He is then not found in the
districts usually resorted to by him when the
berries, fruits, and nuts are in season.

Besides my other collections I embarked a
live gorilla, our little friend Tom, and had full
hopes that he would arrive safely and gratify
the world of London with a sight of this rare and
wonderful ape in the living state; unfortunately,
he died on the passage. He did very well for a
few weeks, I am told, as long as the supply of
bananas lasted which I placed on board for his
sustenance. The repugnance of the gorilla to
cooked food, or any sort of food except the fruits
and juicy plants he obtains in his own wilds, will
always be a difficulty in the way of bringing
him to Europe alive. I had sent him consigned
to Messrs. Baring, who, I am sure, never had
any such consignment before. I promised the
Captain that he should receive one hundred
pounds if he succeeded in taking the animal
alive to London.

During the few days Tom was in my possession
he remained, like all the others of his species
that I had seen, utterly untractable. The food
that was offered to him he would come and
snatch from the hand, and then bolt with it to
the length of his tether. If I looked at him he
would make a feint of darting at me, and in

giving him water I had to push the bowl towards him with a stick, for fear of his biting me. When he was angry I saw him often beat the ground and his legs with his fists, thus showing a similar habit to that of the adult gorillas, which I described as beating their breasts with their fists when confronting an enemy. Before lying down to rest he used to pack his straw very carefully as a bed to lie on. Tom used to wake me in the night by screaming suddenly, and in the morning I more than once detected him in the attempt to strangle himself with his chain, no doubt through rage at being kept prisoner. He used to twist the chain round and round the post to which it was attached until it became quite short and then pressed with his feet the lower part of the post until he had nearly done the business.

As I have before related, I took photographs of Tom, and succeeded very well. These photographs I was unwilling to send home, and kept them until I should have completed my whole series of photographs of African subjects. They are now, unfortunately, lost forever; for they were left behind in the bush during my hurried retreat from Ashango-land, as will be related in the sequel.

When the last boat which took on board the Captain and the live animals left the shore for the vessel, I trembled for the safety of the cargo, for the surf was very rough. The negroes, however, could have managed to get her safely through if they had not been too careful. They were nervous at having a white man on board, and did not seize the proper moment to pass the breakers; their hesitation was very near proving fatal, for a huge billow broke over them and filled the boat. It did not, happily, upset, but they had to return. Captain Berridge thus escaped with a wetting, and the Potamochoerus and eagles were half drowned. As to poor Tom, the bath, instead of cooling his courage, made him more violent than ever. He shouted furiously, and as soon as I opened the door of his cage he pounced on the bystanders, clinging to them and screaming. A present of a banana, which he ate voraciously, quieted him down, and the passage was again tried in the afternoon with a better result.

THE CLOUD

PERCY BYSSHE SHELLEY

I bring fresh showers for the thirsting flowers,
    From the seas and the streams;
I bear light shade for the leaves when laid
    In their noonday dreams.
From my wings are shaken the dews that waken
    The sweet buds every one,
When rocked to rest on their mother's breast,
    As she dances about the sun.
I wield the flail of the lashing hail,
    And whiten the green plains under;
And then again I dissolve it in rain,
    And laugh as I pass in thunder.

I sift the snow on the mountains below,
    And their great pines groan aghast;
And all the night 'tis my pillow white,
    While I sleep in the arms of the blast.
Sublime on the towers of my skyey bowers
    Lightning, my pilot, sits,
In a cavern under is fettered the thunder;
    It struggles and howls by fits.
Over earth and ocean, with gentle motion,
    This pilot is guiding me,
Lured by the love of the genii that move
    In the depths of the purple sea;
Over the rills and the crags and the hills,
    Over the lakes and the plains,
Wherever he dream, under mountain or stream,
    The spirit he loves remains;

And I all the while bask in heaven's blue smile,
    Whilst he is dissolving in rains.

The sanguine sunrise, with his meteor eyes,
    And his burning plumes outspread,
Leaps on the back of my sailing rack,
    When the morning star shines dead.
As, on the jag of a mountain crag
    Which an earthquake rocks and swings,
An eagle, alit, one moment may sit
    In the light of its golden wings;
And when sunset may breathe, from the lit sea
       beneath,
    Its ardors of rest and of love,
And the crimson pall of eve may fall
    From the depth of heaven above,
With wings folded I rest on mine airy nest,
    As still as a brooding dove.

That orbéd maiden with white fire laden,
    Whom mortals call the moon,
Glides glimmering o'er my fleece-like floor
    By the midnight breezes strewn;
And wherever the beat of her unseen feet,
    Which only the angels hear,
May have broken the woof of my tent's thin roof,
    The stars peep behind her and peer;
And I laugh to see them whirl and flee,
    Like a swarm of golden bees,
When I widen the rent in my wind-built tent,
    Till the calm rivers, lakes, and seas,
Like strips of the sky fallen through me on high,
    Are each paved with the moon and these.

I bind the sun's throne with a burning zone,
    And the moon's with a girdle of pearl;
The volcanoes are dim, and the stars reel and
       swim,
    When the whirlwinds my banner unfurl.
From cape to cape, with a bridge-like shape,
    Over a torrent sea,
Sunbeam-proof, I hang like a roof,
    The mountains its columns be.
The triumphal arch, through which I march,
    With hurricane, fire, and snow,
When the powers of the air are chained to my
       chair,
    Is the million-colored bow;
The sphere-fire above its soft colors wove,
    While the moist earth was laughing below.

I am the daughter of earth and water,
    And the nursling of the sky;
I pass through the pores of the ocean and shores;
    I change, but I cannot die.
For after the rain, when, with never a stain,
    The pavilion of heaven is bare,
And the winds and sunbeams, with their convex
      gleams,
    Build up the blue dome of air,—
I silently laugh at my own cenotaph,
    And out of the caverns of rain,
Like a child from the womb, like a ghost from
      the tomb,
    I rise and upbuild it again.

BRUTE NEIGHBORS

HENRY DAVID THOREAU

NOTE,—The author of this sketch, Henry David Thoreau, who lived from 1817 to 1862, was one of the oddest of American men of genius. He was educated at Harvard University, but he did not care, in the common phrase, to "turn his learning to practical account;" that is, save for a short time when he taught school, he did not make it earn his living for him. His theory was that life and energy were being wasted when a man spent in working more time than he absolutely needed to in order to provide himself with necessities; and this theory he carried out in his own life. While he lived in Concord, he did odd jobs at carpentering, surveying, and gardening, and worked for a time at his father's trade of pencil making. However, he contended that a man was doing himself an injustice if he kept on at that work after he had reached the point where he could make no further improvement in his pencils.

From 1845 to 1847 Thoreau lived as a hermit in a hut which he had built on the shore of Walden Pond, and the simple life he led there gave him plenty of leisure for the things he liked best—the study of nature, the grappling with philosophical problems, and the society of friends. The result of the two years at Walden Pond was his best book, *Walden, or Life in the*

Woods, a work which is distinguished for its peculiarly truthful and sympathetic studies of nature.

Thoreau refused to perform any of the ordinary duties of a citizen: he never voted, he never paid taxes. Once he was arrested because he refused to pay his taxes, and was thrown into jail; his friends remonstrated with him, but still he refused to pay. However, when his friends paid the sum he made no objections to accepting his release, nor did he in the future make any objections when his friends quietly paid his taxes.

The Pond in Winter and *Winter Animals*, which are contained in this volume, are also from Thoreau.

HY do precisely these objects which we behold make a world? Why has man just these species of animals for his neighbors; as if nothing but a mouse could have filled this crevice? I suspect that Pilpay & Co. have put animals to their best use, for they are all beasts of burden, in a sense, made to carry some portion of our thoughts.

The mice which haunted my house were not the common ones, which are said to have been introduced into the country, but a wild native kind not found in the village. I sent one to a distinguished naturalist, and it interested him much. When I was building, one of these had its nest underneath the house, and before I had

laid the second floor, and swept out the shavings,
would come out regularly at lunch time and pick
up the crumbs at my feet. It probably had
never seen a man before; and it soon became
quite familiar, and would run over my shoes and
up my clothes. It could readily ascend the sides
of the room by short impulses, like a squirrel,
which it resembled in its motions. At length,
as I leaned with my elbow on the bench one day,
it ran up my clothes, and along my sleeve, and
round and round the paper which held my
dinner, while I kept the latter close, and dodged
and played at bo-peep with it; and when at last
I held still a piece of cheese between my thumb
and finger, it came and nibbled it, sitting in my
hand, and afterward cleaned its face and paws,
like a fly, and walked away.

A phœbe soon built in my shed, and a robin
for protection in a pine which grew against the
house. In June the partridge (*Tetrao umbellus*),
which is so shy a bird, led her brood past my
windows, from the woods in the rear to the front
of my house, clucking and calling to them like a
hen, and in all her behavior proving herself the
hen of the woods. The young suddenly disperse on your approach, at a signal from the
mother, as if a whirlwind had swept them away,
and they so exactly resemble the dried leaves
and twigs that many a traveler has placed his
foot in the midst of a brood, and heard the whir
of the old bird as she flew off, and her anxious
calls and mewing, or seen her trail her wings to
attract his attention, without suspecting their

neighborhood. The parent will sometimes roll
and spin round before you in such a dishabille,
that you cannot, for a few moments, detect what
kind of creature it is. The young squat still
and flat, often running their heads under a leaf,
and mind only their mother's directions given
from a distance, nor will your approach make
them run again and betray themselves. You
may even tread on them, or have your eyes on
them for a minute, without discovering them. I
have held them in my open hand at such a time,
and still their only care, obedient to their
mother and their instinct, was to squat there
without fear or trembling. So perfect is this
instinct, that once, when I had laid them on the
leaves again, and one accidentally fell on its
side, it was found with the rest in exactly the
same position ten minutes afterward. They
are not callow like the young of most birds, but
more perfectly developed and precocious even
than chickens. The remarkably adult yet innocent expression of their open and serene eyes is
very memorable. All intelligence seems reflected in them. They suggest not merely the
purity of infancy, but a wisdom clarified by
experience. Such an eye was not born when the
bird was, but is coeval with the sky it reflects.
The woods do not yield another such gem. The
traveler does not often look into such a limpid
well. The ignorant or reckless sportsman often
shoots the parent at such a time, and leaves
these innocents to fall a prey to some prowling
beast or bird, or gradually mingle with the

oecaying leaves which they so much resemble. It is said that when hatched by a hen they will directly disperse on some alarm, and are so lost, for they never hear the mother's call which gathers them again. These were my hens and chickens.

It is remarkable how many creatures live wild and free though secret in the woods, and still sustain themselves in the neighborhood of towns, suspected by hunters only. How retired the otter manages to live here! He grows to be four feet long, as big as a small boy, perhaps without any human being getting a glimpse of him. I formerly saw the raccoon in the woods behind where my house is built, and probably still heard their whinnering at night. Commonly I rested an hour or two in the shade at noon, after planting, and ate my lunch, and read a little by a spring which was the source of a swamp and of a brook, oozing from under Brister's Hill, half a mile from my field. The approach to this was through a succession of descending grassy hollows, full of young pitch pines, into a larger wood about the swamp. There, in a very secluded and shaded spot, under a spreading white pine, there was yet a clean firm sward to sit on. I had dug out the spring and made a well of clear gray water, where I could dip up a pailful without roiling it, and thither I went for this purpose almost every day in midsummer, when the pond was warmest. Thither, too, the woodcock led her brood, to probe the mud for worms, flying but a foot above them down the

bank, while they ran in a troop beneath; but at
last, spying me, she would leave her young and
circle round and round me, nearer and nearer
till within four or five feet, pretending broken
wings and legs, to attract my attention, and get
off her young, who would already have taken up
their march, with faint wiry peep, single file
through the swamp, as she directed.   Or I heard
the peep of the young when I could not see the
parent bird.   There too the turtledoves sat over
the spring, or fluttered from bough to bough of
the soft white pines over my head; or the red
squirrel, coursing down the nearest bough, was
particularly familiar and inquisitive.   You only
need sit still long enough in some attractive
spot in the woods that all its inhabitants may
exhibit themselves to you by turns.

I was witness to events of a less peaceful character.   One day when I went out to my wood
pile, or rather my pile of stumps, I observed two
large ants, the one red, the other much larger,
nearly half an inch long, and black, fiercely con-
tending with one another.   Having once got
hold they never let go, but struggled and wrestled
and rolled on the chips incessantly.   Looking
further, I was surprised to find that the chips
were covered with such combatants, that it was
not a *duellum*, but a *bellum*, a war between two
races of ants, the red always pitted against the
black, and frequently two red ones to one black.
The legions of these Myrmidons covered all the
hills and vales in my wood yard, and the ground
was already strewn with the dead and dying,

both red and black. It was the only battle which I have ever witnessed, the only battlefield I ever trod while the battle was raging; internecine war; the red republicans on the one hand, and the black imperialists on the other. On every side they were engaged in deadly combat, yet without any noise that I could hear, and human soldiers never fought so resolutely. I

THE BATTLE OF THE ANTS

watched a couple that were fast locked in each other's embraces, in a little sunny valley amid the chips, now at noonday prepared to fight till the sun went down, or life went out. The smaller red champion had fastened himself like a vise to his adversary's front, and through all the tumblings on that field never for an instant ceased to gnaw at one of his feelers near the root, having already caused the other to go by the board; while the stronger black one dashed

him from side to side, and, as I saw on looking
nearer, had already divested him of several of
his members. They fought with more perti-
nacity than bulldogs. Neither manifested the
least disposition to retreat. It was evident that
their battle-cry was "Conquer or die." In the
meanwhile there came along a single red ant on
the hillside of this valley, evidently full of excitement, who either had despatched his foe, or
had not yet taken part in the battle; probably
the latter, for he had lost none of his limbs;
whose mother had charged him to return with
his shield or upon it. Or perchance he was
some Achilles, who had nourished his wrath
apart, and had now come to avenge or rescue his
Patroclus. He saw this unequal combat from
afar—for the blacks were nearly twice the size
of the red—he drew near with rapid pace till he
stood on his guard within half an inch of the
combatants; then, watching his opportunity, he
sprang upon the black warrior, and commenced
his operations near the root of his right fore-leg,
leaving the foe to select among his own members;
and so there were three united for life, as if a new
kind of attraction had been invented which put
all other locks and cements to shame. I should
not have wondered by this time to find that they
had their respective musical bands stationed on
some eminent chip, and playing their national
airs the while, to excite the slow and cheer the
dying combatants. I was myself excited somewhat even as if they had been men. The more
you think of it, the less the difference. And

certainly there is not the fight recorded in Concord history, at least, if in the history of America,
that will bear a moment's comparison with this,
whether for the numbers engaged in it, or for the
patriotism and heroism displayed. For numbers and for carnage it was an Austerlitz or
Dresden. Concord Fight! Two killed on the
patriots' side, and Luther Blanchard wounded!
Why, here every ant was a Butterick—"Fire! for
God's sake, fire!"—and thousands shared the
fate of Davis and Hosmer. There was not one
hireling there. I have no doubt that it was a
principle they fought for, as much as our ances-
tors, and not to avoid a three-penny tax on their
tea; and the results of this battle will be as important and memorable to those whom it concerns as those of the battle of Bunker Hill, at
least.

I took up the chip on which the three I have
particularly described were struggling, carried it
into my house, and placed it under a tumbler on
my window sill, in order to see the issue. Holding a microscope to the first-mentioned red ant,
I saw that, though he was assiduously gnawing
at the near fore-leg of his enemy, having severed
his remaining feeler, his own breast was all torn
away, exposing what vitals he had there to the
jaws of the black warrior, whose breastplate was
apparently too thick for him to pierce; and the
dark carbuncles of the sufferer's eyes shone with
ferocity such as war only could excite. They
struggled half an hour longer under the tumbler,
and when I looked again the black soldier had

severed the heads of his foes from their bodies,
and the still living heads were hanging on either
side of him like ghastly trophies at his saddle-
bow, still apparently as firmly fastened as ever,
and he was endeavoring with feeble struggles,
being without feelers and with only the remnant
of a leg, and I know not how many other wounds,
to divest himself of them; which at length, after
half an hour more, he accomplished. I raised
the glass, and he went off over the window sill
in that crippled state. Whether he finally survived that combat, and spent the remainder of
his days in some Hotel des Invalides, I do not
know; but I thought that his industry would not
be worth much thereafter. I never learned
which party was victorious, nor the cause of the
war; but I felt for the rest of that day as if I had
had my feelings excited and harrowed by witnessing the struggle, the ferocity and carnage, of
a human battle before my door.

Kirby and Spence tell us that the battles of
ants have long been celebrated and the date of
them recorded, though they say that Huber is
the only modern author who appears to have
witnessed them. "Æneas Sylvius," say they,
"after giving a very circumstantial account of
one contested with great obstinacy by a great
and small species on the trunk of a pear tree,"
adds that "'This action was fought in the
pontificate of Eugenius the Fourth, in the
presence of Nicholas Pistoriensis, an eminent
lawyer, who related the whole history of the
battle with the greatest fidelity.' A similar

engagement between great and small ants is
recorded by Olaus Magnus, in which the small
ones, being victorious, are said to have buried
the bodies of their own soldiers, and left those
of their giant enemies a prey to the birds. This
event happened previous to the expulsion of the
tyrant Christiern the Second from Sweden.''
The battle which I witnessed took place in the
Presidency of Polk, five years before the passage
of Webster's Fugitive-Slave Bill.

Many a village Bose, fit only to course a
mud-turtle in a victualling cellar, sported his
heavy quarters in the woods, without the knowledge of his master, and ineffectually smelled
at old fox burrows and woodchucks' holes; led
perchance by some slight cur which nimbly
threaded the wood, and might still inspire a
natural terror in its denizens; now far behind
his guide, barking like a canine bull toward
some small squirrel which had treed itself for
scrutiny, then, cantering off, bending the bushes
with his weight, imagining that he is on the
track of some stray member of the jerbilla
family. Once I was surprised to see a cat
walking along the stony shore of the pond, for
they rarely wander so far from home. The
surprise was mutual. Nevertheless the most
domestic cat, which has lain on a rug all her
days, appears quite at home in the woods, and,
by her sly and stealthy behavior, proves herself
more native there than the regular inhabitants.
Once, when berrying, I met with a cat with
young kittens in the woods, quite wild, and they

all, like their mother, had their backs up and were fiercely spitting at me. A few years before I lived in the woods there was what was called a "winged cat" in one of the farmhouses in Lincoln nearest the pond, Mr. Gilian Baker's. When I called to see her in June, 1842, she was gone a-hunting in the woods, as was her wont (I am not sure whether it was a male or female, and so use the more common pronoun), but her mistress told me that she came into the neighborhood a little more than a year before, in April, and was finally taken into their house; that she was of a dark brownish gray color, with a white spot on her throat, and white feet, and had a large bushy tail like a fox; that in the winter the fur grew thick and flatted out along her sides, forming strips ten or twelve inches long by two and a half wide, and under her chin like a muff, the upper side loose, the under matted like felt, and in the spring these appendages dropped off. They gave me a pair of her "wings," which I keep still. There is no appearance of a membrane about them. Some thought it was part flying-squirrel or some other wild animal, which is not impossible, for, according to naturalists, prolific hybrids have been produced by the union of the marten and domestic cat. This would have been the right kind of cat for me to keep, if I had kept any; for why should not a poet's cat be winged as well as his horse?

In the fall the loon (*Colymbus glacialis*) came, as usual, to moult and bathe in the pond, making the woods ring with his wild laughter before I had risen. At rumor of his arrival all the Mill-dam sportsmen are on the alert, in gigs and on foot, two by two and three by three, with patent rifles and conical balls and spyglasses. They come rustling through the woods like autumn leaves, at least ten men to one loon. Some station themselves on this side of the pond, some on that, for the poor bird cannot be omnipresent; if he dive here he must come up there. But now the kind October wind rises, rustling the leaves and rippling the surface of the water, so that no loon can be heard or seen, though his foes sweep the pond with spyglasses, and make the woods resound with their discharges. The waves generally rise and dash angrily, taking sides with all waterfowl, and our sportsmen must beat a retreat to town and shop and unfinished jobs. But they were too often successful. When I went to get a pail of water early in the morning I frequently saw this stately bird sailing out of my cove within a few rods. If I endeavored to overtake him in a boat, in order to see how he would manœuvre, he would dive and be completely lost, so that I did not discover him again sometimes till the latter part of the day. But I was more than a match for him on the surface. He commonly went off in a rain.

As I was paddling along the north shore one very calm October afternoon, for such days especially they settle on to the lakes, like the milkweed down, having looked in vain over the pond for a loon, suddenly one, sailing out from the shore toward the middle a few rods in front

of me, set up his wild laugh and betrayed himself. I pursued with a paddle and he dived, but
when he came up I was nearer than before. He
dived again, but I miscalculated the direction
he would take, and we were fifty rods apart when
he came to the surface this time, for I had helped
to widen the interval; and again he laughed long
and loud, and with more reason than before.

He manœuvred so cunningly that I could not
get within half a dozen rods of him. Each time,
when he came to the surface, turning his head
this way and that, he coolly surveyed the water
and the land, and apparently chose his course
so that he might come up where there was the
widest expanse of water, and at the greatest
distance from the boat. It was surprising how
quickly he made up his mind and put his
resolve into execution. He led me at once to the
widest part of the pond, and could not be driven
from it. While he was thinking one thing in his
brain, I was endeavoring to divine his thought in
mine. It was a pretty game, played on the
smooth surface of the pond, a man against a
loon. Suddenly your adversary's checker dis-
appears beneath the board, and the problem is
to place yours nearest to where his will appear
again. Sometimes he would come up unexpectedly on the opposite side of me, having
apparently passed directly under the boat. So
long-winded was he and so unweariable, that
when he had swum furthest he would immediately plunge again, nevertheless; and then no
wit could divine where in the deep pond, beneath

WATCHING FOR THE LOON

the smooth surface, he might be speeding his
way like a fish, for he had time and ability to
visit the bottom of the pond in its deepest part.

It is said that loons have been caught in the
New York lakes eighty feet beneath the surface,
with hooks set for trout—though Walden is deeper
than that.   How surprised must the fishes be to
see this ungainly visitor from another sphere
speeding his way amid their schools!   Yet he
appeared to know his course as surely under
water as on the surface, and swam much faster

there.   Once or twice I saw a ripple where he
approached the surface, just put his head out to
reconnoitre, and instantly dived again.   I found
that it was as well for me to rest on my oars and
wait his reappearing as to endeavor to calculate
where he would rise; for again and again, when
I was straining my eyes over the surface one
way, I would suddenly be startled by his unearthly laugh behind me.   But why, after dis-
playing so much cunning, did he invariably
betray himself the moment he came up by that
loud laugh?   Did not his white breast enough
betray him?   He was indeed a silly loon, I
thought.   I could commonly hear the splash of
the water when he came up, and so also detected
him.   But after an hour he seemed as fresh as
ever, dived as willingly and swam yet further
than at first.   It was surprising to see how
serenely he sailed off with unruffled breast when
he came to the surface, doing all the work with
his webbed feet beneath.   His usual note was
this demoniac laughter, yet somewhat like that
of a waterfowl; but occasionally, when he had
balked me most successfully and come up a long
way off, he uttered a long-drawn unearthly howl,
probably more like that of a wolf than any bird;
as when a beast puts his muzzle to the ground
and deliberately howls.   This was his looning—
perhaps the wildest sound that is ever heard
here, making the woods ring far and wide.   I
concluded that he laughed in derision of my
efforts, confident of his own resources.   Though
the sky was by this time overcast, the pond was

so smooth that I could see where he broke the surface when I did not hear him. His white breast, the stillness of the air, and the smoothness of the water were all against him. At length, having come up fifty rods off, he uttered one of those prolonged howls, as if calling on the god of loons to aid him, and immediately there came a wind from the east and rippled the surface, and filled the whole air with misty rain, and I was impressed as if it were the prayer of the loon answered, and his god was angry with me; and so I left him disappearing far away on the tumultuous surface.

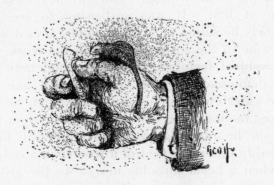

ODE TO A SKYLARK

PERCY BYSSHE SHELLEY

NOTE,—There are a few places in the United States where the skylark has been naturalized, but most of us have never heard it sing. In Europe, however, and especially in Great Britain, it is very common; and despite the fact that it is dull of plumage, there are few birds which are more universally loved. For the song which it pours forth as it soars upward in spiral curves and floats in the air is wonderfully sweet and cheerful. Strangely enough, this bird, which seems to like best to sing when far, far above the earth, does not refuse to sing when confined in a cage.

Though none of us may ever hear a skylark sing, we shall always feel grateful to the one which inspired the writing of Shelley's *Skylark*, one of the most beautiful of English lyrics.

Hail to thee, blithe spirit!—
Bird thou never wert—
That from heaven, or near it,
Pourest thy full heart
In profuse strains of unpremeditated art.

Higher still and higher
From the earth thou springest
Like a cloud of fire;
The blue deep thou wingest,
And singing still dost soar, and soaring ever singest.

In the golden lightning
Of the sunken sun,
O'er which clouds are brightening,
Thou dost float and run;
Like an unbodied joy whose race is just begun.

The pale purple even
Melts around thy flight;
Like a star of heaven
In the broad day-light,
Thou art unseen, but yet I hear thy shrill delight,

Keen as are the arrows
Of that silver sphere
Whose intense lamp narrows
In the white dawn clear,
Until we hardly see, we feel that it is there.

All the earth and air
With thy voice is loud,
As, when night is bare,
From one lonely cloud
The moon rains out her beams, and heaven is
overflowed.

What thou art we know not;
What is most like thee?
From rainbow clouds there flow not
Drops so bright to see,
As from thy presence showers a rain of melody.

Like a poet hidden
In the light of thought,
Singing hymns unbidden,

THE SKYLARK

Till the world is wrought
To sympathy with hopes and fears it heeded not:

Like a high-born maiden
In a palace tower,
Soothing her love-laden
Soul in secret hour
With music sweet as love, which overflows her
bower:

Like a glowworm golden
In a dell of dew,
Scattering unbeholden
Its aërial hue
Among the flowers and grass, which screen it
from the view:

Like a rose embowered
In its own green leaves,
By warm winds deflowered,
Till the scent it gives
Makes faint with too much sweet these heavy-
wingèd thieves.

Sound of vernal showers
On the twinkling grass,
Rain-awakened flowers,
All that ever was
Joyous, and clear, and fresh, thy music doth
surpass.

Teach us, sprite or bird,
What sweet thoughts are thine:
I have never heard
Praise of love or wine
That panted forth a flood of rapture so di-
vine.

Chorus Hymenæal,
Or triumphal chaunt,
Matched with thine would be all
But an empty vaunt,
A thing wherein we feel there is some hidden
want.

What objects are the fountains
    Of thy happy strain?
What fields, or waves, or mountains?
    What shapes of sky or plain?
What love of thine own kind? what ignorance
        of pain?

With thy clear, keen joyance
    Languor cannot be:
Shadow of annoyance
    Never came near thee:
Thou lovest; but ne'er knew love's sad satiety.

Waking or asleep,
    Thou of death must deem
Things more true and deep
    Than we mortals dream,
Or how could thy notes flow in such a crystal
        stream!

We look before and after,
    And pine for what is not:
Our sincerest laughter
    With some pain is fraught;
Our sweetest songs are those that tell of saddest
        thought.

Yet if we could scorn
    Hate, and pride, and fear;
If we were things born
    Not to shed a tear,
I know not how thy joy we ever should come
        near.

Better than all measures
Of delightful sound,
Better than all treasures
That in books are found,
Thy skill to poet were, thou scorner of the
ground!

Teach me half the gladness
That thy brain must know,
Such harmonious madness
From my lips would flow,
The world should listen then, as I am listening
now!

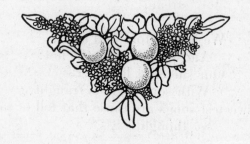

THE POND IN WINTER

HENRY DAVID THOREAU

AFTER a still winter night I awoke with the impression that some question had been put to me, which I had been endeavoring in vain to answer in my sleep, as what—how—when—where? But there was dawning Nature, in whom all creatures live, looking in at my broad windows with serene and satisfied face, and no question on *her* lips. I awoke to an answered question, to Nature and daylight. The snow lying deep on the earth dotted with young pines, and the very slope of the hill on which my house is placed, seemed to say, Forward! Nature puts no question and answers none which we mortals ask. She has long ago taken her resolution. "O Prince, our eyes contemplate with admiration and transmit to the soul the wonderful and varied spectacle of this universe. The night veils without doubt a part of this glorious creation; but day comes to reveal to us this great work, which extends from earth even into the plains of the ether."

Then to my morning work. First I take an axe and pail and go in search of water if that be not a dream. After a cold and snowy night it needed a divining rod to find it. Every winter the liquid and trembling surface of the pond,

KNEELING TO DRINK

which was so sensitive to every breath, and
reflected every light and shadow, becomes solid
to the depth of a foot or a foot and a half, so that
it will support the heaviest teams, and perchance
the snow covers it to an equal depth, and it is
not to be distinguished from any level field.
Like the marmots in the surrounding hills, it

closes its eyelids and becomes dormant for three months or more. Standing on the snow-covered plain, as if in a pasture amid the hills, I cut my way first through a foot of snow, and then a foot of ice, and open a window under my feet, where, kneeling to drink, I look down into the quiet parlor of the fishes, pervaded by a softened light as through a window of ground glass, with its bright sanded floor the same as in summer; there a perennial waveless serenity reigns as in the amber twilight sky, corresponding to the cool and even temperament of the inhabitants. Heaven is under our feet as well as over our heads.

Early in the morning, while all things are crisp with frost, men come with fishing reels and slender lunch, and let down their fine lines through the snowy field to take pickerel and perch; wild men, who instinctively follow other fashions and trust other authorities than their townsmen, and by their goings and comings stitch towns together in parts where else they would be ripped. They sit and eat their luncheon in stout fearnaughts on the dry oak leaves on the shore, as wise in natural lore as the citizen is in artificial. They never consulted with books, and know and can tell much less than they have done. The things which they practice are said not yet to be known. Here is one fishing for pickerel with grown perch for bait. You look into his pail with wonder as into a summer pond, as if he kept summer locked up at home, or knew where she had retreated. How, pray, did he get

these in midwinter? Oh, he got worms out of
rotten logs since the ground froze, and so he
caught them. His life itself passes deeper in Nature than the studies of the naturalist penetrate;
himself a subject for the naturalist. The latter
raises the moss and bark gently with his knife
in search of insects; the former lays open logs to
their core with his axe, and moss and bark fly
far and wide. He gets his living by barking
trees. Such a man has some right to fish, and
I love to see Nature carried out in him. The
perch swallows the grubworm, the pickerel
swallows the perch, and the fisherman swallows
the pickerel; and so all the chinks in the scale of
being are filled.

When I strolled around the pond in misty
weather I was sometimes amused by the primi-
tive mode which some ruder fisherman had
adopted. He would perhaps have placed alder
branches over the narrow holes in the ice, which
were four or five rods apart and an equal distance
from the shore, and having fastened the end of
the line to a stick to prevent its being pulled
through, have passed the slack line over a twig
of the alder, a foot or more above the ice, and
tied a dry oak leaf to it, which, being pulled
down, would show when he had a bite. These
alders loomed through the mist at regular intervals as you walked halfway round the pond.

Ah, the pickerel of Walden! when I see them
lying on the ice, or in the well which the fisherman cuts in the ice, making a little hole to admit
the water, I am always surprised by their rare

beauty, as if they were fabulous fishes, they are so foreign to the streets, even to the woods, foreign as Arabia to our Concord life. They possess a quite dazzling and transcendent beauty which separates them by a wide interval from the cadaverous cod and haddock whose fame is trumpeted in our streets. They are not green like the pines, nor gray like the stones, nor blue like the sky; but they have, to my eyes, if possible, yet rarer colors, like flowers and precious stones, as if they were the pearls, the animalized *nuclei* or crystals of the Walden water. They, of course, are Walden all over and all through; are themselves small Waldens in the animal kingdom, Waldenses. It is surprising that they are caught here—that in this deep and capacious spring, far beneath the rattling teams and chaises and tinkling sleighs that travel the Walden road, this great gold and emerald fish swims. I never chanced to see its kind in any market; it would be the cynosure of all eyes there. Easily, with a few convulsive quirks, they give up their watery ghosts, like a mortal translated before his time to the thin air of heaven.

SALMON FISHING

RUDYARD KIPLING

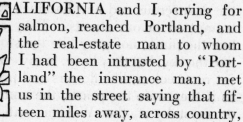ALIFORNIA and I, crying for salmon, reached Portland, and the real-estate man to whom I had been intrusted by "Portland" the insurance man, met us in the street saying that fifteen miles away, across country, we should come upon a place called Clackamas where we might perchance find what we desired. And California, his coat-tails flying in the wind, ran to a livery stable and chartered a wagon and team forthwith. I could push the wagon about with one hand, so light was its structure. The team was purely American—that is to say, almost human in its intelligence and docility. Some one said that the roads were not good on the way to Clackamas and warned us against smashing the springs. "Portland," who had watched the preparations, finally reckoned "he'd come along too," and under heavenly skies we three companions of a day set forth; California carefully lashing our rods into the carriage, and the bystanders overwhelming us with directions as to the sawmills we were to pass, the ferries we were to cross, and the signposts we were to seek signs from. Half a mile from this city of fifty thousand souls we struck (and this must be taken literally) a plank-

road that would have been a disgrace to an Irish village.

Then six miles of macadamized road showed us that the team could move. A railway ran between us and the banks of the Willamette, and another above us through the mountains. All the land was dotted with small townships, and the roads were full of farmers in their town wagons, bunches of tow-haired, boggle-eyed urchins sitting in the hay behind. The men generally looked like loafers, but their women were all well dressed. Brown hussar braiding on a tailor-made jacket does not, however, consort with hay wagons. Then we struck into the woods along what California called a "*camina reale*,"—a good road,—and Portland a "fair track." It wound in and out among fire-blackened stumps, under pine trees, along the corners of log-fences, through hollows which must be hopeless marsh in winter, and up absurd gradients. But nowhere throughout its length did I see any evidence of road-making. There was a track,—you couldn't well get off it,—and it was all you could do to stay on it. The dust lay a foot thick in the blind ruts, and under the dust we found bits of planking and bundles of brushwood that sent the wagon bounding into the air. Sometimes we crashed through bracken; anon where the blackberries grew rankest we found a lonely little cemetery, the wooden rails all awry, and the pitiful stumpy headstones nodding drunkenly at the soft green mulleins. Then with oaths and the sound of rent underwood a yoke of mighty bulls would swing down a "skid" road, hauling a forty-foot log along a rudely made slide.

A valley full of wheat and cherry trees succeeded, and halting at a house we bought ten pound weight of luscious black cherries for something less than a rupee and got a drink of icy-cold water for nothing, while the untended team browsed sagaciously by the roadside. Once we found a wayside camp of horse dealers lounging by a pool, ready for a sale or a swap, and once two sun-tanned youngsters shot down a hill on Indian ponies, their full creels banging from their high-pommeled saddles. They had been fishing, and were our brethren therefore. We shouted aloud in chorus to scare a wild cat; we squabbled over the reasons that had led a snake to cross a road; we heaved bits of bark at a venturesome chipmunk, who was really the little gray squirrel of India and had come to call on me; we lost our way and got the wagon so beautifully fixed on a steep road that we had to tie the two hind-wheels to get it down. Above all, California told tales of Nevada and Arizona, of lonely nights spent out prospecting, of the slaughter of deer and the chase of men; of woman, lovely woman, who is a firebrand in a western city, and leads to the popping of pistols, and of the sudden changes and chances of fortune, who delights in making the miner or the lumberman a quadruplicate millionaire, and in "busting" the railroad king. That was a day to be remembered, and it had only begun when

WHERE THE GOOD SALMON GOES TO SMOKE HIS PIPE

we drew rein at a tiny farmhouse on the banks of the Clackamas and sought horse-feed and lodging ere we hastened to the river that broke over a weir not over a quarter of a mile away.

Imagine a stream seventy yards broad divided by a pebbly island, running over seductive riffles and swirling into deep, quiet pools where the good salmon goes to smoke his pipe after meals.

Set such a stream amid fields of breast-high crops surrounded by hills of pine, throw in where you please quiet water, log-fenced meadows, and a hundred foot bluff just to keep the scenery from growing too monotonous, and you will get some faint notion of the Clackamas.

Portland had no rod. He held the gaff and the whiskey. California sniffed, upstream and downstream across the racing water, chose his ground, and let the gaudy spoon drop in the tail of a riffle. I was getting my rod together when I heard the joyous shriek of the reel and the yells of California, and three feet of shining silver leaped into the air far across the water. The forces were engaged. The salmon tore upstream, the tense line cutting the water like a tide-rip behind him, and the light bamboo bowed to breaking. What happened after I cannot tell. California swore and prayed, and Portland shouted advice, and I did all three for what appeared to be half a day, but was in reality a little over a quarter of an hour, and sullenly our fish came home with spurts of temper, dashes head-on, and sarabands in the air; but home to the bank came he, and the remorseless reel gathered up the thread of his life inch by inch. We landed him in a little bay, and the spring weight checked him at eleven and a half pounds. Eleven and a half pounds of fighting salmon! We danced a war dance on the pebbles, and California caught me around the waist in a hug that went near to breaking my ribs, while he shouted: "Partner! Partner! This is glory!

Now you catch your fish! Twenty-four years I've waited for this!"

I went into that icy-cold river and made my cast just above a weir, and all but foul-hooked a blue and black water-snake with a coral mouth who coiled herself on a stone and hissed maledictions. The next cast—ah, the pride of it, the regal splendor of it! the thrill that ran down from finger-tip to toe! The water boiled. He broke for the fly and got it! There remained enough sense in me to give him all he wanted when he jumped not once but twenty times before the upstream flight that ran my line out to the last half-dozen turns, and I saw the nickeled reel-bar glitter under the thinning green coils. My thumb was burned deep when I strove to stopper the line, but I did not feel it till later, for my soul was out in the dancing water praying for him to turn ere he took my tackle away. The prayer was heard. As I bowed back, the butt of the rod on my left hip-bone and the top joint dipping like unto a weeping willow, he turned, and I accepted each inch of slack that I could by any means get in as a favor from on high. There be several sorts of success in this world that taste well in the moment of enjoyment, but I question whether the stealthy theft of line from an able-bodied salmon who knows exactly what you are doing and why you are doing it is not sweeter than any other victory within human scope. Like California's fish, he ran at me head-on and leaped against the line, but the Lord gave me two hundred and fifty pairs of fingers in that

hour. The banks and the pine trees danced
dizzily around me, but I only reeled as for life—
reeled for hours, and at the end of the reeling
continued to give him the butt while he sulked
in a pool. California was farther up the reach,
and with the corner of my eye I could see him
casting with long casts and much skill. Then
he struck, and my fish broke for the weir at the
same instant, and down the reach went California
and I, reel answering reel, even as the morning
stars sung together.

The first wild enthusiasm of capture had died
away. We were both at work now in deadly
earnest to prevent the lines fouling, to stall off a
downstream rush for deep water just above the
weir, and at the same time to get the fish into the
shallow bay downstream that gave the best
practicable landing. Portland bade us both be
of good heart, and volunteered to take the rod
from my hands. I would rather have died
among the pebbles than surrender the right to
play and land my first salmon, weight unknown,
on an eight-ounce rod. I heard California, at
my ear it seemed, gasping: "He's a fighter
from Fightersville, sure!" as his fish made a fresh
break across the stream. I saw Portland fall
off a log fence, break the overhanging bank, and
clatter down to the pebbles all sand and landing
net, and I dropped on a log to rest for a moment.

As I drew breath the weary hands slackened
their hold, and I forgot to give him the butt. A
wild scutter in the water, a plunge and a break
for the head-waters of the Clackamas was my

reward, and the hot toil of reeling-in with one
eye under the water and the other on the top
joint of the rod, was renewed. Worst of all, I
was blocking California's path to the little landing bay aforesaid, and he had to halt and tire
his prize where he was. "The father of all
salmon!" he shouted. "For the love of heaven,
get your *trout* to bank, Johnny Bull." But I
could no more. Even the insult failed to move
me. The rest of the game was with the salmon.
He suffered himself to be drawn, skipping with
pretended delight at getting to the haven where
I fain would have him. Yet no sooner did he
feel shoal water under his ponderous belly than
he backed like a torpedo boat, and the snarl of
the reel told me that my labor was in vain. A
dozen times at least this happened ere the line
hinted that he had given up the battle and would
be towed in. He was towed. The landing net
was useless for one of his size, and I would not
have him gaffed. I stepped into the shallows
and heaved him out with a respectful hand under
the gill, for which kindness he battered me about
the legs with his tail, and I felt the strength of
him and was proud. California had taken my
place in the shallows, his fish hard held. I was
up on the bank lying full length on the sweet-
scented grass, gasping in company with my first
salmon caught, played, and landed on an eight-
ounce rod. My hands were cut and bleeding.
I was dripping with sweat, spangled like harle-
quin with scales, wet from the waist down, nose
peeled by the sun, but utterly, supremely, and

consummately happy.   He, the beauty, the daisy,
the darling, my Salmon Bahadur, weighed twelve
pounds, and I had been seven and thirty minutes
bringing him to bank! He had been lightly
hooked on the angle of the right jaw, and the
hook had not wearied him. That hour I sat
among princes and crowned heads—greater than
them all. Below the bank we heard California
scuffling with his salmon, and swearing Spanish
oaths. Portland and I assisted at the capture,
and the fish dragged the spring-balance out by
the roots. It was only constructed to weigh up
to fifteen pounds. We stretched the three fish
on the grass,—the eleven-and-a-half, the twelve,
and the fifteen-pounder,—and we swore an oath
that all who came after should merely be weighed
and put back again.

How shall I tell the glories of that day so that
you may be interested? Again and again did
California and I prance down that little reach
to the little bay, each with a salmon in tow, and
land him in the shallows. Then Portland took
my rod, and caught some ten-pounders, and my
spoon was carried away by an unknown levia-
than. Each fish, for the merits of the three that
had died so gamely, was hastily hooked on the
balance and flung back, Portland recording the
weight in a pocketbook, for he was a real-estate
man. Each fish fought for all he was worth,
and none more savagely than the smallest—a
game little six-pounder. At the end of six hours
we added up the list. Total: 16 fish, aggregate
weight, 142 lbs. The score in detail runs some-

thing like this—it is only interesting to those concerned: 15, 11½, 12, 10, 9¾, 8, and so forth; as I have said, nothing under six pounds, and three ten-pounders.

Very solemnly and thankfully we put up our rods—it was glory enough for all time—and returned weeping in each other's arms—weeping tears of pure joy—to that simple, barelegged family in the packing-case house by the water-side.

WINTER ANIMALS

HENRY DAVID THOREAU

WHEN the ponds were firmly frozen, they afforded not only new and shorter routes to many points, but new views from their surfaces of the familiar landscape around them. When I crossed Flint's Pond, after it was covered with snow, though I had often paddled about and skated over it, it was so unexpectedly wide and so strange that I could think of nothing but Baffin's Bay. The Lincoln hills rose up around me at the extremity of a snowy plain, in which I did not remember to have stood before; and the fishermen, at an indeterminable distance over the ice, moving slowly about with their wolfish dogs, passed for sealers or Esquimaux, or in misty weather loomed like fabulous creatures, and I did not know whether they were giants or pygmies. I took this course when I went to lecture in Lincoln in the evening, traveling in no road and passing no house between my own hut and the lecture room. In Goose Pond, which lay in my way, a colony of muskrats dwelt, and raised their cabins high above the ice, though none could be seen abroad when I crossed it. Walden, being like the rest usually bare of snow, or with only shallow and interrupted drifts on it, was my yard, where I

could walk freely when the snow was nearly two
feet deep on a level elsewhere and the villagers
were confined to their streets. There, far from
the village street, and, except at very long intervals, from the jingle of sleigh bells, I slid and
skated, as in a vast moose-yard well trodden,
overhung by oak woods and solemn pines bent
down with snow or bristling with icicles.

For sounds in winter nights, and often in winter
days, I heard the forlorn but melodious note of a
hooting owl indefinitely far; such a sound as the
frozen earth would yield if struck with a suitable
plectrum, the very *lingua vernacula* of Walden
Wood, and quite familiar to me at last, though I
never saw the bird while it was making it. I
seldom opened my door in a winter evening without hearing it; *Hoo hoo hoo, hoorer hoo*, sounded
sonorously, and the first three syllables accented
somewhat like *how der do;* or sometimes *hoo
hoo* only. One night in the beginning of winter,
before the pond froze over, about nine o'clock,
I was startled by the loud honking of a goose,
and, stepping to the door, heard the sound of
their wings like a tempest in the woods as they
flew low over my house. They passed over the
pond toward Fair Haven, seemingly deterred
from settling by my light, their commodore honking all the while with a regular beat. Suddenly
an unmistakable cat-owl from very near me,
with the most harsh and tremendous voice I ever
heard from any inhabitant of the woods, responded at regular intervals to the goose, as if
determined to expose and disgrace this intruder

from Hudson's Bay by exhibiting a greater compass and volume of voice in a native, and *boo-hoo* him out of Concord horizon. "What do you mean by alarming the citadel at this time of night consecrated to me? Do you think I am ever caught napping at such an hour, and that I have not got lungs and a larynx as well as yourself? *Boo-hoo, boo-hoo, boo-hoo!*" It was one of the most thrilling discords I ever heard. And yet, if you had a discriminating ear, there were in it the elements of a concord such as these plains never saw nor heard.

I also heard the whooping of the ice in the pond, my great bedfellow in that part of Concord, as if it were restless in its bed and would fain turn over, were troubled with flatulency and bad dreams; or I was waked by the cracking of the ground by the frost, as if some one had driven a team against my door, and in the morning would find a crack in the earth a quarter of a mile long and a third of an inch wide.

Sometimes I heard the foxes as they ranged over the snow crust, in moonlight nights, in search of a partridge or other game, barking raggedly and demoniacally like forest dogs, as if laboring with some anxiety, or seeking expression, struggling for light and to be dogs outright and run freely in the streets; for if we take the ages into our account, may there not be a civilization going on among brutes as well as men? They seemed to me to be rudimental, burrowing men, still standing on their defence, awaiting their transformation. Sometimes one came near

to my window, attracted by my light, barked a
vulpine curse at me, and then retreated.

Usually the red squirrel (*Sciurus Hudsonius*)
waked me in the dawn, coursing over the roof
and up and down the sides of the house, as if
sent out of the woods for this purpose. In the
course of the winter I threw out half a bushel of
ears of sweet corn, which had not got ripe, on to
the snow crust by my door, and was amused by
watching the motions of the various animals
which were baited by it. In the twilight and the
night the rabbits came regularly and made a
hearty meal. All day long the red squirrels
came and went, and afforded me much entertainment by their manœuvres. One would approach
at first warily through the shrub-oaks, running
over the snow crust by fits and starts like a leaf
blown by the wind, now a few paces this way,
with wonderful speed and waste of energy, making inconceivable haste with his "trotters," as if
it were for a wager, and now as many paces that
way, but never getting on more than half a rod
at a time; and then suddenly pausing with a
ludicrous expression and a gratuitous somerset,
as if all the eyes in the universe were fixed on
him—for all the motions of a squirrel, even in the
most solitary recesses of the forest, imply spectators as much as those of a dancing girl—wasting
more time in delay and circumspection than
would have sufficed to walk the whole distance—
I never saw one walk—and then suddenly, before you could say Jack Robinson, he would be
in the top of a young pitch-pine, winding up his

clock and chiding all imaginary spectators,
soliloquizing and talking to all the universe at
the same time—for no reason that I could ever
detect, or he himself was aware of, I suspect.

At length he would reach the corn, and selecting
a suitable ear, brisk about in the same uncertain
trigonometrical way to the topmost stick of my
wood-pile, before my window, where he looked
me in the face, and there sit for hours, supplying
himself with a new ear from time to time, nib-
bling at first voraciously and throwing the half-
naked cobs about; till at length he grew more
dainty still and played with his food, tasting only
the inside of the kernel, and the ear, which was
held balanced over the stick by one paw, slipped
from his careless grasp and fell to the ground,
when he would look over at it with a ludicrous
expression of uncertainty, as if suspecting that
it had life, with a mind not made up whether to
get it again, or a new one, or be off; now thinking
of corn, then listening to hear what was in the
wind. So the little impudent fellow would waste
many an ear in a forenoon; till at last, seizing
some longer and plumper one, considerably
bigger than himself, and skilfully balancing it,
he would set out with it to the woods, like a tiger
with a buffalo, by the same zigzag course and
frequent pauses, scratching along with it as if it
were too heavy for him and falling all the while,
making its fall a diagonal between a perpendicu-
lar and horizontal, being determined to put it
through at any rate—a singularly frivolous and
whimsical fellow—and so he would get off with

THE RED SQUIRREL STEALING CORN

it to where he lived, perhaps carry it to the top
of a pine tree forty or fifty rods distant, and I
would afterward find the cobs strewed about the
woods in various directions.

At length the jays arrive, whose discordant
screams were heard long before, as they were
warily making their approach an eighth of a mile
off; and in a stealthy and sneaking manner they
flit from tree to tree, nearer and nearer, and pick
up the kernels which the squirrels have dropped.
Then, sitting on a pitch-pine bough, they attempt
to swallow in their haste a kernel which is too big

for their throats and chokes them; and after great labor they disgorge it, and spend an hour in the endeavor to crack it by repeated blows with their bills. They were manifestly thieves, and I had not much respect for them; but the squirrels, though at first shy, went to work as if they were taking what was their own.

Meanwhile also came the chickadees in flocks, which, picking up the crumbs the squirrels had dropped, flew to the nearest twig, and, placing them under their claws, hammered away at them with their little bills, as if it were an insect in the bark, till they were sufficiently reduced for their slender throats. A little flock of these titmice came daily to pick a dinner out of my wood pile, or the crumbs at my door, with faint flitting lisping notes, like the tinkling of icicles in the grass, or else with sprightly *day day day*, or more rarely, in spring-like days, a wiry summery *phe-be* from the wood-side. They were so familiar that at length one alighted on an armful of wood which I was carrying in, and pecked at the sticks without fear. I once had a sparrow alight upon my shoulder for a moment while I was hoeing in a village garden, and I felt that I was more distinguished by that circumstance than I should have been by any epaulet I could have worn. The squirrels also grew at last to be quite familiar and occasionally stepped upon my shoe, when that was the nearest way.

When the ground was not yet quite covered, and again near the end of winter, when the snow was melted on my south hillside and about my

wood-pile, the partridges came out of the woods
morning and evening to feed there. Whichever
side you walk in the woods the partridge bursts
away on whirring wings, jarring the snow from
the dry leaves and twigs on high, which comes
sifting down in the sunbeams like golden dust;
for this brave bird is not to be scared by winter.
It is frequently covered up by drifts, and, it is
said, "sometimes plunges from on wing into the
soft snow, where it remains concealed for a day
or two." I used to start them in the open land
also, where they had come out of the woods at
sunset to "bud" the wild apple trees. They will
come regularly every evening to particular trees,
where the cunning sportsman lies in wait for
them, and the distant orchards next the woods
suffer thus not a little. I am glad that the partridge gets fed, at any rate. It is Nature's own
bird which lives on buds and diet-drink.

In dark winter mornings, or in short winter
afternoons, I sometimes heard a pack of hounds
threading all the woods with hounding cry and
yelp, unable to resist the instinct of the chase,
and the note of the hunting horn at intervals,
proving that man was in the rear. The woods
ring again, and yet no fox bursts forth on to the
open level of the pond, nor following pack pursuing their Actæon. And perhaps at evening I see
the hunters returning with a single brush trailing
from their sleigh for a trophy, seeking their inn.
They tell me that if the fox would remain in the
bosom of the frozen earth he would be safe, or
if he would run in a straight line away no fox-

hound could overtake him; but, having left his
pursuers far behind, he stops to rest and listen
till they come up, and when he runs he circles
round to his old haunts, where the hunters await
him.   Sometimes, however, he will run upon a
wall many rods, and then leap off far to one side,
and he appears to know that water will not retain
his scent.   A hunter told me that he once saw a
fox pursued by hounds burst out on to Walden
when the ice was covered with shallow puddles,
run part way across, and then return to the
same shore. Ere long the hounds arrived, but here
they lost the scent.   Sometimes a pack hunting
by themselves would pass my door, and circle
round my house, and yelp and hound without
regarding me, as if afflicted by a species of madness, so that nothing could divert them from the
pursuit.   Thus they circle until they fall upon
the recent trail of a fox, for a wise hound will
forsake everything else for this.   One day a
man came to my hut from Lexington to inquire
after his hound that made a large track, and had
been hunting for a week by himself.   But I fear
that he was not the wiser for all I told him, for
every time I attempted to answer his questions
he interrupted me by asking, "What do you do
here?"   He had lost a dog, but found a man.

One old hunter who has a dry tongue, who
used to come to bathe in Walden once every year
when the water was warmest, and at such times
looked in upon me, told me that many years ago
he took his gun one afternoon and went out for
a cruise in Walden Wood, and as he walked the

Wayland road he heard the cry of hounds approaching, and ere long a fox leaped the wall into the road, and as quick as thought leaped the other wall out of the road, and his swift bullet had not touched him. Some way behind came an old hound and her three pups in full pursuit, hunting on their own account, and disappeared again in the woods. Later in the afternoon, as he was resting in the thick woods south of Walden, he heard the voice of the hounds far over toward Fair Haven still pursuing the fox; and on they came, their hounding cry which made all the woods ring sounding nearer and nearer, now from Well Meadow, now from the Baker Farm. For a long time he stood still and listened to their music, so sweet to a hunter's ear, when suddenly the fox appeared, threading the solemn aisles with an easy coursing pace, whose sound was concealed by a sympathetic rustle of the leaves, swift and still, keeping the ground, leaving his pursuers far behind; and, leaping upon a rock amid the woods, he sat erect and listening, with his back to the hunter. For a moment compassion restrained the latter's arm; but that was a short-lived mood, and as quick as thought can follow thought his piece was levelled, and *whang!* —the fox rolling over the rock lay dead on the ground. The hunter still kept his place and listened to the hounds. Still on they came, and now the near woods resounded through all their aisles with their demoniac cry. At length the old hound burst into view with muzzle to the ground, and snapping the air as if possessed, and

ran directly to the rock; but spying the dead fox
she suddenly ceased her hounding, as if struck
dumb with amazement, and walked round and
round him in silence; and one by one her pups
arrived, and, like their mother, were sobered
into silence by the mystery. Then the hunter
came forward and stood in their midst, and the
mystery was solved. They waited in silence
while he skinned the fox, then followed the brush
awhile, and at length turned off into the woods
again. That evening a Weston Squire came to
the Concord hunter's cottage to inquire for his
hounds, and told how for a week they had been
hunting on their own account from Weston
woods. The Concord hunter told him what he
knew and offered him the skin; but the other
declined it and departed. He did not find his
hounds that night, but the next day learned that
they had crossed the river and put up at a farmhouse for the night, whence, having been well
fed, they took their departure early in the morning.

The hunter who told me this could remember
one Sam Nutting, who used to hunt bears on
Fair-Haven Ledges, and exchange their skins
for rum in Concord village; who told him, even,
that he had seen a moose there. Nutting had a
famous foxhound named Burgoyne,—he pronounced it Bugine,—which my informant used
to borrow. In the "Wast Book" of an old
trader of this town, who was also a captain,
townclerk, and representative, I find the following entry: Jan. 18th, 1742-3, "John Melven Cr.

by 1 Grey Fox 0—2—3;" they are not found
here; and in his ledger, Feb. 7th, 1743, Hezekiah
Stratton has credit "by $\frac{1}{2}$ a Catt skin 0—1—
$4\frac{1}{2}$;" of course a wild cat, for Stratton was a
sergeant in the old French war, and would not
have got credit for hunting less noble game.
Credit is given for deerskins also, and they were
daily sold. One man still preserves the horns
of the last deer that was killed in this vicinity,
and another has told me the particulars of the
hunt in which his uncle was engaged. The
hunters were formerly a numerous and merry
crew here. I remember well one gaunt Nimrod
who would catch up a leaf by the road-side and
play a strain on it wilder and more melodious,
if my memory serves me, than any hunting horn.

At midnight, when there was a moon, I sometimes met with hounds in my path prowling
about the woods, which would skulk out of my
way as if afraid, and stand silent amid the bushes
till I had passed.

Squirrels and wild mice disputed for my store
of nuts. There were scores of pitch-pines
around my house, from one to four inches in
diameter, which had been gnawed by mice the
previous winter,—a Norwegian winter for them,
for the snow lay long and deep, and they were
obliged to mix a large proportion of pine bark
with their other diet. These trees were alive
and apparently flourishing at midsummer, and
many of them had grown a foot, though completely girdled; but after another winter such
were without exception dead. It is remarkable

that a single mouse should thus be allowed a
whole pine tree for its dinner, gnawing round
instead of up and down it; but perhaps it is
necessary in order to thin these trees, which are
wont to grow up densely.

The hares (*Lepus Americanus*) were very
familiar. One had her form under my house
all winter, separated from me only by the floor-
ing, and she startled me each morning by her
hasty departure when I began to stir—thump,
thump, thump, striking her head against the
floor timbers in her hurry. They used to come
round my door at dusk to nibble the potato par-
ings which I had thrown out, and were so nearly
the color of the ground that they could hardly
be distinguished when still. Sometimes in the
twilight I alternately lost and recovered sight of
one sitting motionless under my window. When
I opened my door in the evening, off they would
go with a squeak and a bounce. Near at hand
they only excited my pity. One evening one
sat by my door two paces from me, at first trembling with fear, yet unwilling to move; a poor
wee thing, lean and bony, with ragged ears and
sharp nose, scant tail and slender paws. It
looked as if Nature no longer contained the breed
of nobler bloods, but stood on her last toes. Its
large eyes appeared young and unhealthy, almost
dropsical. I took a step, and lo, away it scudded
with an elastic spring over the snow crust,
straightening its body and its limbs into graceful
length, and soon put the forest between me and
itself—the wild free venison, asserting its vigor

and the dignity of Nature. Not without reason was its slenderness. Such then was its nature. (*Lepus, levipes,* lightfoot, some think.)

What is a country without rabbits and partridges? They are among the most simple and indigenous animal products; ancient and venerable families known to antiquity as to modern times; of the very hue and substance of Nature, nearest allied to leaves and to the ground—and to one another; it is either winged or it is legged. It is hardly as if you had seen a wild creature when a rabbit or a partridge bursts away, only a natural one, as much to be expected as rustling leaves. The partridge and the rabbit are still sure to thrive, like true natives of the soil, whatever revolutions occur. If the forest is cut off, the sprouts and bushes which spring up afford them concealment, and they become more numerous than ever. That must be a poor country indeed that does not support a hare. Our woods teem with them both, and around every swamp may be seen the partridge or rabbit walk, beset with twiggy fences and horsehair snares, which some cow-boy tends.

TREES AND ANTS THAT HELP EACH OTHER[1]

THOMAS BELT

ONE low tree, very characteristic of the dry savannahs, is a species of acacia, belonging to the section *Gummiferæ*, with bipinnate leaves, growing to a height of fifteen or twenty feet. The branches and trunk are covered with strong curved spines, set in pairs, from which it receives the name of the bull's-horn, they having a very strong resemblance to the horns of that quadruped. These horns are hollow, and are tenanted by ants, that make a small hole for their entrance and exit near one end of the thorn, and also burrow through the partition that separates the two horns; so that the one entrance serves for both. Here they rear their young, and in the wet season every one of the thorns is tenanted, and hundreds of ants are to be seen running about, especially over the young leaves. If one of these be touched, or a branch shaken, the little ants swarm out from the hollow thorns, and attack the aggressor with jaws and sting. They sting severely, raising a little white lump that does not disappear in less than twenty-four hours.

1. From *The Naturalist in Nicaragua.*

These ants form a most efficient standing army for the plant, which prevents not only the mammalia from browsing on the leaves, but delivers it from the attacks of a much more dangerous enemy—the leaf-cutting ants. For these services the ants are not only securely housed by the plant, but are provided with a bountiful supply of food; and to secure their attendance at the right time and place, this food is so arranged and distributed as to effect that object with wonderful perfection. The leaves are bi-pinnate. At the base of each pair of leaflets, on the midrib, is a crater-formed gland, which, when the leaves are young, secretes a honey-like liquid. Of this the ants are very fond; they are constantly running about from one gland to another to sip up the honey as it is secreted. But this is not all; there is a still more wonderful provision of more solid food. At the end of each of the small divisions of the compound leaflet there is, when the leaf first unfolds, a little yellow fruit-like body united by a point at its base to the end of the pinnule. Examined through a microscope, this little appendage looks like a golden pear. When the leaf first unfolds, the little pears are not quite ripe, and the ants are continually employed going from one to another, examining them. When an ant finds one sufficiently advanced, it bites the small point of attachment; then, bending down the fruit-like body, it breaks it off and bears it away in triumph to the nest. All the fruit-like bodies do not ripen at once, but successively, so

that the ants are kept about the young leaf for
some time after it unfolds. Thus the young
leaves are always guarded by the ants; and no
caterpillar or large animal could attempt to
injure them without being attacked by the little
warriors. The fruit-like bodies are about one-
twelfth of an inch long, and are about one third
of the size of the ants; so that the ant bearing
one away is as heavily laden as a man bearing a
large bunch of plantains. I think these facts
show that the ants are really kept by the acacia
as a standing army, to protect its leaves from
the attacks of herbivorous mammals and insects.

The bull's-horn thorn does not grow at the
mines in the forest, nor are the small ants attending on them found there. They seem
specially adapted for the tree, and I have seen
them nowhere else. Besides the little ants, I
found another ant that lives on these acacias,
whose habits appear to be rather different. It
makes the holes of entrance to the thorns near
the centre of one of each pair, and not near the
end, and it is not so active as the other species.
It is also rather scarce; but when it does occur,
it occupies the whole tree, to the exclusion of
the other. The glands on the acacia are also
frequented by a small species of wasp. I sowed
the seeds of the acacia in my garden, and reared
some young plants. Ants of many kinds were
numerous; but none of them took to the thorns
for shelter, nor the glands and fruit-like bodies
for food; for, as I have already mentioned, the
species that attend on the thorns are not found

in the forest. The leaf-cutting ants attacked
the young plants, and defoliated them; but I
have never seen any of the trees out on the
savannahs that are guarded touched by them,
and have no doubt the acacia is protected from
them by its little warriors. The thorns, when
they are first developed, are soft, and filled with
a sweetish, pulpy substance; so that the ant,
when it makes an entrance into them, finds its
new house full of food. It hollows this out,
leaving only the hardened shell of the thorn.
Strange to say, this treatment seems to favour
the development of the thorn, as it increases in
size, bulging out towards the base; whilst in my
plants that were not touched by the ants, the
thorns turned yellow and dried up into dead but
persistent prickles. I am not sure, however, that
this may not have been due to the habitat of the
plant not suiting it.

These ants seem to lead the happiest of existences. Protected by their stings, they fear no
foe. Habitations full of food are provided for
them to commence housekeeping with; and cups
of nectar and luscious fruits await them every
day. But there is a reverse to the picture. In
the dry season on the plains, the acacias cease
to grow. No young leaves are produced, and
the old glands do not secrete honey. Then
want and hunger overtake the ants that have
revelled in luxury all the wet season; many of
the thorns are depopulated, and only a few ants
live through the season of scarcity. As soon,
however, as the first rains set in, the trees throw

out numerous vigorous shoots, and the ants multiply again with astonishing rapidity.

Both in Brazil and in Nicaragua I paid much attention to the relation between the presence of honey-secreting glands on plants, and the protection the latter secured by the attendance of ants attracted by the honey. I found many plants so protected; the glands being specially developed on the young leaves, and on the sepals of the flowers. Besides the bull's-horn acacias, I, however, only met with two other genera of plants that furnished the ants with houses, namely, the trumpet tree and some of the evergreen shrubs; but I have no doubt that there are many others. The stem of the Cecropia, or trumpet tree, is hollow, and divided into cells by partitions that extend across the interior of the hollow trunk. The ants gain access by making a hole from the outside, and then burrow through the partitions, thus getting the run of the whole stem. They do not obtain their food directly from the tree, but keep brown scale insects in the cells, which suck the juices from the tree, and secrete a honey-like fluid that exudes from a pore on the back, and is lapped up by the ants. In one cell eggs will be found, in another grubs, and in a third pupæ, all lying loosely. In another cell, by itself, a queen ant will be found, surrounded by walls made of a brown waxy-looking substance, along with about a dozen scale insects to supply her with food. I suppose the eggs are removed as soon as laid, for I never found any along with the queen ant. If the tree be shaken, the ants rush out in myriads, and search about for the molester. This case is not like the last one, where the tree has provided food and shelter for the ants, but rather one where the ant has taken possession of the tree, and brought with it the scale insects; but I believe that its presence must be beneficial. I have cut into some dozens of the trumpet trees, and never could find one that was not tenanted by ants. I noticed three different species, all, as far as I know, confined to the trumpet tree, and all farming scale insects. As in the bull's-horn thorn, there is never more than one species of ant on the same tree.

In some species of evergreen shrub there is a direct provision of houses for the ants. In each leaf, at the base of the laminæ, the petiole, or stalk, is furnished with a couple of pouches, divided from each other by the midrib. Into each of these pouches there is an entrance from the lower side of the leaf. I noticed them first in Northern Brazil, in the province of Maranham; and afterwards at Pará. Every pouch was occupied by a nest of small black ants; and if the leaf was shaken ever so little, they would rush out and scour all over it in search of the aggressor. I must have tested some hundreds of leaves, and never shook one without the ants coming out, excepting one sickly-looking plant at Pará. In many of the pouches I noticed the eggs and young ants, and in some I saw a few dark-colored scale insects or plant lice; but my attention had not been at that time directed to

the latter as supplying the ants with food, and I
did not examine a sufficient number of pouches
to determine whether they were constant occu-
pants of the nests or not; but my experience since
with the trumpet trees would lead me to expect
that they were. If so, we have an instance of
two insects and a plant living together, and all
benefited by the companionship. The leaves of
the plant are guarded by the ants; the ants are
provided with houses by the plant, and food by
the scale insects and plant lice; and the latter
are effectually protected by the ants in their
common habitation.

Amongst the numerous plants that do not
provide houses, but attract ants to their leaves
and flower buds by means of glands secreting a
honey-like liquid, are many orchids, and I think
all the species of passion flowers. I had the
common red passion flower growing over the
front on my verandah, where it was continually
under my notice. It had honey-secreting glands
on its young leaves and on the sepals of the
flower buds. For two years I noticed that the
glands were constantly attended by a small ant,
and, night and day, every young leaf and every
flower bud had a few on them. They did not
sting, but attacked and bit my finger when I
touched the plant. I have no doubt that the
primary object of these honey-glands was to
attract the ants, and keep them about the most
tender and vulnerable parts of the plant, to
prevent them being injured; and I further believe that one of the principal enemies that they

serve to guard against in tropical America is the leaf-cutting ant, as I have noticed that the latter are very much afraid of the small black ants.

On the third year after I had noticed the attendance of the ants on my passion flower, I found that the glands were not so well looked after as before, and soon discovered that a number of scale insects had established themselves on the stems, and that the ants had in a great measure transferred their attentions to them. An ant would stand over a scale insect and stroke it alternately on each side with its antennæ, whereupon every now and then a clear drop of honey would exude from a pore on the back of the scale insect and be imbibed by the ant. Here it was clear that the scale insect was competing successfully with the leaves and sepals for the attendance and protection of the ants, and was successful either through the fluid it furnished being more attractive or more abundant. I have, from these facts, been led to the conclusion that the use of honey-secreting glands in plants is to attract insects that will protect the flower buds and leaves from being injured by herbivorous insects and mammals; but I do not mean to infer that this is the use of all glands, for many of the small appendicular bodies, called "glands" by botanists, do not secrete honey. The common dog-rose of England is furnished with glands on the stipules, and in other species they are more numerous, until in the wild rose of the northern counties the leaves are thickly edged, and the fruit and sepals covered with stalked glands. I have only observed the wild roses in the north of England, but there I have never seen insects attending the glands. These glands, however, do not secrete honey; but a dark, resinous, sticky liquid, that probably is useful by being distasteful to both insects and mammals.

THE FAMILY OF MICHAEL AROUT[1]

FROM THE FRENCH OF EMILE SOUVESTRE

EPTEMBER *15th, Eight O'clock.*—
This morning, while I was arranging
my books, Mother Genevieve came
in and brought me the basket of
fruit I buy of her every Sunday. For
nearly twenty years that I have lived
in this quarter I have dealt in her
little fruit shop. Perhaps I should be better
served elsewhere, but Mother Genevieve has but
little custom; to leave her would do her harm and
cause her unnecessary pain. It seems to me
that the length of our acquaintance has made me
incur a sort of tacit obligation to her; my patron-
age has become her property.

She has put the basket upon my table, and as
I wanted her husband, who is a joiner, to add
some shelves to my bookcase, she has gone
downstairs again immediately to send him to me.

At first I did not notice either her looks or the
sound of her voice: but, now that I recall them,
it seems to me that she was not as jovial as
usual. Can Mother Genevieve be in trouble
about anything?

Poor woman! All her best years were subject
to such bitter trials that she might think she had
received her full share already. Were I to live
a hundred years I should never forget the cir-

---

1. This is adapted from *An Attic Philosopher in Paris.*

cumstances which first made her known to me
and which obtained her my respect.

It was at the time of my first settling in the
faubourg. I had noticed her empty fruit shop,
which nobody came into, and being attracted by
its forsaken appearance I made my little purchases in it. I have always instinctively preferred the poor shops; there is less choice in
them, but it seems to me that my purchase is a
sign of sympathy with a brother in poverty.
These little dealings are almost always an anchor
of hope to those whose very existence is in peril—
the only means by which some orphan gains a
livelihood. There the aim of the tradesman is
not to enrich himself, but to live! The purchase
you make of him is more than an exchange—it
is a good action.

Mother Genevieve at that time was still young,
but had already lost that fresh bloom of youth
which suffering causes to wither so soon among
the poor. Her husband, a clever joiner, gradually left off working to become, according to the
picturesque expression of the workshops, "a
worshiper of Saint Monday." The wages of the
week, which was always reduced to two or three
working days, were completely dedicated by him
to the worship of this god of the Barriers,[2] and
Genevieve was obliged herself to provide for all
the wants of the household.

One evening, when I went to make some
trifling purchases of her, I heard a sound of

<hr>

[2] The cheap wine shops of Paris are outside the Barriers, to avoid
the city tax.

quarreling in the back shop. There were the
voices of several women, among which I distinguished that of Genevieve, broken by sobs.
On looking further in, I perceived the fruit-
woman with a child in her arms, and kissing it,
while a country nurse seemed to be claiming her
wages from her. The poor woman, who without
doubt had exhausted every explanation and
every excuse, was crying in silence, and one of
her neighbors was trying in vain to appease the
countrywoman. Excited by that love of money
which the evils of a hard peasant life but too
well excuse, and disappointed by the refusal
of her expected wages, the nurse was launching
forth in recriminations, threats, and abuse. In
spite of myself, I listened to the quarrel, not
daring to interfere, and not thinking of going
away, when Michael Arout appeared at the shop
door.

The joiner had just come from the Barrier,
where he had passed part of the day at the public-
house. His blouse, without a belt, and untied at
the throat, showed none of the noble stains of
work: in his hand he held his cap, which he had
just picked up out of the mud; his hair was in
disorder, his eye fixed, and the pallor of drunkenness in his face. He came reeling in, looked
wildly around him, and called Genevieve.

She heard his voice, gave a start, and rushed
into the shop; but at the sight of the miserable
man, who was trying in vain to steady himself,
she pressed the child in her arms and bent over
it with tears.

THE DRUNKARD RAISED HIS HEAD

The countrywoman and the neighbor had
followed her.

"Come! come! do you intend to pay me, after
all?" cried the former in a rage.

"Ask the master for the money," ironically
answered the woman from the next door, point-

ing to the joiner, who had just fallen against the counter.

The countrywoman looked at him.

"Ah! he is the father," returned she.   "Well, what idle beggars! not to have a penny to pay honest people, and get tipsy with wine in that way."

The drunkard raised his head.

"What! what!" stammered he; "who is it that talks of wine? I've had nothing but brandy! But I am going back again to get some wine! Wife, give me your money; there are some friends waiting for me at the wine shop."

Genevieve did not answer: he went round the counter, opened the till, and began to rummage in it.

"You see where the money of the house goes!" observed the neighbor to the countrywoman; "how can the poor unhappy woman pay you when he takes all?"

"Is that my fault?" replied the nurse angrily. "They owe it to me and somehow or other they must pay me!"

And letting loose her tongue, as those women out of the country do, she began relating at length all the care she had taken of the child and all the expense it had been to her.   In proportion as she recalled all she had done, her words seemed to convince her more than ever of her rights and to increase her anger.   The poor mother, who no doubt feared that her violence would frighten the child, returned into the back shop and put it into its cradle.

Whether it is that the countrywoman saw in this act a determination to escape her claims, or that she was blinded by passion, I cannot say; but she rushed into the next room, where I heard the sounds of quarreling, with which the cries of the child were soon mingled. The joiner, who was still rummaging in the till, was startled and raised his head.

At the same moment Genevieve appeared at the door, holding in her arms the baby that the countrywoman was trying to tear from her. She ran toward the counter, and throwing herself behind her husband cried:

"Michael, defend your son!"

The drunken man quickly stood up erect, like one who awakes with a start.

"My son!" stammered he; "what son?"

His looks fell upon the child; a vague ray of intelligence passed over his features.

"Robert," resumed he; "it is Robert!"

He tried to steady himself on his feet, that he might take the baby, but he tottered. The nurse approached him in a rage.

"My money, or I shall take the child away!" cried she. "It is I who have fed and brought it up: if you don't pay me for what has made it live, it ought to be the same to you as if it were dead. I shall not go until I have my due or the baby."

"And what would you do with him?" murmured Genevieve, pressing Robert against her bosom.

"Take it to the Foundling!" replied the countrywoman harshly; "the hospital is a better

mother than you are, for it pays for the food of its
little ones."

At the word "Foundling," Genevieve had exclaimed aloud in horror.   With her arms wound
round her son, whose head she hid in her bosom,
and her two hands spread over him, she had retreated to the wall, and remained with her back
against it, like a lioness defending her young ones.
The neighbor and I contemplated this scene,
without knowing how we could interfere.   As
for Michael, he looked at us by turns, making a
visible effort to comprehend it all.   When his
eye rested upon Genevieve and the child, it lit up
with a gleam of pleasure; but when he turned
toward us, he again became stupid and hesitating.

At last, apparently making a prodigious effort,
he cried out, "Wait!"

And going to a tub full of water, he plunged
his face into it several times.

Every eye was turned upon him; the countrywoman herself seemed astonished.   At length
he raised his dripping head.   This ablution had
partly dispelled his drunkenness; he looked at
us for a moment, then he turned to Genevieve,
and his face brightened up.

"Robert!" cried he, going up to the child and
taking him in his arms.   "Ah! give him me,
wife; I must look at him."

The mother seemed to give up his son to him
with reluctance, and stayed before him with her
arms extended, as if she feared the child would
have a fall.   The nurse began again in her turn
to speak, and renewed her claims, this time

threatening to appeal to law. At first Michael
listened to her attentively, and when he comprehended her meaning he gave the child back
to its mother.

"How much do we owe you?" asked he.

The countrywoman began to reckon up the
different expenses, which amounted to nearly 30
francs. The joiner felt to the bottom of his
pockets, but could find nothing. His forehead
became contracted by frowns; low curses began
to escape him. All of a sudden he rummaged
in his breast, drew forth a large watch, and
holding it up above his head—

"Here it is—here's your money!" cried he
with a joyful laugh; "a watch, number one! I
always said it would keep for a drink on a dry
day; but it is not I who will drink it, but the
young one. Ah! ah! ah! go and sell it for me,
neighbor, and if that is not enough, I have my
earrings. Eh! Genevieve, take them off for me;
the earrings will square all! They shall not say
you have been disgraced on account of the child—
no, not even if I must pledge a bit of my flesh!
My watch, my earrings, and my ring—get rid of
all of them for me at the goldsmith's; pay the
woman and let the little fool go to sleep. Give
him me, Genevieve; I will put him to bed."

And taking the baby from the arms of his
mother, he carried him with a firm step to his
cradle.

It was easy to perceive the change which took
place in Michael from this day. He cut all his
old drinking acquaintances. He went early

every morning to his work, and returned regularly in the evening to finish the day with Genevieve and Robert. Very soon he would not
leave them at all, and he hired a place near
the fruit shop and worked in it on his own account.

They would soon have been able to live in
comfort, had it not been for the expenses which
the child required. Everything was given up to
his education. He had gone through the regular
school training, had studied mathematics, drawing, and the carpenter's trade, and had only
begun to work a few months ago. Till now,
they had been exhausting every resource which
their laborious industry could provide to push
him forward in his business; but, happily, all
these exertions had not proved useless: the
seed had brought forth its fruits, and the days of
harvest were close by.

While I was thus recalling these remembrances
to my mind, Michael had come in and was occupied in fixing shelves where they were wanted.

During the time I was writing the notes of my
journal, I was also scrutinizing the joiner.

The excesses of his youth and the labor of his
manhood have deeply marked his face; his hair
is thin and gray, his shoulders stooping, his legs
shrunken and slightly bent. There seems a sort
of weight in his whole being. His very features
have an expression of sorrow and despondency.
He answered my questions by monosyllables,
and like a man who wishes to avoid conversation.
From whence is this dejection, when one would

think he had all he could wish for? I should like to know!

Ten O'clock.—Michael is just gone downstairs to look for a tool he has forgotten. I have at last succeeded in drawing from him the secret of his and Genevieve's sorrow. Their son Robert is the cause of it!

Not that he has turned out ill after all their care—not that he is idle and dissipated; but both were in hopes he would never leave them any more. The presence of the young man was to have renewed and made glad their lives once more; his mother counted the days, his father prepared everything to receive their dear associate in their toils; and at the moment when they were thus about to be repaid for all their sacrifices, Robert had suddenly informed them that he had just engaged himself to a contractor at Versailles.

Every remonstrance and every prayer were useless; he brought forward the necessity of initiating himself into all the details of an important contract, the facilities he should have in his new position of improving himself in his trade, and the hopes he had of turning his knowledge to advantage. At last, when his mother, having come to the end of her arguments, began to cry, he hastily kissed her and went away that he might avoid any further remonstrances.

He had been absent a year, and there was nothing to give them hopes of his return. His parents hardly saw him once a month, and then he only stayed a few moments with them.

"I have been punished where I had hoped to
be rewarded," Michael said to me just now.   "I
had wished for a saving and industrious son, and
God has given me an ambitious and avaricious
one! I had always said to myself that when
once he was grown up we should have him
always with us, to recall our youth and to enliven
our hearts. His mother was always thinking
of getting him married and having children again
to care for. You know women always will busy
themselves about others. As for me, I thought
of him working near my bench and singing his
new songs; for he has learned music and is one
of the best singers at the Orphéon. A dream,
sir, truly! Directly the bird was fledged, he
took to flight, and remembers neither father nor
mother. Yesterday, for instance, was the day
we expected him; he should have come to supper
with us. No Robert to-day either! He has had
some plan to finish, or some bargain to arrange,
and his old parents are put down last in the
accounts, after the customer's and the joiner's
work. Ah! if I could have guessed how it would
have turned out! Fool! to have sacrificed my
likings and my money, for nearly twenty years,
to the education of a thankless son! Was it for
this I took the trouble to cure myself of drinking,
to break with my friends, to become an example
to the neighborhood? The jovial good fellow
has made a goose of himself. Oh! if I had to
begin again! No, no! you see women and
children are our bane. They soften our hearts;
they lead us a life of hope and affection; we pass

a quarter of our lives in fostering the growth of a grain of corn which is to be everything to us in our old age, and when the harvest-time comes—good night, the ear is empty!"

While he was speaking, Michael's voice became hoarse, his eye fierce, and his lips quivered. I wished to answer him, but I could only think of commonplace consolations, and I remained silent. The joiner pretended he wanted a tool and left me.

Poor father! Ah! I know those moments of temptation when virtue has failed to reward us and we regret having obeyed her! Who has not felt this weakness in hours of trial, and who has not uttered, at least once, the mournful exclamation of Brutus?

But if virtue is only a word, what is there then in life which is true and real? No, I will not believe that goodness is in vain! It does not always give the happiness we had hoped for, but it brings some other. In the world everything is ruled by order and has its proper and necessary consequences, and virtue cannot be the sole exception to the general law. If it had been prejudicial to those who practice it, experience would have avenged them; but experience has, on the contrary, made it more universal and more holy. We only accuse it of being a faithless debtor because we demand an immediate payment, and one apparent to our senses. We always consider life as a fairy tale, in which every good action must be rewarded by a visible wonder. We do not accept as payment a peaceful

conscience, self-content, or a good name among
men—treasures that are more precious than any
other, but the value of which we do not feel till
after we have lost them!

Michael is come back and returned to his
work. His son had not yet arrived.

By telling me of his hopes and his grievous
disappointments, he became excited; he un-
ceasingly went over again the same subject,
always adding something to his griefs. He has
just wound up his confidential discourse by
speaking to me of a joiner's business which he
had hoped to buy and work to good account with
Robert's help. The present owner had made a
fortune by it, and after thirty years of business
he was thinking of retiring to one of the ornamental cottages in the outskirts of the city, a
usual retreat for the frugal and successful
workingman. Michael had not indeed the 2,000
francs which must be paid down; but perhaps he
could have persuaded Master Benoit to wait.
Robert's presence would have been a security
for him, for the young man could not fail to insure
the prosperity of a workshop; besides science and
skill, he had the power of invention and bringing
to perfection. His father had discovered among
his drawings a new plan for a staircase, which
had occupied his thoughts for a long time;
and he even suspected him of having engaged
himself to the Versailles contractor for the very
purpose of executing it. The youth was tor-
mented by this spirit of invention, which took
possession of all his thoughts, and while devoting

GENEVIEVE ENTERED WITH ROBERT

his mind to study he had not time to listen to his feelings.

Michael told me all this with a mixed feeling of pride and vexation. I saw he was proud of the son he was abusing, and that his very pride made him more sensible of that son's neglect.

Six O'clock P. M.—I have just finished a
happy day. How many events have happened
within a few hours, and what a change for
Genevieve and Michael!

He had just finished fixing the shelves and
telling me of his son, while I laid the cloth for my
breakfast.

Suddenly we heard hurried steps in the passage, the door opened, and Genevieve entered
with Robert.

The joiner gave a start of joyful surprise, but
he repressed it immediately, as if he wished to
keep up the appearance of displeasure.

The young man did not appear to notice it, but
threw himself into his arms in an open-hearted
manner which surprised me. Genevieve, whose
face shone with happiness, seemed to wish to
speak, and to restrain herself with difficulty.

I told Robert I was glad to see him, and he
answered me with ease and civility.

"I expected you yesterday," said Michael
Arout rather dryly.

"Forgive me, father," replied the young work-
man, "but I had business at St. Germain's. I
was not able to come back till it was very late,
and then the master kept me."

The joiner looked at his son sideways, and
then took up his hammer again.

"All right," muttered he in a grumbling tone;
"when we are with other people we must do as
they wish; but there are some who would like
better to eat brown bread with their own knife
than partridges with the silver fork of a master."

"And I am one of those, father," replied Robert merrily; "but, as the proverb says, 'you must shell the peas before you can eat them.' It was necessary that I should first work in a great workshop——"

"To go on with your plan of the staircase," interrupted Michael, ironically.

"You must now say M. Raymond's plan, father," replied Robert, smiling.

"Why?"

"Because I have sold it to him."

The joiner, who was planing a board, turned round quickly.

"Sold it!" cried he, with sparkling eyes.

"For the reason that I was not rich enough to give it him."

Michael threw down the board and tool.

"There he is again!" resumed he angrily; "his good genius puts an idea into his head which would have made him known, and he goes and sells it to a rich man, who will take all the honor of it himself."

"Well, what harm is there done?" asked Genevieve.

"What harm!" cried the joiner in a passion. "You understand nothing about it—you are a woman; but he—he knows well that a true work-man never gives up his own inventions for money, no more than a soldier would give up his cross. That is his glory; he is bound to keep it for the honor it does him! Ah! thunder! if I had ever made a discovery, rather than put it up at auction I would have sold one of my eyes! Don't you

see that a new invention is like a child to a work-
man? He takes care of it, he brings it up, he
makes a way for it in the world, and it is only
poor creatures who sell it."

Robert colored a little.

"You will think differently, father," said he,
"when you know why I sold my plan."

"Yes, and you will thank him for it," added
Genevieve, who could no longer keep silence.

"Never!" replied Michael.

"But, wretched man!" cried she, "he only
sold it for our sakes!"

The joiner looked at his wife and son with
astonishment. It was necessary to come to an
explanation. The latter related how he had
entered into a negotiation with Master Benoit,
who had positively refused to sell his business
unless one half of the 2,000 francs were first
paid down. It was in the hopes of obtaining
this sum that he had gone to work with the contractor at Versailles; he had had an opportunity
of trying his invention and of finding a purchaser.
Thanks to the money he received for it, he had
just concluded the bargain with Benoit, and had
brought his father the key of the new work-yard.

This explanation was given by the young work-
man with so much modesty and simplicity that
I was quite affected by it. Genevieve cried;
Michael pressed his son to his heart, and in a long
embrace he seemed to ask his pardon for having
unjustly accused him.

All was now explained with honor to Robert.
The conduct which his parents had ascribed to

indifference really sprang from affection; he had neither obeyed the voice of ambition nor of avarice, nor even the nobler inspiration of inventive genius; his whole motive and single aim had been the happiness of Genevieve and Michael. The day for proving his gratitude had come, and he had returned them sacrifice for sacrifice!

After the explanations and exclamations of joy were over, all three were about to leave me; but the cloth being laid, I added three more places, and kept them to breakfast.

The meal was prolonged: the fare was only tolerable, but the overflowings of affection made it delicious. Never had I better understood the unspeakable charm of family love. What calm enjoyment in that happiness which is always shared with others; in that community of interests which unites such various feeling; in that association of existences which forms one single being of so many! What is man without those home affections which, like so many roots, fix him firmly in the earth and permit him to imbibe all the juices of life? Energy, happiness—does it not all come from them? Without family life where would man learn to love, to associate, to deny himself? A community in little, is it not this which teaches us how to live in the great one? Such is the holiness of home, that to express our relation with God we have been obliged to borrow the words invented for our family life. Men have named themselves the sons of a heavenly Father!

Ah! let us carefully preserve these chains of domestic union; do not let us unbind the human sheaf and scatter its ears to all the caprices of chance and of the winds; but let us rather enlarge this holy law; let us carry the principles and the habits of home beyond its bounds; and, if it may be, let us realize the prayer of the Apostle of the Gentiles when he exclaimed to the newborn children of Christ:

"Be ye like-minded, having the same love, being of one accord, of one mind."

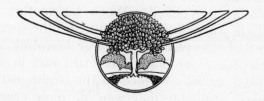

ON THE RECEIPT OF MY MOTHER'S PICTURE

WILLIAM COWPER

INTRODUCTORY NOTE

BEFORE we read this beautiful little poem, let us prepare ourselves by learning something about the author.

William Cowper, the son of an English clergyman, was born in 1731. He was a delicate, sensitive little boy whose life was made miserable by his companions in play and at school. So timid was he that the larger boys tyrannized over him shamefully, and the smaller ones teased him as much as they liked. When his mother died, William was but six years old, and the shrinking little lad was placed in a large boarding school where the other boys were cruel and heartless. At least, so they seemed to the frightened newcomer. Probably they were no more cruel and heartless than most strong and healthy youngsters who are accustomed to give and take without whimpering. Young Cowper was merely the strange lad whose timid and hesitating manner seemed to call for discipline. Years afterward, still remembering the agony of these years, he wrote of one big boy in particular:

"His savage treatment of me impressed such

a dread of his figure upon my mind that I well
remember of being afraid to lift my eyes up
higher than to his knees, and that I knew him
better by his shoe-buckles than by any other part
of his dress."

At ten he was removed to Westminster School,
where he made some good friends. Here, too,
he took a more manly stand, played football and
cricket with the other boys, and redeemed himself from some of his weakness. But he had
numerous spells of moodiness and sadness,
during which he hid himself from his fellows and
refused to join their plays even. He was unusually intelligent, distinguished himself in his
studies, and became a favorite with his teachers.

Among his friends here was Warren Hastings,
who long years afterwards, as governor of India,
was convicted of cruelty and extortion. Cowper
showed the loyalty of his nature by refusing
utterly to believe in the guilt of his old friend.

William's father wished to make a lawyer of
his son, and when the boy had finished at Westminster he was sent to study law in London. If
he had been unhappy in school, he became even
more so now, for there was nothing in the legal
profession to attract him. Instead of reading
law he read literature; instead of writing legal
papers he wrote poems and sketches. Finally,
however, he became a lawyer, but he could never
bring himself to practice his profession.

At one time he was given a clerkship, but in
preparation for it he was asked to take an ex-
amination before the bar at the House of Lords.

Here his old nervousness and timidity overpowered him, and he failed to appear; in fact, he ran away, planning to kill himself, but at the last moment his courage again failed him. After this, his mind gave way, and he was for a time in an asylum. In fact, at intervals thereafter, he had attacks of despondency and moodiness, of fear and discouragement, which showed how seriously his mind was affected.

So far this is not a very attractive picture; but it is one side of the great poet's character. That there was another we know, for he made the most loyal friends, who opened their homes to him and were ever willing to care for him.

At one time he was engaged to be married, but an attack of insanity prevented the union, though it did not destroy the ardent friendship of the lovers. Cowper could never wholly throw off the fear of the future. "Day and night," he once wrote, "I was upon the rack, lying down in horror and rising up in despair."

His most attached friends, the Unwins, were deeply religious people, and at their house Cowper spent his happiest years. It was a great shock to him when Mr. Unwin was thrown from a horse and killed. From that time a succession of kind friends aided him, watched him through his periods of despair and provided for his simple wants. He was passionately fond of pets, and was happiest in caring for his rabbits, cats and other animals. He liked gardening, too, and spent a great deal of energy upon his plants.

Cowper was one of the finest correspondents that ever wrote, and his graceful and humorous letters are still read with pleasure by all who know them. Strangely enough, his gloominess rarely found its way into his poetry, which often was highly amusing, as you know who have read *John Gilpin*. *The Task* is his greatest poem, though there are many short ones of great beauty.

Cowper was sincere and honest, and used good judgment in everything that did not concern himself. Occasionally he became dissatisfied with the style of poetry then most popular, because it was written so strictly according to rule and because heart and nature were all forgotten. What he wrote was different; putting his truthful eyes on birds and flowers, on fine scenery and on noble men and women, he wrote exactly as he saw, and let his fine sentiment and loving heart find gracious expression. The result was that he led the way for Wordsworth, the greater man, who brought our poetry back from the bonds of formality and made it beautiful, sincere and true.

The final years of Cowper were sad ones. Mrs. Unwin was stricken with paralysis, and the poet repaid her years of care and protection by an unfailing attention that lasted till she died. It is said that after the one heart-breaking cry he uttered when he saw her dead body, he never again mentioned her name, though he lived for four years. His end came peacefully enough, in April, 1800.

When Cowper was fifty-six years old his cousin sent to him from Norfolk a picture of his mother, who had then been dead for half a century. How vivid a recollection of her loving care remained to the saddened man may be seen in the poem.

MY MOTHER'S PICTURE

OUT OF NORFOLK, THE GIFT OF MY COUSIN,
ANN BODHAM

 THAT those lips had language! Life has passed
   With me but roughly since I heard thee last.
Those lips are thine,—thy own sweet smile I see,
The same that oft in childhood solaced me;
Voice only fails, else how distinct they say,
"Grieve not, my child; chase all thy fears away!"
The meek intelligence of those dear eyes
(Blest be the art that can immortalize,—
The art that baffles time's tyrannic claim
To quench it!) here shines on me still the same.

Faithful remembrancer of one so dear!
O welcome guest, though unexpected here!
Who bid'st me honor with an artless song,
Affectionate, a mother lost so long.
I will obey,—not willingly alone,
But gladly, as[1] the precept were her own;

1. As *though* the request were her own.

"MY MOTHER!"

And, while that face renews my filial grief,
Fancy shall weave a charm for my relief,—
Shall steep me in Elysian[2] revery,
A momentary dream that thou art she.

2. The Elysian Fields were the blessed lands of beauty and joy to which the Greeks hoped to go at their death.

My mother! when I learned that thou wast
    dead,
Say, wast thou conscious of the tears I shed?
Hovered thy spirit o'er thy sorrowing son,—
Wretch even then, life's journey just begun?
Perhaps thou gavest me, though unfelt, a kiss;
Perhaps a tear, if souls can weep in bliss—
Ah, that maternal smile! it answers—Yes.
I heard the bell tolled on thy burial day;
I saw the hearse that bore thee slow away;
And, turning from my nursery window, drew
A long, long sigh, and wept a last adieu!
But was it such?—It was.—Where thou art
    gone
Adieus and farewells are a sound unknown;
May I but meet thee on that peaceful shore,
The parting word shall pass my lips no more.
Thy maidens, grieved themselves at my concern,
Oft gave me promise of thy quick return;
What ardently I wished I long believed,
And, disappointed still, was still deceived,—
By expectation every day beguiled,
Dupe of to-morrow even from a child.
Thus many a sad to-morrow came and went,
Till, all my stock of infant sorrows spent,
I learned at last submission to my lot;
But, though I less deplored thee, ne'er forgot.

Where once we dwelt our name is heard no
    more;
Children not thine have trod my nursery floor;
And where the gardener Robin, day by day,
Drew me to school along the public way,

Delighted with my bauble coach, and wrapt
In scarlet mantle warm, and velvet capped,
'Tis now become a history little known,
That once we call'd the pastoral house[3] our
    own.
Shortlived possession! but the record fair,
That memory keeps of all thy kindness there,
Still outlives many a storm, that has effaced
A thousand other themes less deeply traced.
Thy nightly visits to my chamber made,
That thou mightst know me safe and warmly
    laid;
Thy morning bounties ere I left my home,
The biscuit, or confectionery plum;
The fragrant waters on my cheeks bestow'd
By thy own hand, till fresh they shone and
    glow'd;
All this, and more endearing still than all,
Thy constant flow of love, that knew no
    fall,
Ne'er roughen'd by those cataracts and breaks,
That humour[4] interposed too often makes;
All this still legible in memory's page,
And still to be so to my latest age,
Adds joy to duty, makes me glad to pay
Such honours to thee as my numbers[5] may;
Perhaps a frail memorial, but sincere,
Not scorn'd in Heaven, though little noticed
    here.

---

3. The *pastoral house* means the rectory, the home of the clergy-man.

4. *Humour* here means *temper*.

5. *Numbers* is used for *poetic measures; poetry*.

Could Time, his flight reversed, restore the
    hours,
When, playing with thy vesture's tissued[6]
    flowers,
The violet, the pink, the jessamine,
I prick'd them into paper with a pin,[7]
(And thou wast happier than myself the while—
Wouldst softly speak, and stroke my head and
    smile,)—
Could those few pleasant days again appear,
Might one wish bring them, would I wish them
    here?
I would not trust my heart,—the dear delight
Seems so to be desired, perhaps I might.
But no,—what here we call our life is such,
So little to be loved, and thou so much,
That I should ill requite thee to constrain
Thy unbound spirit into bonds again.

    Thou—as a gallant bark, from Albion's[8] coast,
(The storms all weathered and the ocean
    crossed,)
Shoots into port at some well-havened isle,
Where spices breathe and brighter seasons
    smile;
There sits quiescent on the floods, that show
Her beauteous form reflected clear below,
While airs impregnated with incense play
Around her, fanning light her streamers gay,—

6. *Tissued* is a poetic word for *variegated*.

7. He pricked into paper with a pin the outlines of the variegated
forms of violets, pinks and jessamine that decorated his mother's dress.

8. *England's*. The old name Albion, which means *white*, is still used
in poetry. Just how the name originated no one knows. Perhaps it
alluded to the white chalk cliffs of England which the Gauls could see.

So thou, with sails how swift! hast reached the
    shore
"Where tempests never beat nor billows roar":
And thy loved consort[9] on the dangerous tide
Of life long since has anchored by thy side.
But me,[10] scarce hoping to attain the rest,
Always from port withheld, always distressed,—
Me[10] howling blasts drive devious, tempest-
    tossed,
Sails ripped, seams opening wide, and compass
    lost;[11]
And day by day some current's thwarting force
Sets me more distant from a prosperous course.
Yet O, the thought that thou art safe, and he!—[12]
That thought is joy, arrive what may to me.
My boast is not that I deduce my birth
From loins enthroned,[13] and rulers of the earth;
But higher far my proud pretensions rise,—
The son of parents passed into the skies.
And now, farewell!—Time, unrevoked,[14] has run
His wonted course; yet what I wished is done.
By contemplation's help, not sought in vain,
I seem to have lived my childhood o'er again,—

---

9. Cowper's father died in 1756; his mother in 1737.

10. *Me* is repeated for emphasis; it is the object of *drive:* "Howling
blasts drive me out of the straight line," is what the lines mean.

11. Cowper was too strongly conscious of his weakness and his difference from other men. He wrote in a letter to a friend, "Certainly I am
not an absolute fool, but I have more weaknesses than the greatest of all
the fools I can recollect at present. In short, if I was as fit for the next
world as I am unfit for this,—and God forbid I should speak of it in
vanity,—I would not change conditions with any saint in Christendom."

12. "That thou art safe, and that he is safe."

13. As a matter of fact Cowper's descent was from ancient and high
lineage on both sides.

14. *Unrevoked* means *not called back.*

To have renewed the joys that once were mine,
Without the sin of violating thine;
And, while the wings of fancy still are free,
And I can view this mimic show of thee,
Time has but half succeeded in his theft,—
Thyself removed, thy power to soothe me left.

ANNABEL LEE

EDGAR ALLAN POE

It was many and many a year ago,
   In a kingdom by the sea,
That a maiden lived, whom you may know
   By the name of Annabel Lee;
And this maiden she lived with no other thought
   Than to love, and be loved by me.

I was a child and she was a child,
   In this kingdom by the sea;
But we loved with a love that was more than
     love,
   I and my Annabel Lee,—
With a love that the wingéd seraphs of heaven
   Coveted her and me.

And this was the reason that long ago,
   In this kingdom by the sea,
A wind blew out of a cloud, chilling
   My beautiful Annabel Lee;
So that her highborn kinsmen came,
   And bore her away from me,
To shut her up in a sepulchre,
   In this kingdom by the sea.

IN HER SEPULCHRE THERE BY THE SEA

The angels, not so happy in heaven,
    Went envying her and me.
Yes! that was the reason (as all men know)
    In this kingdom by the sea,
That the wind came out of the cloud by
        night,
    Chilling and killing my Annabel Lee.

But our love it was stronger by far than the love
    Of those who were older than we,
    Of many far wiser than we;

And neither the angels in heaven above,
  Nor the demons down under the sea,
Can ever dissever my soul from the soul
  Of the beautiful Annabel Lee.

For the moon never beams without bringing me
      dreams
  Of the beautiful Annabel Lee,
And the stars never rise but I feel the bright
      eyes
  Of the beautiful Annabel Lee.
And so, all the night-tide I lie down by the side
Of my darling, my darling, my life, and my bride,
  In her sepulchre there by the sea,
  In her tomb by the sounding sea.

THOSE EVENING BELLS

THOMAS MOORE

  Those evening bells! those evening bells.
  How many a tale their music tells,
  Of youth, and home, and that sweet time
  When last I heard their soothing chime!

  Those joyous hours are passed away;
  And many a heart that once was gay,
  Within the tomb now darkly dwells,
  And hears no more those evening bells.

  And so 'twill be when I am gone—
  That tuneful peal will still ring on;
  While other bards shall walk these dells,
  And sing your praise, sweet evening bells.

THE THREE FISHERS

CHARLES KINGSLEY

Three fishers went sailing out into the west—
    Out into the west as the sun went down;
Each thought on the woman who loved him the
      best,
    And the children stood watching them out of
      the town;
For men must work, and women must weep;

THE NIGHT RACK CAME ROLLING UP

And there's little to earn, and many to keep,
    Though the harbor bar be moaning.[1]

---

    1. Off the mouths of harbors there are frequently shallow bars over
which the waves roll softly when there is little wind; but as the wind is
rising, the breakers form on the bar and make a moaning sound, which
sailors and their families have learned to regard as the warning of a
storm.

Three wives sat up in the lighthouse tower,
  And trimmed the lamps as the sun went down;
And they looked at the squall, and they looked
    at the shower,
  And the night rack[2] came rolling up, ragged
    and brown;
But men must work, and women must weep,—
Though storms be sudden, and waters deep,
  And the harbor bar be moaning.

Three corpses lay out on the shining sands
  In the morning gleam as the tide went down,
And the women are weeping and wringing their
    hands,
  For those who will never come back to the
    town;
For men must work, and women must weep,
And the sooner it's over, the sooner to sleep,—
  And good-bye to the bar and its moaning.

2. *Rack* is a word applied to those light, fleecy, flying clouds, which
are often seen approaching in front of a heavy rainstorm.

CROSSING THE BAR

ALFRED TENNYSON

Sunset and evening star,
   And one clear call for me!
And may there be no moaning of the bar,
   When I put out to sea,

But such a tide as moving seems asleep,
   Too full for sound and foam,

CROSSING THE BAR

When that which drew from out the boundless deep
   Turns again home.

Twilight and evening bell,
   And after that the dark!
And may there be no sadness of farewell,
   When I embark;

For tho' from out our bourne of Time and
  Place
The flood may bear me far,
I hope to see my Pilot face to face
  When I have crost the bar.

English poetry is full of tenderness, reverence,
and deep religious sentiment. The greatest
poems, while they have this religious sentiment,
are not sectarian, but show a strong and abiding
faith in the power and goodness of God.

This beautiful little poem of Tennyson's, written when he was nearing the close of his long
and useful life, breathes the sentiment we have
just mentioned in a most inspiring way.

To appreciate its beauty and its sentiment, we
must understand its basis in nature, and then
learn to feel his application of the ideas.

We may imagine ourselves standing by the
seashore just as the sun is setting and the evening
star begins to shine in the darkening sky. Across
the mouth of the harbor lies the shallow bar.
On such a night as this, the tide rises deeply
over it, and neither dashing wave nor foam
marks its position. The tide has come in to its
full flood, and now draws back silently over the
bar into the great deep from which it came. As
we stand there, twilight fades into night, the
evening bell sounds, and shadows disappear in
the darkness. We may imagine that some one
we love is on the ship which has just safely
crossed the bar, and set forth on its uncertain
voyage to far-away lands.

Some such scene as this was in Tennyson's mind when he wrote the poem. He knew that the waves rise ahead of the approaching storm, and often as they roll across the bar they moan in sad prophecy of coming disaster. He saw in the darkness the approach of death, and his departure seemed to him like that of a ship putting out to sea; but he felt no premonition of coming danger, for there was to him no moaning of the bar. In the quiet darkness, in the bright face of the evening star, in the evening bell and the soundless bar, he saw the prophecy of his own peaceful death. To him the evening star was one of hope, and his great faith convinced him that when he had crossed the bar he would meet his own loved Pilot face to face.

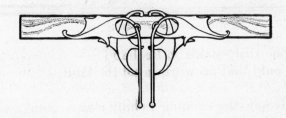

THE REAPER'S DREAM

THOMAS BUCHANAN READ

The road was lone; the grass was dank
With night-dews on the briery bank
Whereon a weary reaper sank.
His garb was old; his visage tanned;

THE CRESCENT MOON WENT BY

The rusty sickle in his hand
Could find no work in all the land.

He saw the evening's chilly star
Above his native vale afar;
A moment on the horizon's bar
It hung, then sank, as with a sigh;
And there the crescent moon went by,
An empty sickle down the sky.

To soothe his pain, Sleep's tender palm
Laid on his brow its touch of balm;
His brain received the slumberous calm;
And soon that angel without name,
Her robe a dream, her face the same,
The giver of sweet visions came.

She touched his eyes; no longer sealed,
They saw a troop of reapers wield
Their swift blades in a ripened field.
At each thrust of their snowy sleeves
A thrill ran through the future sheaves
Rustling like rain on forest leaves.

They were not brawny men who bowed,
With harvest voices rough and loud,
But spirits, moving as a cloud.
Like little lightnings in their hold,
The silver sickles manifold
Slid musically through the gold.

O, bid the morning stars combine
To match the chorus clear and fine,
That rippled lightly down the line,—
A cadence of celestial rhyme,
The language of that cloudless clime,
To which their shining hands kept time!

Behind them lay the gleaming rows,
Like those long clouds the sunset shows
On amber meadows of repose;
But, like a wind, the binders bright
Soon followed in their mirthful might,
And swept them into sheaves of light.

Doubling the splendor of the plain,
There rolled the great celestial wain,
To gather in the fallen grain.
Its frame was built of golden bars;
Its glowing wheels were lit with stars;
The royal Harvest's car of cars.

The snowy yoke that drew the load,
On gleaming hoofs of silver trode;
And music was its only goad.
To no command of word or beck
It moved, and felt no other check
Than one white arm laid on the neck,—

The neck, whose light was overwound
With bells of lilies, ringing round
Their odors till the air was drowned:
The starry foreheads meekly borne,
With garlands looped from horn to horn,
Shone like the many-colored morn.

The field was cleared.   Home went the bands,
Like children, linking happy hands,
While singing through their father's lands;
Or, arms about each other thrown,
With amber tresses backward blown,
They moved as they were music's own.

The vision brightening more and more,
He saw the garner's glowing door,
And sheaves, like sunshine, strew the floor,—
The floor was jasper,—golden flails,
Swift-sailing as a whirlwind sails,
Throbbed mellow music down the vales.

He saw the mansion,—all repose,—
Great corridors and porticos,
Propped with the columns, shining rows;
And these—for beauty was the rule—
The polished pavements, hard and cool,
Redoubled, like a crystal pool.

And there the odorous feast was spread;
The fruity fragrance widely shed
Seemed to the floating music wed.
Seven angels, like the Pleiad seven,
Their lips to silver clarions given,
Blew welcome round the walls of heaven.

In skyey garments, silky thin,
The glad retainers floated in
A thousand forms, and yet no din:
And from the visage of the Lord,
Like splendor from the Orient poured,
A smile illumined all the board.

Far flew the music's circling sound;
Then floated back, with soft rebound,
To join, not mar, the converse round,—
Sweet notes, that, melting, still increased,
Such as ne'er cheered the bridal feast
Of king in the enchanted East.

Did any great door ope or close,
It seemed the birth-time of repose,
The faint sound died where it arose;
And they who passed from door to door,
Their soft feet on the polished floor
Met their soft shadows,—nothing more.

Then once again the groups were drawn
Through corridors, or down the lawn,
Which bloomed in beauty like a dawn.
Where countless fountains leapt alway,
Veiling their silver heights in spray,
The choral people held their way.

There, midst the brightest, brightly shone
Dear forms he loved in years agone,—
The earliest loved,—the earliest flown.
He heard a mother's sainted tongue,
A sister's voice, who vanished young,
While one still dearer sweetly sung!

No further might the scene unfold;
The gazer's voice could not withhold;
The very rapture made him bold:
He cried aloud, with claspéd hands,
"O happy fields! O happy bands!
Who reap the never-failing lands.

"O master of these broad estates,
Behold, before your very gates
A worn and wanting laborer waits!
Let me but toil amid your grain,
Or be a gleaner on the plain,
So I may leave these fields of pain!

"A gleaner, I will follow far,
With never look or word to mar,
Behind the Harvest's yellow car;
All day my hand shall constant be,
And every happy eve shall see
The precious burden borne to thee!"

At morn some reapers neared the place,
Strong men, whose feet recoiled apace;
Then gathering round the upturned face,
They saw the lines of pain and care,
Yet read in the expression there
The look as of an answered prayer.

A poem like the preceding abounds in beautiful word pictures, which add to the charm of the imaginary incident which is related.

Here is the first: It is a country road in the harvest season. On one side, stretching away into the dim distance, lie fields already reaped; upon the other, a bank, covered with briery vines, rises steeply into the darkness. The evening star lies close to the horizon, and in the sky the cold crescent moon hangs like an empty sickle. In the grass under the bank, with night dews thickly gathered upon him, lies a poor and weary reaper. His torn clothes, old and ill-kept, his tanned face, slender figure, and more than all else the rusty sickle in his hand, show that he has been long without work, and has suffered in poverty.

The next four scenes are from the reaper's dream:

1. It is a busy afternoon, and in a field of ripening grain reapers are busy wielding their sickles, but they are not the strong men who talk with loud, rough voices and bind the sheaves with joke and laughter; they are gentle spirits moving like clouds, and their sickles seem like little strokes of lightning as they

slide musically through the golden grain. Their
shining hands keep time to a beautiful song,
and often the reapers glance across the gleaming
rows of grain into the rich red of the sunset.
The binders follow the reapers and place the
sheaves in gleaming rows, while behind them
follows the great wagon gathering in the fallen
grain,—a wagon not of earth, but built of gold.
Beautiful cattle draw the wain, cattle that
tread on silver hoofs and move without other
command than sweet music, or the soft touch
of a white-armed angel. Around the necks of
the cattle are white lilies, and from the horns
droop garlands of many-colored flowers, freshly
picked from the dewy grass.

2.   A jasper floor on which the grain lies like
sunshine, and where golden flails, falling swiftly,
beat out the grain to mellow music, gleams with
increasing brightness.

3.   The great mansion shines with its long
corridors, its gleaming porticos and polished
pavement, all beautiful and hard and cool.
Inside is spread a fragrant feast to which seven
angels sing invitation with their silver clarions.
Softly the invited guests float in, a multitude
in number, but silently as the stars move in
heaven. Sweet music floats around the beautiful room, and smiling faces nod around the
board. Doors are opened and closed without
sound, and the feet of the servants on the polished floor give no more sound than falling
shadows.

4.   The groups of angel guests are gathered

like flowers upon the lawn where countless fountains play, and among them, moving here and there, are the forms of the loved ones who have passed away before him. His mother, his sister, and one still dearer than either, sing sweetly and walk about among fragrant flowers more beautiful than his fancy ever painted.

The last scene is the same as the first, except that it is a cold, chilly morning instead of a damp evening. Some reapers coming near see lying under the briers the poor old reaper with his upturned face, peaceful and quiet, now in death, but bearing the look of an answered prayer.

THE RECOVERY OF THE HISPANIOLA[1]

ROBERT LOUIS STEVENSON

THE coracle—as I had ample reason to know before I was done with her—was a very safe boat for a person of my height and weight, both buoyant and clever in a seaway; but she was the most cross-grained lop-sided craft to manage. Do as you pleased, she always made more leeway than anything else, and turning round and round was the maneuver she was best at.

She turned in every direction but the one I was bound to go; the most part of the time we were broadside on, and I am very sure I never should have made the ship at all but for the tide. By good fortune, paddle as I pleased, the tide was still sweeping me down; and there lay the *Hispaniola* right in the fair way, hardly to be missed.

First she loomed before me like a blot of something yet blacker than darkness, then her spars and hull began to take shape, and the next moment, as it seemed (for, the further I went, the brisker grew the current of the ebb), I was alongside of her hawser, and had laid hold.

The hawser was as taut as a bowstring, and the current so strong she pulled upon her anchor. All round the hull, in the blackness, the rippling

1. From *Treasure Island.*

current bubbled and chattered like a little mountain stream. One cut with my sea-gully, and the *Hispaniola* would go humming down the tide.

So far so good; but it next occurred to my recollection that a taut hawser, suddenly cut, is a thing as dangerous as a kicking horse. Ten to one, if I were so foolhardy as to cut the *Hispaniola* from her anchor, I and the coracle would be knocked clean out of the water.

This brought me to a full stop, and if fortune had not again particularly favored me, I should have had to abandon my design. But the light airs which had begun blowing from the southeast and south had hauled round after nightfall into the southwest. Just while I was meditating, a puff came, caught the *Hispaniola*, and forced her up into the current; and, to my great joy, I felt the hawser slacken in my grasp, and the hand by which I held it dip for a second under water.

With that I made my mind up, took out my gully, opened it with my teeth, and cut one strand after another, till the vessel swung only by two. Then I lay quiet, waiting to sever these last when the strain should be once more lightened by a breath of wind.

All this time I had heard the sound of loud voices from the cabin; but, to say truth, my mind had been so entirely taken up with other thoughts that I had scarcely given ear. Now, however, when I had nothing else to do, I began to pay more heed.

One I recognized for the coxswain's, Israel
Hands, that had been Flint's gunner in former
days. The other was, of course, my friend
of the red nightcap. Both men were plainly
the worse of drink, and they were still drinking;
for, even while I was listening, one of them,
with a drunken cry, opened the stern window
and threw out something, which I divined to be
an empty bottle. But they were not only tipsy;
it was plain that they were furiously angry.
Oaths flew like hailstones, and every now and
then there came forth such an explosion as I
thought was sure to end in blows. But each time
the quarrel passed off, and the voices grumbled
lower for a while, until the next crisis came,
and, in its turn, passed away without result.

On shore I could see the glow of the great
campfire burning warmly through the shore-
side trees. Some one was singing a dull, old,
droning sailor's song, with a droop and a quaver
at the end of every verse, and seemingly no end
to it at all but the patience of the singer. I had
heard it on the voyage more than once, and remembered these words:

"But one man of her crew alive,
    What put to sea with seventy-five."

And I thought it was a ditty rather too dolefully
appropriate for a company that had met such
cruel losses in the morning. But, indeed, from
what I saw, all these buccaneers were as callous
as the sea they sailed on.

At last the breeze came; the schooner sidled and drew nearer in the dark; I felt the hawser slacken once more, and with a good, tough effort, cut the last fibers through.

The breeze had but little action on the coracle, and I was almost instantly swept against the bows of the *Hispaniola*. At the same time the schooner began to turn upon her heel, spinning slowly, end for end, across the current.

I wrought like a fiend, for I expected every moment to be swamped; and since I found I could not push the coracle directly off, I now shoved straight astern. At length I was clear of my dangerous neighbor; and just as I gave the last impulsion, my hands came across a light cord that was trailing overboard across the stern bulwarks. Instantly I grasped it.

Why I should have done so I can hardly say. It was at first mere instinct; but once I had it in my hands and found it fast, curiosity began to get the upper hand, and I determined I should have one look through the cabin window.

I pulled in hand over hand on the cord, and, when I judged myself near enough, rose at infinite risk to about half my height, and thus commanded the roof and a slice of the interior of the cabin.

By this time the schooner and her little consort were gliding pretty swiftly through the water; indeed, we had already fetched up level with the campfire. The ship was talking, as sailors say, loudly, treading the innumerable ripples with an

I LOOKED INTO THE CABIN

incessant weltering splash; and until I got my
eye above the window-sill I could not comprehend why the watchmen had taken no alarm.
One glance, however, was sufficient; and it was
only one glance that I durst take from that un-
steady skiff. It showed me Hands and his

companion locked together in deadly wrestle, each with a hand upon the other's throat.

I dropped upon the thwart again, none too soon, for I was near overboard. I could see nothing for the moment, but these two furious, encrimsoned faces, swaying together under the smoky lamp; and I shut my eyes to let them grow once more familiar with the darkness.

The endless ballad had come to an end at last, and the whole diminished company about the campfire had broken into the chorus I had heard so often:

> "Fifteen men on the dead man's chest—
>   Yo-ho-ho, and a bottle of rum!
> Drink and the devil had done for the rest—
>   Yo-ho-ho, and a bottle of rum!"

I was just thinking how busy drink and the devil were at that very moment in the cabin of the *Hispaniola*, when I was surprised by a sudden lurch of the coracle. At the same moment she yawed sharply and seemed to change her course. The speed in the meantime had strangely increased.

I opened my eyes at once. All round me were little ripples, combing over with a sharp, bristling sound, and slightly phosphorescent. The *Hispaniola* herself, a few yards in whose wake I was still being whirled along, seemed to stagger in her course, and I saw her spars toss a little against the blackness of the night; nay, as I looked longer, I made sure she also was wheeling to the southward.

I glanced over my shoulder, and my heart jumped against my ribs. There, right behind me, was the glow of the campfire. The current had turned at right angles, sweeping round along with it the tall schooner and the little dancing coracle; ever quickening, ever bubbling higher, ever muttering louder, it went spinning through the narrows for the open sea.

Suddenly the schooner in front of me gave a violent yaw, turning, perhaps, through twenty degrees; and almost at the same moment one shout followed another from on board; I could hear feet pounding on the companion ladder; and I knew that the two drunkards had at last been interrupted in their quarrel and awakened to a sense of their disaster.

I lay down flat in the bottom of that wretched skiff, and devoutly recommended my spirit to its Maker. At the end of the straits, I made sure we must fall into some bar of raging breakers, where all my troubles would be ended speedily; and though I could, perhaps, bear to die, I could not bear to look upon my fate as it approached.

So I must have lain for hours, continually beaten to and fro upon the billows, now and again wetted with flying sprays, and never ceasing to expect death at the next plunge. Gradually weariness grew upon me; a numbness, an occasional stupor, fell upon my mind even in the midst of my terrors; until sleep at last supervened,

and in my sea-tossed coracle I lay and dreamed
of home and the old tavern "Benbow."

It was broad day when I awoke, and found
myself tossing at the southwest end of Treasure
Island. The sun was up, but was still hid from
me behind the great bulk of the Spyglass, which
on this side descended almost to the sea in formidable cliffs.

Haulbowline Head and Mizzenmast Hill were
at my elbow; the hill bare and dark, the head
bound with cliffs forty or fifty feet high, and
fringed with great masses of fallen rock. I was
scarce a quarter of a mile to seaward, and it was
my first thought to paddle in and land.

That notion was soon given over. Among the
fallen rocks the breakers spouted and bellowed;
loud reverberations, heavy sprays flying and
falling, succeeded one another from second to
second; and I saw myself, if I ventured nearer,
dashed to death upon the rough shore, or spend-
ing my strength in vain to scale the beetling
crags.

Nor was that all; for crawling together on flat
tables of rock, or letting themselves drop into
the sea with loud reports, I beheld huge slimy
monsters—soft snails, as it were, of incredible
bigness—two or three score of them together,
making the rocks to echo with their barkings.

I have understood since that they were sea
lions, and entirely harmless. But the look of
them added to the difficulty of the shore and the
high running of the surf, was more than enough
to disgust me of that landing place. I felt

willing rather to starve at sea than to confront such perils.

In the meantime I had a better chance, as I supposed, before me. North of Haulbowline Head the land runs in a long way, leaving, at low tide, a long stretch of yellow sand. To the north of that, again, there comes another cape—Cape of the Woods, as it was marked upon the chart— buried in tall green pines, which descended to the margin of the sea.

I remembered that the current sets northward along the whole west coast of Treasure Island; and seeing from my position that I was already under its influence, I preferred to leave Haul- bowline Head behind me, and reserve my strength for an attempt to land upon the kindlier- looking Cape of the Woods.

There was a great, smooth swell upon the sea. The wind blowing steady and gentle from the south, there was no contrariety between that and the current, and the billows rose and fell unbroken.

Had it been otherwise, I must long ago have perished; but as it was, it is surprising how easily and securely my little and light boat could ride. Often, as I still lay at the bottom, and kept no more than an eye above the gunwale, I would see a big blue summit heaving close above me; yet the coracle would but bounce a little, dance as if on springs, and subside on the other side into the trough as lightly as a bird.

I began after a little to grow very bold, and sat up to try my skill at paddling. But even a small

change in the disposition of the weight will produce violent changes in the behavior of a coracle.
And I had hardly moved before the boat, giving
up at once her gentle dancing movement, ran
straight down a slope of water so steep that it
made me giddy, and stuck her nose, with a spout
of spray, deep into the side of the next wave.

I was drenched and terrified, and fell instantly
back into my old position, whereupon the
coracle seemed to find her head again, and led
me as softly as before among the billows. It was
plain she was not to be interfered with, and at
that rate, since I could in no way influence her
course, what hope had I left of reaching land?

I began to be horribly frightened, but I kept
my head, for all that. First, moving with all
care, I gradually bailed out the coracle with my
sea-cap; then getting my eye once more above
the gunwale, I set myself to study how it was
she managed to slip so quietly through the rollers.

I found each wave, instead of the big, smooth,
glossy mountain it looks from shore, or from a
vessel's deck, was for all the world like any
range of hills on the dry land, full of peaks and
smooth places and valleys. The coracle, left to
herself, turning from side to side, threaded, so
to speak, her way through these lower parts, and
avoided the steep slopes and higher, toppling
summits of the waves.

"Well, now," thought I to myself, "it is plain
I must lie where I am, and not disturb the balance; but it is plain, also, that I can put the
paddle over the side, and from time to time, in

smooth places, give her a shove or two toward land." No sooner thought upon than done. There I lay on my elbows, in the most trying attitude, and every now and again gave a weak stroke or two to turn her head to shore.

It was very tiring, and slow work, yet I did visibly gain ground; and, as we drew near the Cape of the Woods, though I saw I must infallibly miss that point, I had still made some hundred yards of easting. I was, indeed, close in. I could see the cool, green tree tops swaying together in the breeze, and I felt sure I should make the next promontory without fail.

It was high time, for I now began to be tortured with thirst. The glow of the sun from above, its thousandfold reflection from the waves, the sea-water that fell and dried upon me, caking my very lips with salt, combined to make my throat burn and my brain ache. The sight of the trees so near at hand had almost made me sick with longing; but the current had soon carried me past the point; and, as the next reach of sea opened out, I beheld a sight that changed the nature of my thoughts.

Right in front of me, not half a mile away, I beheld the *Hispaniola* under sail. I made sure, of course, that I should be taken; but I was so distressed for want of water, that I scarce knew whether to be glad or sorry at the thought; and, long before I had come to a conclusion, surprise had taken entire possession of my mind, and I could do nothing but stare and wonder.

The *Hispaniola* was under her mainsail and

two jibs, and the beautiful white canvas shone
in the sun like snow or silver. When I first
sighted her, all her sails were drawing; she was
lying a course about northwest; and I presumed
the men on board were going round the island
on their way back to the anchorage. Presently
she began to fetch more and more to the west-
ward, so that I thought they had sighted me and
were going about in chase. At last, however,
she fell right into the wind's eye, was taken dead
aback, and stood there awhile helpless, with her
sails shivering.

"Clumsy fellows," said I; "they must still be
drunk as owls." And I thought how Captain
Smollett would have set them skipping.

Meanwhile, the schooner gradually fell off,
and filled again upon another tack, sailed swiftly
for a minute or so, and brought up once more
dead in the wind's eye. Again and again was
this repeated. To and fro, up and down, north,
south, east, and west the *Hispaniola* sailed by
swoops and dashes, and at each repetition ended
as she had begun, with idly-flapping canvas. It
became plain to me that nobody was steering.
And, if so, where were the men? Either they
were dead drunk, or had deserted her, I thought,
and perhaps if I could get on board, I might
return the vessel to her captain.

The current was bearing coracle and schooner
southward at an equal rate. As for the latter's
sailing, it was so wild and intermittent, and she
hung each time so long in irons, that she certainly
gained nothing, if she did not even lose. If only

I dared to sit up and paddle, I made sure that I could overhaul her. The scheme had an air of adventure that inspired me, and the thought of the water-breaker beside the fore companion doubled my growing courage.

Up I got, was welcomed almost instantly by another cloud of spray, but this time stuck to my purpose; and set myself, with all my strength and caution, to paddle after the unsteered *Hispaniola*. Once I shipped a sea so heavy that I had to stop and bail, with my heart fluttering like a bird; but gradually I got into the way of the thing, and guided my coracle among the waves, with only now and then a blow upon her bows and a dash of foam in my face.

I was now gaining rapidly on the schooner. I could see the brass glisten on the tiller as it banged about; and still no soul appeared upon her decks. I could not choose but suppose she was deserted. If not, the men were lying drunk below, where I might batten them down, perhaps, and do what I chose with the ship.

For some time she had been doing the worst thing possible for me—standing still. She headed nearly due south, yawing, of course, all the time. Each time she fell off her sails partly filled, and these brought her in a moment right to the wind again. I have said this was the worst thing possible for me; for helpless as she looked in this situation, with the canvas cracking like cannon and the blocks trundling and banging on the deck, she still continued to run away from me, not only with the speed of the current, but by the whole amount of her leeway, which was naturally great.

But now at last I had my chance. The breeze fell for some seconds very low, and the current gradually turning her, the *Hispaniola* revolved slowly round her center, and at last presented me her stern, with the cabin window still gaping open, and the lamp over the table still burning on into the day. The mainsail hung drooped like a banner. She was stock-still, but for the current.

For the last little while I had even lost; but now, redoubling my efforts, I began once more to overhaul the chase.

I was not a hundred yards from her when the wind came again in a clap; she filled on the port tack and was off again, stooping and skimming like a swallow.

My first impulse was one of despair, but my second was toward joy. Round she came till she was broadside on to me—round still till she had covered a half, and then two thirds, and then three quarters of the distance that separated us. I could see the waves boiling white under her forefoot. Immensely tall she looked to me from my low station in the coracle.

And then, of a sudden, I began to comprehend. I had scarce time to think—scarce time to act and save myself. I was on the summit of one swell when the schooner came stooping over the next. The bowsprit was over my head. I sprang to my feet and leaped, stamping the coracle under water. With one hand I caught

the jib-boom, while my foot was lodged between
the stay and the brace; and as I still clung there
panting a dull blow told me that the schooner
had charged down upon and struck the coracle,
and that I was left without retreat on the *Hispaniola*.

I had scarce gained a position on the bowsprit,
when the flying jib flapped and filled upon the
other tack, with a report like a gun. The
schooner trembled to her keel under the reverse;
but next moment, the other sails still drawing,
the jib flapped back again and hung idle.

This had nearly tossed me off into the sea;
and now I lost no time, crawled back along the
bowsprit, and tumbled head foremost on the
deck.

I was on the lee side of the forecastle, and the
mainsail, which was still drawing, concealed
from me a certain portion of the after-deck. Not
a soul was to be seen. The planks, which had
not been swabbed since the mutiny, bore the
print of many feet; and an empty bottle, broken
by the neck, tumbled to and fro like a live thing
in the scuppers.

Suddenly the *Hispaniola* came right into the
wind. The jibs behind me cracked aloud; the
rudder slammed to; the whole ship gave a sickening heave and shudder, and at the same moment
the main-boom swung inboard, the sheet groan-
ing in the blocks, and showed me the lee after-
deck.

There were the two watchmen, sure enough:
red-cap on his back, as stiff as a handspike, with

his arms stretched out like those of a crucifix, and his teeth showing through his open lips; Israel Hands propped against the bulwarks, his chin on his chest, his hands lying open before him on the deck, his face as white, under its tan, as a tallow candle.

For awhile the ship kept bucking and sidling like a vicious horse, the sails filling, now on one tack, now on another, and the boom swinging to and fro till the mast groaned aloud under the strain. Now and again, too, there would come a cloud of light sprays over the bulwark, and a heavy blow of the ship's bows against the swell: so much heavier weather was made of it by this great rigged ship than by my home-made, lop-sided coracle, now gone to the bottom of the sea.

At every jump of the schooner red-cap slipped to and fro; but—what was ghastly to behold— neither his attitude nor his fixed teeth-disclosing grin was anyway disturbed by this rough usage. At every jump, too, Hands appeared still more to sink into himself and settle down upon the deck, his feet sliding ever the farther out, and the whole body canting toward the stern, so that his face became, little by little, hid from me; and at last I could see nothing beyond his ear and the frayed ringlet of one whisker.

At the same time, I observed, around both of them, splashes of dark blood upon the planks, and began to feel sure that they had killed each other in their drunken wrath.

While I was thus looking and wondering, in a calm moment, when the ship was still, Israel

Hands turned partly round, and, with a low moan, writhed himself back to the position in which I had seen him first. The moan, which told of pain and deadly weakness, and the way in which his jaw hung open, went right to my heart. But when I remembered the talk I had overheard from the apple barrel, all pity left me.

I walked aft until I reached the mainmast.

"Come aboard, Mr. Hands," I said ironically.

He rolled his eyes round heavily; but he was too far gone to express surprise. All he could do was to utter one word: "Brandy."

It occurred to me there was no time to lose; and, dodging the boom as it once more lurched across the deck, I slipped aft, and down the companion stairs into the cabin.

It was such a scene of confusion as you can hardly fancy. All the lockfast places had been broken open in quest of the chart. The floor was thick with mud, where ruffians had sat down to drink or consult after wading in the marshes round their camp. The bulkheads, all painted in clear white, and beaded round with gilt, bore a pattern of dirty hands. Dozens of empty bottles clinked together in corners to the rolling of the ship. One of the doctor's medical books lay open on the table, half of the leaves gutted out, I suppose, for pipelights. In the midst of all this the lamp still cast a smoky glow, obscure and brown as umber.

I went into the cellar; all the barrels were gone, and of the bottles a most surprising number had been drunk out and thrown away. Certainly, since the mutiny began, not a man of them could ever have been sober.

Foraging about I found a bottle with some brandy left, for Hands; and for myself I routed out some biscuit, some pickled fruits, a great bunch of raisins, and a piece of cheese. With these I came on deck, put down my own stock behind the rudder head, and well out of the coxswain's reach, went forward to the water-breaker, and had a good, deep drink of water, and then, and not till then, gave Hands the brandy.

He must have drunk a gill before he took the bottle from his mouth.

"Ay," said he, "by thunder, but I wanted some o' that!"

I had sat down already in my own corner and begun to eat.

"Much hurt?" I asked him.

He grunted, or, rather, I might say, he barked.

"If that doctor was aboard," he said, "I'd be right enough in a couple of turns; but I don't have no manner of luck, you see, and that's what's the matter with me. As for that swab, he's good and dead, he is," he added, indicating the man with the red cap. "He warn't no seaman, anyhow. And where mought you have come from?"

"Well," said I, "I've come aboard to take possession of this ship, Mr. Hands; and you'll please regard me as your captain until further notice."

He looked at me sourly enough, but said nothing. Some of the color had come back into his cheeks, though he still looked very sick, and still continued to slip out and settle down as the ship banged about.

"By the bye," I continued, "I can't have these colors, Mr. Hands; and, by your leave, I'll strike 'em. Better none than these."

And, again dodging the boom, I ran to the color lines, handed down their cursed black flag, and chucked it overboard.

"God save the king!" said I, waving my cap.

He watched me keenly and slyly, his chin all the while on his breast.

"I reckon," he said at last—"I reckon, Cap'n Hawkins, you'll kind of want to get ashore, now. S'pose we talks."

"Why, yes," says I, "with all my heart, Mr. Hands. Say on." And I went back to my meal with a good appetite.

"This man," he began, nodding feebly at the corpse—"O'Brien were his name—a rank Irelander—this man and me got the canvas on her, meaning for to sail her back. Well, *he's* dead now, he is—as dead as bilge; and who's to sail this ship, I don't see. Without I gives you a hint, you ain't that man, as far's I can tell. Now, look here, you gives me food and drink, and an old scarf or ankecher to tie my wound up, you do; and I'll tell you how to sail her; and that's about square all round, I take it."

"I'll tell you one thing," says I: "I'm not going back to Captain Kidd's anchorage. I mean to get into North Inlet, and beach her quietly there."

"To be sure you did," he cried. "Why, I ain't such an infernal lubber, after all. I can see, can't I? I've tried my fling, I have, and I've lost, and it's you has the wind of me. North Inlet? Why, I haven't no ch'ice, not I! I'd help you sail her up to Execution Dock, by thunder! so I would."

Well, as it seemed to me, there was some sense in this. We struck our bargain on the spot. In three minutes I had the *Hispaniola* sailing easily before the wind along the coast of Treasure Island, with good hopes of turning the northern point ere noon, and beating down again as far as North Inlet before high water, when we might beach her safely, and wait till the subsiding tide permitted us to land.

Then I lashed the tiller and went below to my own chest, where I got a soft silk handkerchief of my mother's. With this, and with my aid, Hands bound up the great bleeding stab he had received in the thigh, and after he had eaten a little and had a swallow or two more of the brandy, he began to pick up visibly, sat straighter up, spoke louder and clearer, and looked in every way another man.

The breeze served us admirably. We skimmed before it like a bird, the coast of the island flashing by, and the view changing every minute. Soon we were past the high lands and bowling beside low, sandy country, sparsely dotted with dwarf pines, and soon we were beyond that again, and had turned the corner of the rocky hill that ends the island on the north.

I was greatly elated with my new command, and pleased with the bright, sunshiny weather and these different prospects of the coast. I had now plenty of water and good things to eat, and my conscience, which had smitten me hard for my desertion, was quieted by the great conquest I had made. I should, I think, have had nothing left me to desire but for the eyes of the coxswain as they followed me derisively about the deck, and the odd smile that appeared continually on his face. It was a smile that had in it something both of pain and weakness—a haggard, old man's smile; but there was besides that, a grain of derision, a shadow of treachery in his expression as he craftily watched, and watched, and watched me at my work.

The wind, serving us to a desire, now hauled into the west. We could run so much the easier from the northeast corner of the island to the mouth of the North Inlet. Only, as we had no power to anchor, and dared not beach her till the tide had flowed a good deal farther, time hung on our hands. The coxswain told me how to lay the ship to; after a good many trials I succeeded, and we both sat in silence over another meal.

"Cap'n," said he, at length, with that same uncomfortable smile, "here's my old shipmate, O'Brien; s'pose you was to heave him overboard. I ain't partic'lar as a rule, and I don't take no blame for settling his hash; but I don't reckon him ornamental, now, do you?"

"I'm not strong enough, and I don't like the job; and there he lies, for me," said I.

"This here's an unlucky ship—this *Hispaniola*, Jim," he went on, blinking. "There's a power of men been killed in this *Hispaniola*— a sight o' poor seamen dead and gone since you and me took ship to Bristol. I never seen sich dirty luck, not I. There was this here O'Brien, now—he's dead, ain't he? Well, now, I'm no scholar, and you're a lad as can read and figure; and, to put it straight, do you take it as a dead man is dead for good, or do he come alive again?"

"You can kill the body, Mr. Hands, but not the spirit; you must know that already," I replied. "O'Brien there is in another world, and maybe watching us."

"Ah!" says he. "Well, that's unfort'nate— appears as if killing parties was a waste of time. Howsomever, sperrits don't reckon for much, by what I've seen. I'll chance it with the sperrits, Jim. And now, you've spoke up free, and I'll take it kind if you'd step down into that there cabin and get me a—well, a—shiver my timbers! I can't hit the name on't; well, you get me a bottle of wine, Jim—this here brandy's too strong for my head."

Now, the coxswain's hesitation seemed to be unnatural; and as for the notion of his preferring wine to brandy, I entirely disbelieved it. The whole story was a pretext. He wanted me to leave the deck—so much was plain; but with what purpose I could in no way imagine. His eyes never met mine; they kept wandering to and fro, up and down, now with a look to the sky, now with a flitting glance upon the dead O'Brien.

All the time he kept smiling and putting his tongue out in the most guilty, embarrassed manner, so that a child could have told that he was bent on some deception. I was prompt with my answer, however, for I saw where my advantage lay; and that with a fellow so densely stupid I could easily conceal my suspicions to the end.

"Some wine?" I said. "Far better. Will you have white or red?"

"Well, I reckon it's about the blessed same to me, shipmate," he replied; "so it's strong and plenty of it, what's the odds?"

"All right," I answered. "I'll bring you port, Mr. Hands. But I'll have to dig for it."

With that I scuttled down the companion with all the noise I could, slipped off my shoes, ran quietly along the sparred gallery, mounted the forecastle ladder and popped my head out of the fore companion. I knew he would not expect to see me there; yet I took every precaution possible; and certainly the worst of my suspicions proved too true.

He had risen from his position to his hands and knees; and though his leg obviously hurt him pretty sharply when he moved—for I could hear him stifle a groan—yet it was at a good, rattling rate that he trailed himself across the deck. In half a minute he had reached the port scuppers, and picked, out of a coil of rope, a long knife, or rather a short dirk, discolored to the hilt with blood. He looked upon it for a moment, thrusting forth his under jaw, tried the point upon his hand, and then, hastily concealing it in the bosom of his jacket, trundled back again into his old place against the bulwark.

This was all that I required to know. Israel could move about; he was now armed; and if he had been at so much trouble to get rid of me, it was plain that I was meant to be the victim. What he would do afterward—whether he would try to crawl right across the island from North Inlet to the camp among the swamps, or whether he would fire Long Tom, trusting that his own comrades might come first to help him, was, of course, more than I could say.

Yet I felt sure that I could trust him in one point, since in that our interests jumped together, and that was in the disposition of the schooner. We both desired to have her stranded safe enough, in a sheltered place, and so that, when the time came, she could be got off again with as little labor and danger as might be; and until that was done I considered that my life would certainly be spared.

While I was thus turning the business over in my mind, I had not been idle with my body. I had stolen back to the cabin, slipped once more into my shoes, and laid my hand at random on a bottle of wine, and now, with this for an excuse, I made my reappearance on the deck.

Hands lay as I had left him, all fallen together in a bundle, and with his eyelids lowered, as though he were too weak to bear the light. He looked up, however, at my coming, knocked the neck off the bottle, like a man who had done the same thing often, and took a good swig, with his favorite toast of "Here's luck!" Then he lay quiet for a little, and then, pulling out a stick of tobacco, begged me to cut him a quid.

"Cut me a junk o' that," says he, "for I haven't no knife, and hardly strength enough, so be as I had. Ah, Jim, Jim, I reckon I've missed stays! Cut me a quid, as'll likely be the last, lad; for I'm for my long home, and no mistake."

"Well," said I, "I'll cut you some tobacco; but if I was you and thought myself so badly, I would go to my prayers, like a Christian man."

"Why?" said he. "Now, you tell me why."

"Why?" I cried. "You were asking me just now about the dead. You've broken your trust; you've lived in sin and lies and blood; there's a man you killed lying at your feet this moment; and you ask me why! For God's mercy, Mr. Hands, that's why."

I spoke with a little heat, thinking of the bloody dirk he had hidden in his pocket, and designed, in his ill thoughts, to end me with. He, for his part, took a great draught of the wine, and spoke with the most unusual solemnity.

"For thirty years," he said, "I've sailed the seas, and seen good and bad, better and worse, fair weather and foul, provisions running out, knives going, and what not. Well, now I tell you, I never seen good come o' goodness yet. Him as strikes first is my fancy; dead men don't bite; them's my views—amen, so be it. And now, you look here," he added, suddenly changing his tone, "we've had about enough of this fool-

ery. The tide's made good enough by now.
You just take my orders, Cap'n Hawkins, and
we'll sail slap in and be done with it."

All told, we had scarce two miles to run; but
the navigation was delicate, the entrance to this
northern anchorage was not only narrow and
shoal, but lay east and west, so that the schooner
must be nicely handled to be got in. I think I
was a good, prompt subaltern, and I am very
sure that Hands was an excellent pilot; for we
went about and about, and dodged in, shaving
the banks, with a certainty and a neatness that
were a pleasure to behold.

Scarcely had we passed the heads before the
land closed around us. The shores of North
Inlet were as thickly wooded as those of the
southern anchorage; but the space was longer
and narrower, and more like, what in truth it
was, the estuary of a river. Right before us, at
the southern end, we saw the wreck of a ship in
the last stages of dilapidation. It had been a
great vessel of three masts, but had lain so long
exposed to the injuries of the weather that it was
hung about with great webs of dripping seaweed,
and on the deck of it shore bushes had taken
root, and now flourished thick with flowers. It
was a sad sight, but it showed us that the anchorage was calm.

"Now," said Hands, "look there; there's a
pet bit for to beach a ship in. Fine flat sand,
never a catspaw, trees all around of it, and
flowers a-blowing like a garding on that old
ship."

"And once beached," I inquired, "how shall we get her off again ?"

"Why, so," he replied: "you take a line ashore there on the other side at low water; take a turn about one o' them big pines; bring it back, take a turn round the capstan, and lie-to for the tide. Come high water, all hands take a pull upon the line, and off she comes as sweet as natur'. And now, boy, you stand by. We're near the bit now, and she's too much way on her. Starboard a little—so—steady—starboard—larboard a little —steady—steady!"

So he issued his commands, which I breath-lessly obeyed; till, all of a sudden, he cried: "Now, my hearty, luff!" And I put the helm hard up, and the *Hispaniola* swung round rap-idly, and ran stem on for the low wooded shore.

The excitement of these last maneuvers had somewhat interfered with the watch I had kept hitherto, sharply enough, upon the coxswain. Even then I was still so much interested, waiting for the ship to touch, that I had quite forgot the peril that hung over my head, and stood craning over the starboard bulwarks and watching the ripples spreading wide before the bows. I might have fallen without a struggle for my life, had not a sudden disquietude seized upon me, and made me turn my head. Perhaps I had heard a creak, or seen his shadow moving with the tail of my eye; perhaps it was an instinct like a cat's; but, sure enough, when I looked round, there was Hands, already halfway toward me, with the dirk in his right hand.

We must both have cried out aloud when our
eyes met; but while mine was the shrill cry of
terror, his was a roar of fury like a charging
bull's.   At the same instant he threw himself
forward, and I leaped sideways toward the bows.
As I did so I let go of the tiller, which sprang
sharp to leeward; and I think this saved my life,
for it struck Hands across the chest and stopped
him, for the moment, dead.

Before he could recover, I was safe out of the
corner where he had me trapped, with all the
deck to dodge about.   Just forward of the mainmast I stopped, drew a pistol from my pocket,
took a cool aim, though he had already turned
and was once more coming directly after me, and
drew the trigger.   The hammer fell, but there
followed neither flash nor sound; the priming
was useless with sea-water.   I cursed myself for
my neglect.   Why had not I, long before, re-
primed and reloaded my only weapons?   Then
I should not have been as now, a mere fleeing
sheep before this butcher.

Wounded as he was, it was wonderful how
fast he could move, his grizzled hair tumbling
over his face, and his face itself as red as a red
ensign with his haste and fury.   I had no time
to try my other pistol, nor, indeed, much inclina-
tion, for I was sure it would be useless.   One
thing I saw plainly: I must not simply retreat
before him, or he would speedily hold me boxed
into the bows, as a moment since he had so nearly
boxed me in the stern.   Once so caught, and
nine or ten inches of the blood-stained dirk would

be my last experience on this side of eternity. I placed my palms against the mainmast, which was of a goodish bigness, and waited, every nerve upon the stretch.

Seeing that I meant to dodge, he also paused; and a moment or two passed in feints on his part, and corresponding movements upon mine. It was such a game as I had often played at home about the rocks of Black Hill Cove; but never before, you may be sure, with such a wildly beating heart as now. Still, as I say, it was a boy's game, and I thought I could hold my own at it, against an elderly seaman with a wounded thigh. Indeed, my courage had begun to rise so high that I allowed myself a few darting thoughts on what would be the end of the affair; and while I saw certainly that I could spin it out for long, I saw no hope of any ultimate escape.

Well, while things stood thus, suddenly the *Hispaniola* struck, staggered, ground for an instant in the sand, and then, swift as a blow, canted over to the port side, till the deck stood at an angle of forty-five degrees, and about a puncheon of water splashed into the scupper-holes, and lay in a pool between the deck and bulwark.

We were both of us capsized in a second, and both of us rolled, almost together, into the scuppers; the dead red-cap, with his arms still spread out, tumbled stiffly after us. So near were we, indeed, that my head came against the coxswain's foot with a crack that made my teeth rattle. Blow and all, I was the first afoot again; for

Hands had got involved with the dead body. The sudden canting of the ship had made the deck no place for running on; I had to find some new way of escape, and that upon the instant, for my foe was almost touching me. Quick as thought I sprang into the mizzen shrouds, rattled up hand over hand, and did not draw a breath till I was seated on the crosstrees.

I had been saved by being prompt; the dirk had struck not half a foot below me, as I pursued my upward flight; and there stood Israel Hands with his mouth open and his face upturned to mine, a perfect statue of surprise and disappointment.

Now that I had a moment to myself, I lost no time in changing the priming of my pistol, and then, having one ready for service, and to make assurance doubly sure, I proceeded to draw the load of the other, and recharge it afresh from the beginning.

My new employment struck Hands all of a heap; he began to see the dice going against him; and after an obvious hesitation, he also hauled himself heavily into the shrouds, and, with the dirk in his teeth, began slowly and painfully to mount. It cost him no end of time and groans to haul his wounded leg behind him; and I had quietly finished my arrangements before he was much more than a third of the way up. Then, with a pistol in either hand, I addressed him.

"One more step, Mr. Hands," said I, "and I'll blow your brains out! Dead men don't bite, you know," I added, with a chuckle.

He stopped instantly. I could see by the working of his face that he was trying to think, and the process was so slow and laborious that, in my new-found security, I laughed aloud. Then with a swallow or two, he spoke, his face still wearing the same expression of extreme perplexity. In order to speak he had to take the dagger from his mouth, but, in all else, he remained unmoved.

"Jim," says he, "I reckon we're fouled, you and me, and we'll have to sign articles. I'd have had you but for that there lurch: but I don't have no luck, not I; and I reckon I'll have to strike, which comes hard, you see, for a master mariner to a ship's younker like you, Jim."

I was drinking in his words and smiling away, as conceited as a cock upon a wall, when, all in a breath back went his right hand over his shoulder. Something sang like an arrow through the air; I felt a blow and then a sharp pang, and there I was pinned by the shoulder to the mast. In the horrid pain and surprise of the moment—I scarce can say it was by my own volition, and I am sure it was without a conscious aim—both my pistols went off, and both escaped out of my hands. They did not fall alone; with a choked cry, the coxswain loosed his grasp upon the shrouds, and plunged head first into the water.

Stevenson was not one of the men who can write only one sort of thing. The numerous little poems contained in the first volume of this series show his sympathetic knowledge of children, while his essays prove that he could handle

THE DEATH OF ISRAEL HANDS

serious subjects in a most masterly manner. The extract from *Treasure Island* which you have just been reading displays his skill in still another field—the writing of stories of pure adventure.

In the days when Stevenson began writing, novel writers seemed to feel that to write a story that was simply a story was beneath them; they led their readers off into analysis of motives and of feelings, and treated the narrative as if it were of secondary importance. Stevenson, however, had a different idea of a story, and the immense popularity of his tales shows that many people believe with him.

One of the striking things in all Stevenson's writings is his power of vivid description, his ability to make us see things. Nor does he make us wait while he gives us page-long descriptions; he suggests pictures to us with a few words. The "glow of the great camp-fire burning warmly through the shore-side trees," with "some one singing a dull, old, droning sailor's song," makes the scene very real to us, and lets us feel the *aloneness* of the man in the coracle. And the dead man and his wounded companion could not be more clearly brought before us than they are in the few lines on page 209. It may be safely said of descriptions, when they are part of a story, that those which are given in the fewest words, if those few words are the right ones, are most effective. Stevenson fully grasped this fact, and that is the reason he is able to bring all his scenes before us so vividly, without wearying our patience.

JOHN GREENLEAF WHITTIER

GRACE E. SELLON

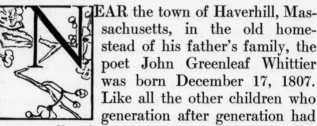

NEAR the town of Haverhill, Massachusetts, in the old homestead of his father's family, the poet John Greenleaf Whittier was born December 17, 1807. Like all the other children who generation after generation had come to live in this Quaker dwelling, he was brought up in simple, useful ways, and was early given his full share of the duties about the farm. No matter how sharply the cold of the harsh New England winter pierced his homespun clothes, the snow must be shoveled from the paths, firewood must be brought, the stalls in the barn must be littered, and, worst task of all for him, seven cows must be milked. Yet there was plenty of fun to be had, too. When the snow fell so heavily that it blocked all the roads and closed in tightly about the house, the two Whittier boys found it exciting work to dig their way to the outside world.

When the early twilight fell and passed into night, the boys with their sisters joined the group gathered about the great hearth, and there listened to stories of Indians, witches and Christian martyrs, and to many another weird or adventurous tale told by the older members of the family. While they were being thus enter-

tained, the blaze of the red logs went roaring up
the chimney,

"The house-dog on his paws outspread
Laid to the fire his drowsy head,
The cat's dark silhouette on the wall
A couchant tiger's seemed to fall;
And, for the winter fireside meet,
Between the andirons' straddling feet,
The mug of cider simmered slow,
The apples sputtered in a row,
And, close at hand, the basket stood
With nuts from brown October's wood."[1]

All too soon this pleasant time came to an end,
and the boys must go to their bare, unheated
room upstairs.   There, the poet has written,

"Within our beds awhile we heard
The wind that round the gables roared,
With now and then a ruder shock,
Which made our very bedsteads rock.
We heard the loosened clapboards tost,
The board-nails snapping in the frost;
And on us, through the unplastered wall,
Felt the lightsifted snowflakes fall;
But sleep stole on, as sleep will do
When hearts are light and life is new;
Faint and more faint the murmurs grew,
Till in the summer-land of dreams
They softened to the sound of streams,
Low stir of leaves, and dip of oars,
And lapsing waves on quiet shores."

1. The poetical quotations given in this article are from *Snow-Bound*.

In the warm season, though there was much to
do in helping plant and harvest the crops, there
were good times to be had in climbing to the top
of Job's hill, next to the house, where the friendly
oxen were pastured, or in gathering berries or
nuts, or in watching the birds, bees and squirrels as they worked or played about their homes.
It was these delights of his childhood that the
poet was calling to remembrance when he wrote
The Barefoot Boy, which may be found elsewhere
in these volumes.

Probably there are few country lads to-day
who know so little as did the Whittier boys of the
common sights and pleasures of city life. The
strict Quaker belief regarding children's amusement barred them from most of the enjoyment
familiar to the young people in the great world
that lay beyond their home. So little were they
acquainted with the forbidden attractions at the
circus that one time when President Monroe
visited Haverhill, Greenleaf (as the poet was
known in his home), looking next day for traces
of the presence of the great man, whom he had
not been allowed to see, came upon the tracks
of an elephant that had been in town with a
traveling menagerie, and in his ignorance believed that these were the footsteps of the famous
visitor. The theater, so the children were
taught, was to be shunned as a place of wicked-
ness. Once while Greenleaf was visiting in
Boston he was asked to go to a play by a lady
whom he met in the home where he was staying.
When he found that the lady was an actress, he

became so much afraid of being led into sinful ways that, not daring to remain longer, he started off at once for home.

Though young Whittier was a wide-awake boy and eager to learn, there was only the district school, held for a few weeks each winter, for him to attend. Yet an opportunity was not lacking for bringing to light his poetic gift. One of his schoolmasters, who lived for part of the term in the Whittier home, used to read to the family from various interesting books, and one night chose for their entertainment a volume of Burns's poems. As the lines of the much-loved Scotch poet fell from the reader's lips, the young boy listened as he had never before listened in his life. His own power awakened and responded warmly to that of the older poet. From that hour, whether he was at home or at school, he found great pleasure in writing verses, which he often showed to his young friends. Thus it was that his older sister Mary was able, all unknown to him, to send off one of his poems to the Newburyport *Free Press*. When the paper containing the verses came, the young poet read the lines over and over again, almost too dazed to recognize them as his own. This contribution was followed by another made to the same paper. By this time the editor's interest had been so much aroused that, learning from the postman of the author's whereabouts, he traveled to Haverhill to visit him. This editor was no other than William Lloyd Garrison, who later became famous as a leader of the cause of abolition. He

urged strongly that the boy's education be continued.   Perhaps his words would have counted
for nothing, however, had it not been that somewhat later the editor of the Haverhill *Gazette*,
in which some of young Whittier's verses had
been published, entreated the boy's parents to
send him to the new Haverhill Academy.   His
father's consent having been gained, Greenleaf
learned from a man who worked on the farm
how to make slippers, and thus he became able
to pay his own expenses during a term at the
Academy.   By teaching school in the winter,
and by helping to keep the books of a Haverhill
merchant, he was able to provide for a second
term.   Thus was completed his regular schooling.

In the meanwhile his friend Garrison had kept
an eye on him, and at the close of 1825 secured
for him the editorship of *The American Manufacturer*, a weekly magazine published in Boston.
Young Whittier entered with great interest into
the work, contributing articles on politics and
temperance as well as numerous poems.   Though
he received only nine dollars a week, he was able,
when called back to Haverhill in 1829, by his
father's illness, to give about one half of what he
had earned to help remove the mortgage on the
farm.

He remained at home until his father's death
in 1830, editing for a time the Haverhill *Gazette*
and sending to the *New England Review*, of
Hartford, Connecticut, various poems and articles.   So much favor did these find with the

editor, George D. Prentice, that he invited the
young writer to fill his position during a temporary absence.   The offer was highly compli-
mentary, for the *Review* was the principal
political journal in Connecticut supporting Henry
Clay.   However, Whittier was well prepared
for the work, for he had become acquainted with
the leaders and with the chief interests of the
Whig party while editing the *Manufacturer*, and
was himself an enthusiastic follower of Clay.
His common sense and shrewd but kindly
reading of human nature, united with a high
sense of honor and justice, enabled him to fill
this responsible position with marked success
until his failing health forced him to give it up
in January, 1832.

There was much reason for Whittier to look
for success in political life, for his editorial work
had made him widely known as a man of sane
and practical views, and he was so highly regarded in the district where he lived that had he
reached the required age of twenty-five, he
would in all probability have been made a
candidate for Congress in 1832.   Thus it was
that although he had published more than a
hundred favorably received poems between 1828
and 1832, he wrote in the latter year: "My
prospects are too good to be sacrificed for any
uncertainty. I have done with poetry and
literature."

A far nobler mission, however, and greater
usefulness than he could have planned for himself lay before Whittier. It was not political

success that was to draw forth the greatness of his nature. The strong and fearless interest with which his friend Garrison had begun to champion the abolition of slavery in the United States appealed to him, he felt with all his heart that the cause was right, and, closing his eyes to the bright promise of political success, he chose to unite himself with the scorned and mistreated upholders of freedom. After thorough consideration and study, he wrote and published in 1833 the pamphlet *Justice and Expediency*, in which he set forth fully the arguments against slavery. This was the first of his strong and stirring protests against oppression. From that time until the close of the Civil War his fervent, fearless love of liberty voiced itself through ringing verses, in constant appeals to the conscience of the nation. The greatness of this influence, as it worked silently in men's hearts, who can estimate?

Whittier's part in the anti-slavery struggle was not always a quiet one. On one occasion, when in company with a famous but unpopular English reformer he was to address an audience on the subject of abolition, he was attacked by a mob while passing quietly along the street with a friend, and narrowly escaped being tarred and feathered. Somewhat later he was set upon in another town by a crowd armed with sticks and stones and other missiles, from which he fled with more haste than dignity. It was while he was editor of the *Freeman* that Pennsylvania Hall, where the Philadelphia Abolitionists held

JOHN GREENLEAF WHITTIER

their meetings, was burned by a mob, and the papers from Whittier's editorial room in this building were used to help start the blaze.

In 1836 the farm at Haverhill had been sold, and a cottage was bought in Amesbury near the Quaker meetinghouse. It was in this quiet place, under the loving care of his mother and sister, that Whittier made his home after resigning his position with the *Freeman*. These two women were in their way as unselfishly devoted to the cause of freedom as was the poet himself, for they encouraged his loyalty and bore privation uncomplainingly. In the darkest hour of their need, when it seemed as if their home must be mortgaged, Whittier was invited to become a contributor to the *Atlantic Monthly*, then being founded, and thus the long period of want was brought to an end.

After the death of his mother, in the following year (1858), Whittier's association with his sister Elizabeth became even closer than before, though they had always shared each other's hopes and interests with unusual sympathy and understanding. When she died, in 1864, it seemed to him that part of his life had gone with her. It was with this grief still fresh in his mind that he wrote the best known of his poems, *Snow-Bound, A Winter Idyl,* in which he pictures in the most simple and lifelike manner the quiet loveliness of his childhood home. With especial tenderness he tells of the much-loved sister, and lets his mingled grief and hope of reunion be seen:

"As one who held herself a part
  Of all she saw, and let her heart
    Against the household bosom lean,
Upon the motley-braided mat
Our youngest and our dearest sat,
Lifting her large, sweet, asking eyes,
Now bathed within the fadeless green
And holy peace of Paradise.
Oh, looking from some heavenly hill,
  Or from the shade of saintly palms,
  Or silver reach of river calms,
Do those large eyes behold me still?
With me one little year ago:—
The chill weight of the winter snow
  For months upon her grave has lain;
And now, when summer south-winds blow,
  And brier and harebell bloom again,
I tread the pleasant paths we trod,
I see the violet-sprinkled sod,
Whereon she leaned, too frail and weak,
The hillside flowers she loved to seek,
Yet following me where'er I went
With dark eyes full of love's content.
The birds are glad; the brier-rose fills
The air with sweetness; all the hills
Stretch green to June's unclouded sky;
But still I wait with ear and eye
For something gone which should be nigh,
A loss in all familiar things,
In flower that blooms, and bird that sings.
And yet, dear heart! remembering thee,
    Am I not richer than of old?
Safe in thy immortality,

What change can reach the wealth I hold?
What chance can mar the pearl and gold
Thy love hath left in trust with me?
And while in life's late afternoon
  Where cool and long the shadows grow,
I walk to meet the night that soon
  Shall shape and shadow overflow,
I cannot feel that thou art far,
Since near at need the angels are;
And when the sunset gates unbar,
  Shall I not see thee waiting stand,
And, white against the evening star,
  The welcome of thy beckoning hand?"

After the death of Elizabeth Whittier, the Amesbury home was cared for by the poet's niece. During the remaining years of his life Whittier passed his time here or in the country. He lived in comparative comfort, for the publication of *Snow-Bound* in 1866 had brought very good returns. These were years of great peace, in which he remained actively interested in the affairs of the nation, yet liked most to dwell upon the beauty of nature and especially upon the thought of God's goodness that must triumph over all the evil in the world. *Among the Hills* and the collections *Tent on the Beach* and *At Sundown* were produced in the last period; but his religious poems seem best to represent his thought and feeling in the closing years. From these were taken the beautiful verses *At Last*, read as the poet passed away from earth, September 7, 1892.

Though Whittier remained throughout his life a Quaker not only in dress and speech but in belief and character, yet with his quietness and quaint simplicity was blended no severity nor gloom. He had a great love of fun, which alone can account for his mischievous habit of teasing, and for his keeping such pets as the little bantam rooster that aroused the household each morning with its crowing, and the parrot "Charlie" that swore when excited, stopped the horses in the street with its cries of "whoa," and nipped the ankles of unwary visitors. Then, too, he was always attractive to children, and often preferred their society to that of older people. But above all else, with each succeeding year he became more just and compassionate towards others. The kindliness of his nature was untouched by the sorrow and sickness that he bore. "Love—love to all the world," he would often repeat in his last years, and the sweet influence of the benediction is felt by all who read his life and works:

"Best loved and saintliest of our singing train,
Earth's noblest tributes to thy name belong.
A lifelong record closed without a stain,
A blameless memory shrined in deathless song." [2]

2. From an ode written by Oliver Wendell Holmes upon the death of Whittier.

WILLIAM CULLEN BRYANT

PLAIN indeed was the little home among the hills of Western Massachusetts, near the town of Cummington, where was born on November 3, 1794, the first great American poet, William Cullen Bryant. His father was a physician of scholarly tastes, and his mother, though not highly educated, was a woman of much practical wisdom. Both parents were kind and affectionate, but followed the custom of that time in treating their children with a strictness unknown to American boys and girls of to-day. Even small acts of disrespect or disobedience were promptly punished, and to aid in the work of correction the Bryant home as well as that of almost every neighbor was provided with a good-sized bundle of birch sticks hanging warningly on the kitchen wall. As the poet himself tells us in a sketch of his early life, the children looked upon the older people of the family with so much awe that they could not go to them freely nor act naturally in their presence.

This severity in his home must have made young Bryant, who was by nature grave and thoughtful, even more serious. Then, too, his mental powers developed with surprising quickness, so that by the time he had reached his teens, he was thinking and expressing himself upon subjects usually discussed by men rather than boys. Having begun to write verses when only nine years old, he had had enough practice in this kind of exercise to compose when thirteen years of age a satirical poem addressed to President Jefferson, because of his part in passing the Embargo Act by which New England commerce had been greatly injured. These verses were published and met with a ready sale. But far more remarkable as an early expression of genius was *Thanatopsis*, written several months before Bryant's eighteenth birthday. This poem deals with the subject of death with such deep thoughtfulness and in such a stately and powerful style that although it did not appear until six years later, it was even then believed to have been written by the poet's father, who had sent it to the publisher.

Though he was thoughtful beyond his years and had shown unusual poetic power, young Bryant was in other ways quite an ordinary boy. He was quiet and studious in the schoolroom, but was active enough in the games played outside. Of the sports enjoyed by himself and the other boys of the district school, he writes: "We amused ourselves with building dams across the rivulet, and launching rafts made of old boards on the collected water; and in winter, with sliding on the ice and building snow barricades, which we called forts, and, dividing the boys into two armies, and using snowballs for ammunition, we contended for the possession of these strong-

WILLIAM CULLEN BRYANT

holds. I was one of their swiftest runners in the race, and not inexpert at playing ball, but, being of a slight frame, I did not distinguish myself in these sieges." Sometimes, on long evenings, Cullen and his elder brother Austin would play that they were the heroes of whom they had read in the *Iliad*, and, fitted out with swords and spears and homemade armor, they would enact in the barn 'the great battles of the Trojan War.

Not only the *Iliad*, but other carefully chosen works of literature were discovered by the boy in his father's library, and he read widely and well. It proved that this reading had to take the place of a much hoped-for course at college. After attending Williams College for only two terms, he left there, expecting to enter Yale, but was forced to give up his plan, owing to his father's inability to supply him with the necessary means. He did not let this great disappointment overcome him, however, but a few months later began the study of law, with the result that in 1815 he was admitted to the bar.

It is a fact well worth noting that at the very beginning of his career as a lawyer, on the day when he was walking from his home to the little village where he was to start his practice, having learned, in his doubt and loneliness, a great lesson in faith, he wrote the beautiful poem that shows his genius at its best, and probably more than any other has made him famous, the ode *To a Waterfowl*.

When a little boy, he had prayed, in his simple way, that he might be a great poet, and though he had outgrown the prayer, his desire was unchanged. More than this, he had now produced two works that undoubtedly showed genius. It is not surprising, then, that in a few years a literary career was opened to him and he was able to give up the law, for which he had no especial liking.

In 1825, after his marriage to a Miss Fairchild of Great Barrington, he removed from that town to New York. There he became editor of the *New York Review* and *Athenæum Magazine*; and a year later he accepted the position of assistant editor of the *Evening Post*, a newspaper with which he remained for the rest of his life, assuming in 1829 the office of editor-in-chief. Though his contributions to this paper were not a poet's work, they enabled him to unite his literary power with his deep interest in the political concerns of the country, and for many years to help direct public opinion during the most critical periods in the history of the new nation. More than this, while steadily provided with a good income he could spend his leisure hours among the quiet country scenes where he found inspiration for his greatest works, his simple nature poems.

The busy years of his life as a journalist were several times interrupted by travel. Besides visiting Mexico, Cuba and various parts of the United States, he made six voyages to Europe, and on the fourth extended the journey to Egypt and the Holy Land. His *Letters of a Traveller* and *Letters from the East* tell of the impressions he received in these countries.

Besides translating the *Iliad* and the *Odyssey* and writing the two fairy stories in verse, *Sella* and *The Little People of the Snow*, Bryant undertook no poetic work of any length. The poems for which his name is most honored are the little lyrics in which the calm and beauty of nature tell us of truths that never change. Among these, some that are best liked by readers both young and old are *The Yellow Violet*, *The Fringed Gentian*, *A Forest Hymn*, *The Planting of the Apple Tree*, *Robert of Lincoln*, *The Gladness of Nature*, *March* and *To a Waterfowl*.

These poems, when studied, are sure to reveal the simplicity and sincerity not only of Bryant's love for nature, but of his character as a man. They show the freedom from affectation that marks alike his writings and his everyday life. He followed almost sternly his high ideals both of moral right and literary correctness, and this has made him seem somewhat cold and formal. But probably all who can read most clearly the meaning of his life and works feel that so true-hearted a man could not have been lacking in warm and generous kindliness.

TO A WATERFOWL

WILLIAM CULLEN BRYANT

NOTE,—"He says in a letter that he felt, as he walked up the hills, very forlorn and desolate indeed, not knowing what was to become of him in the big world, which grew bigger as he ascended, and yet darker with the coming on of night. The sun had already set, leaving behind it one of those brilliant seas of chrysolite and opal which often flood the New England skies; and, while he was looking upon the rosy splendor with rapt admiration, a solitary bird made wing along the illuminated horizon. He watched the lone wanderer until it was lost in the distance, asking himself whither it had come and to what far home it was flying. When he went to the house where he was to stop for the night, his mind was still full of what he had seen and felt, and he wrote these lines, as imperishable as our language, *The Waterfowl.*"—Parke Godwin, in Biography of Bryant.

———————

Whither, 'midst falling dew,
While glow the heavens with the last steps of
    day,
Far through their rosy depths dost thou pursue
    Thy solitary way?

Vainly the fowler's eye
Might mark thy distant flight to do thee wrong,

THY FIGURE FLOATS ALONG

As, darkly painted on the crimson sky,
    Thy figure floats along.

    Seek'st thou the plashy brink
Of weedy lake, or marge of river wide,
Or where the rocking billows rise and sink
    On the chafed ocean side?

    There is a Power whose care
Teaches thy way along that pathless coast—
The desert and illimitable air—
    Lone wandering, but not lost.

All day thy wings have fanned,
At that far height, the cold, thin atmosphere,
Yet stoop not, weary, to the welcome land,
    Though the dark night is near.

And soon that toil shall end;
Soon shalt thou find a summer home and rest,
And scream among thy fellows; reeds shall bend,
    Soon, o'er thy sheltered nest.

Thou'rt gone, the abyss of heaven
Hath swallowed up thy form; yet on my heart
Deeply hath sunk the lesson thou hast given,
    And shall not soon depart.

He who, from zone to zone,
Guides through the boundless sky thy certain
    flight,
In the long way that I must tread alone,
    Will lead my steps aright.

OLIVER WENDELL HOLMES

GRACE E. SELLON

BESIDES giving to the United States her great president, Abraham Lincoln, the year 1809 also bestowed upon us one of the most gifted and warmly esteemed of American authors, Oliver Wendell Holmes. It was in a pleasant home in Cambridge, not far from the great university in which he was to serve ably for so many years, that Holmes was born. His mother was a bright and sociable little woman, well liked for her lively ways and quick sympathy, and his father, though a grave and scholarly man, was of a kindly nature. Both parents were descended from families that were looked upon as among the best in New England, and this became a matter of no little pride to their son.

The old colonial house where his boyhood and youth were spent contained a well-chosen library. Here, he has written, "he bumped about among books from the time when he was hardly taller than one of his father's or grandfather's folios." Yet he did not read many of these volumes thoroughly. He liked to "read *in* books rather than *through* them" and would hunt out a paragraph here and there that especially pleased and satisfied him. The collections of sermons were always passed by, the lives of pious children met with the same neglect, and even *The Pilgrim's Progress* seemed to picture the world as such a cruel, gloomy place that this great book too was shunned.

The truth was that, being a lively and cheerful boy, he rebelled against the dark and fear-awakening religion preached by his father, a Congregational minister, discussed by visiting pastors and taught in many of the books that he avoided in the library. He seemed to know by instinct which of the clergymen who called at his father's home were kind and friendly, and which of them looked on children as "a set of little fallen wretches," and for the forlorn looks and solemn ways of the latter he had an especial dislike. "Now and then," he has written, "would come along a clerical visitor with a sad face and a wailing voice, which sounded exactly as if somebody must be lying dead upstairs, who took no interest in us children, except a painful one, as being in a bad way with our cheery looks, and did more to unchristianize us with his woebegone ways than all his sermons were like to accomplish in the other direction." In fact, he might have pleased his father by becoming a minister if a certain preacher that he knew had not, to use his own words, "looked and talked so like an undertaker."

But the dreary sermons, the visits of the long-faced clergymen and the drill in the Catechism were only shadows that came and went. Most of the time young Holmes was as light-hearted a boy as was to be found in all New England. He

OLIVER WENDELL HOLMES

liked best of all to go hunting, carrying on such
trips an old gun of the kind used in the Revolution.   A good many of his hours at home were
spent in working with tools, and thus he became
skilful enough to carve out of wood a skate on
which he learned to travel about on the ice.   He
was active and industrious at school, too, and he
made such a good record there that though he
whispered a great part of the time he got along
peaceably with the schoolmaster.   The only
serious troubles that he had came from two great
fears.   Many times after he had gone to bed at
night he would be awakened by strange noises
that he believed to be made by ghosts or evil
spirits mysteriously roaming through the house.
Perhaps he was ashamed to tell of this dread to
his mother or father, and so the foolish belief
that there might be ghosts about stayed with him
through boyhood.   His other fear was of the
doctor's visits.   In helpless terror he would look
on while the old physician pronounced his doom
and began to measure out the bitter medicine.

In his fifteenth year Holmes left the school at
Cambridgeport to attend Phillips Academy, at
Andover, and in the following year, 1825, entered Harvard College.   During his four years
at Harvard he took quite as active an interest in
the social life of the college as in his classes.   He
joined the society known as the Knights of the
Square Table, and at the lively meetings of this
club, where wine and wit passed freely about the
table, he was introduced to a kind of gayety un-
dreamed of in his quiet home.   In a humorous

description of himself, given at this time in a
letter to a former classmate at Andover, he
writes:

"I, then, Oliver Wendell Holmes, Junior in
Harvard University, am a plumeless biped of
the height of exactly five feet three inches when
standing in a pair of substantial boots made by
Mr. Russell of this town, having eyes which I
call blue, and hair which I do not know what to
call. . . . . Secondly, with regard to my moral
qualities, I am rather lazy than otherwise, and
certainly do not study as hard as I ought to. I
am not dissipated and I am not sedate, and when
I last ascertained my college rank, I stood in the
humble situation of seventeenth scholar."

After graduating from Harvard, Holmes entered the Dane Law School at Cambridge. He
did not feel at all sure, however, that he wished
to be a lawyer, and at the end of a year he had
so far lost interest in his studies that he gave
them up. As the physician's calling seemed
much more to his liking, he took two courses of
study in a private school of medicine. This
preparation was not of course sufficient to fit
him for a large practice, so a trip to Europe
where he could study under the great professors
of the School of Medicine at Paris became
necessary. Accordingly, his parents, at some
sacrifice to themselves, provided him with the
required means, and he set sail from New York
in the spring of 1833.

During the two years spent abroad, Holmes
gave himself up wholly to his chosen study. "I

am more and more attached every day to the study of my profession. . . . I am occupied from morning to night, and as every one is happy when he is occupied, I enjoy myself as much as I could wish," he wrote home. This period of hard work, however, was interrupted by summer vacations spent in the countries along the Rhine, in England and in Italy.

Early in 1836, the young physician established himself in Boston. Perhaps it was that people thought him too much of a wit to take their troubles seriously, or perhaps it was that he was better fitted to teach than to practice the doctor's art. At any rate, his success was very moderate. He was very glad, then, to be appointed Professor of Anatomy at Dartmouth College in 1838, a position that he held until 1840. About this time, too, he received prizes for some *Medical Essays* that are even to-day regarded as valuable. Thus he was gradually fitting himself for the honorable office offered him in 1847, that of Professor of Anatomy and Physiology in the Medical School of Harvard University. For thirty-five years Holmes filled this position with the greatest success. He was given the fifth hour in the day as his lecture period because he was the only one able to hold the attention of students who had already been listening to four long and difficult lectures. He enlivened the dry subject with funny stories, droll comparisons and interesting descriptions, teaching while he entertained.

In 1840 the young doctor had married Amelia

Lee Jackson, daughter of a highly respected Boston family. His wife was of so gentle and tactful a nature that their home was always a well-ordered and pleasant place of rest for the busy doctor, where unwelcome visitors and other annoyances were not allowed to take his time. Yet he was never too much occupied to find pleasure in what interested his wife and his three children.

During all these years when the profession of medicine had been of chief concern to him, and even before he had begun his medical studies, he had occasionally written poems that won a good deal of praise from friends, but brought no widespread notice. From his very earliest years he could feel very keenly and remember the melody of verse. "The low, soft chirp of the little bird heard in the nest, while his mother is brooding over him," he has written, "lives in his memory, I doubt not, through all the noisy carols of the singing season; so I remember the little songs my mother sang to me when I was old enough to run about, and had not outgrown the rhymes of the nursery." He enjoyed writing poems for the yearly meetings held by his college class long after their graduation, and while he was at the law school he had made several contributions to the Harvard *Collegian*. Just once in these early years had his fame traveled far, and that was the occasion when he wrote *Old Ironsides*. The frigate *Constitution* that had served the country so well was to be done away with as a useless vessel. Learning of this,

Holmes penned in haste the stanzas that stirred the nation's feelings and saved the old boat from destruction.

It came, then, as a surprise to the American people, when upon the founding of the *Atlantic Monthly* in 1857, the name of Holmes was signed to the articles that probably were most popular of all published in that magazine, to which the greatest literary men in the country were contributing. *The Autocrat of the Breakfast Table* was the title of the delightful series of humorous essays in which the author seemed really to be talking to his readers. A sort of story bound the numbers together. In the fourth issue appeared perhaps the best poem written by Holmes —*The Chambered Nautilus.* This was a favorite with him and was one of those poems of which he said: "I did not write it, but it was written through me," for he believed it to be a work of inspiration.

The Autocrat, which is Holmes's greatest work, was followed by two similar but inferior series, *The Professor at the Breakfast Table* and *The Poet at the Breakfast Table.* Between the last two series he had published in 1861 his novel *Elsie Venner,* followed in 1867 by *The Guardian Angel,* and in 1885 by *A Mortal Antipathy.* The first of these novels is considerably the best, but none of them ranks high, for they all deal with unusual people who because of weird inherited traits of mind are forced to go through strange if not impossible experiences.

Still another kind of writing was attempted by

Holmes.   In 1878 he completed a biography of
his intimate friend, the historian Motley, and in
1884 wrote a life of Emerson.   These are not,
however, among his best productions.   *Over
the Teacups*, similar to the *Breakfast Table*
papers, appeared in 1890, and was his last important work.

In 1886, accompanied by his daughter, he
spent four months in Europe, chiefly in England.
The warm welcome and high honor given him
by the English people were very gratifying to the
aged professor.   He was always at his best when
talking, and so brilliant and easy was his wit
that had not politeness forbidden he could have
entertained a roomful of people during a whole
evening.   This fact as well as his literary achieve-
ments made him popular everywhere.

On the occasion when he received a degree of
honor from Cambridge University, the young
collegemen greeted him by singing at the tops
of their voices a song of "Holmes, sweet
Holmes;" and on a similar occasion at Oxford
one of the students, making good use of the title
of a poem especially known to Holmes's young
readers, asked from the gallery whether the
Doctor had come in the "One-Hoss Shay."   It
is likely that the worthy old gentleman was quite
as pleased with this hearty good will as with the
more dignified tributes received during his
memorable visit.

After 1890, Holmes wrote only occasionally.
Yet he continued to take his usual walks and to
answer a part of his large correspondence, leav-

ing the rest to a secretary.   Now and then he
would go to a concert or to a dinner among
friends, and in other ways he showed himself
remarkably active.   In fact, he had not become
feeble in mind or body when death quietly came
to him, October 7th, 1894.

Though the brightness of his wit makes
Holmes one of the most entertaining of writers,
it is his deep kindness that gives to what he has
written an even greater power and attractive-
ness.   More than all else, he tried both in his
writings and in his everyday living to drive
away the shadows of all kinds of suffering, and
to share with others the cheerfulness of his own
genial nature.

"Long be it ere the table shall be set
For the last breakfast of the Autocrat,
And love repeat with smiles and tears thereat
His own sweet songs that time shall not forget."[1]

1. Whittier's ode on the eightieth birthday of Holmes.

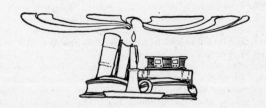

THE CUBES OF TRUTH

OLIVER WENDELL HOLMES

ISTEN, Benjamin Franklin![1] This is for you, and such others of tender age as you may tell it to.

When we are as yet small children, long before the time when those two grown ladies offer us the choice of Hercules,[2] there comes up to us a youthful angel, holding in his right hand cubes like dice, and in his left spheres like marbles. The cubes are of stainless ivory, and on each is written in letters of gold—TRUTH. The spheres are veined and streaked and spotted beneath, with a dark crimson flush above where the light falls on them and in a certain aspect you can make out upon every one of them the three letters, L, I, E.

The child to whom they are offered very prob-

---

1. *The Autocrat of the Breakfast Table* is the most famous and the best of the prose works of Oliver Wendell Holmes. It consists of a series of rambling talks on a great variety of subjects, addressed to the people who sit at his table in a boarding house. Holmes himself is the "Autocrat," and his sparkling talks are full of wit and wisdom. Among those who regularly sit at the Autocrat's table is a schoolboy, whom he calls Benjamin Franklin, and to whom he tells this beautiful story of the Cubes of Truth.

2. When the old Greek hero, Hercules, was a youth, and nearing manhood, two women appeared to him, both offering beautiful gifts. One of the women was Duty, the other Pleasure. Hercules chose to accept the gifts of Duty and to follow her. The opportunity to make this choice did not come till he was old enough to understand. In Holmes's beautiful allegory the cubes and spheres are presented long before that time, even in early childhood.

ably clutches at both. The spheres are the most convenient things in the world; they roll with the least possible impulse just where the child would have them. The cubes will not roll at all; they have a great talent for standing still, and always keep right side up. But very soon the young philosopher finds that things which roll so easily are very apt to roll into the wrong corner, and to get out of his way when he most wants them, while he always knows where to find the others, which stay where they are left.

Thus he learns—thus we learn—to drop the streaked and speckled globes of falsehood, and to hold fast the white angular blocks of truth. But then comes Timidity, and after her Good-nature, and last of all Polite-behaviour, all insisting that truth must *roll*, or nobody can do anything with it; and so the first with her coarse rasp, and the second with her broad file, and the third with her silken sleeve, do so round off and smooth and polish the snow-white cubes of truth, that, when they have got a little dingy by use, it becomes hard to tell them from the rolling spheres of falsehood.

The schoolmistress[3] was polite enough to say that she was pleased with this, and that she would read it to her little flock the next day. But she should tell the children, she said, that there were better reasons for truth than could be found in

3. The schoolmistress is one of the most lovable of the characters introduced by Mr. Holmes into *The Autocrat of the Breakfast Table*. At first she appears and speaks only at intervals, but toward the end of the book her love story and her marriage to the Autocrat afford the chief interest to the reader.

mere experience of its convenience, and the in
convenience of lying.

Yes—I said—but education always begins
through the senses, and works up to the idea of
absolute right and wrong. The first thing the
child has to learn about this matter is, that lying
is unprofitable—afterwards, that it is against the
peace and dignity of the universe.

———————

1. What does the stainless ivory in the cubes
indicate?

2. What is the meaning of the veins, streaks,
and spots and the dark crimson flush in the
spheres?

3. Are the letters L, I, E, always visible?
Does this mean that lies are not always known
to be lies to the person who tells them, or that
they may deceive the person to whom they are
told?

4. Does Dr. Holmes mean to imply that it is
natural for a little child to lie when he says that
the spheres are the most convenient things in the
world?

5. What does Dr. Holmes mean when he
says that the spheres are apt to roll into the
wrong corner?

6. How does Timidity teach a child to lie?
How does Good-nature lead him to lie? What
are some of the "polite lies" that help to make
the cubes roll?

7. Which cuts most deeply a substance upon
which it is rubbed—a rasp, a file, or a silken
sleeve?

8.   Which causes the most lies, Timidity, Good-nature or Polite-behavior?

9.   Do you think the schoolmistress is right? If so, what better reasons are there for telling the truth than mere convenience and the inconvenience of lying?

10.   What do you understand by "against the peace and dignity of the universe?"

11.   Do you think the schoolmistress would agree with the Autocrat in his last statement as to the way in which children are taught the difference between right and wrong?

12.   Do you think if a child is first taught that lying is unprofitable he will without further assistance learn that lying is wrong in itself?

13.   Do you gain from the whole selection the idea that all lies, even the polite lies of society and the common and apparently harmless lies of business life, are always and wholly wrong?

THE LOST CHILD

JAMES RUSSELL LOWELL

I wandered down the sunny glade
  And ever mused, my love, of thee;
My thoughts, like little children, played,
  As gayly and as guilelessly.

If any chanced to go astray,
  Moaning in fear of coming harms,
Hope brought the wanderer back alway,
  Safe nestled in her snowy arms.

DOWN THE SUNNY GLADE

From that soft nest the happy one
   Looked up at me and calmly smiled;
Its hair shone golden in the sun,
   And made it seem a heavenly child.

Dear Hope's blue eyes smiled mildly down,
   And blest it with a love so deep,
That, like a nursling of her own,
   It clasped her neck and fell asleep.

JAMES RUSSELL LOWELL

GRACE E. SELLON.

OWN the street, about a mile from the center of Cambridge, Massachusetts, stands a square, three-story colonial dwelling house, sheltered by pines and great English elms and surrounded by flowering shrubs. In this home, for many years known as Elmwood, the great American poet and essayist was born February 22, 1819, and it was here that he lived during the greater part of his life. In the woods and meadows that lay about Elmwood in the poet's childhood he spent much time, for he liked especially to be out-of-doors; and so it was that in his earliest years he began to feel the great love for flowers, birds and trees that made him able in later life to show to the readers of his poems how much beauty there is in the very commonest things of nature.

However, all of the things he liked were not out-of-doors. In his father's library were more than three thousand books, and he began when only a small boy to choose for himself favorite authors. He seems to have been unusually fond of books, for in a little note written when he was eight years old,—his first letter, so far as any one knows,—he tells his brother, "I read French stories," and adds in a postscript, "I

have got three books." The next year, in a
letter to the same brother he writes, "I have
got quite a library."

After learning his letters and other simple
things at an elementary school, Lowell was sent
when about nine years old to a higher school,
where he was thoroughly taught Latin, and
otherwise prepared for his entrance into Harvard College in 1834. He was then only fifteen
years of age, yet he had such decided tastes in
his studies that he was not always willing to give
attention to the work required in his college
courses, but would follow his own inclinations
in his reading. The result was, that though he
gained such a reputation among his class-mates
for appreciation of literature and ability in
original composition that he was made one of the
editors of *Harvardiana*, the college paper, and
was chosen in his senior year to write the class
poem, yet he was looked upon with growing dis-
approval by his instructors, because of his irregular ways. At length, it is told, he completely
disgraced himself, on the day he was chosen
class poet, by rising at the close of the evening
prayer service and bowing solemnly to right and
left. As punishment for this and all preceding
misconduct, he was sent to Concord to continue
his studies under a private teacher, and was not
allowed to return to Harvard until after classday.
Nevertheless, he wrote his poem and later had it
printed, for his friends, in a little pamphlet.

After receiving his degree from Harvard in
1838, Lowell decided upon the law as the pro-

JAMES RUSSELL LOWELL

fession most suitable for him to follow, for at that time a literary career in the United States held out no assurance of a living, even to the best writers. In the preceding year he had written to his intimate friend Shackford: "I thought your brother Charles was studying law. I intend to study that myself, and probably shall be Chief Justice of the United States." This modest prediction, however, was not to be fulfilled, for after completing a course at the Harvard Law School in 1840 and practicing with but slight interest and success for two years, he gave up the law for a more congenial occupation.

His letters to his confidants "Shack" and Loring during the years at college show his aspiration to become a poet. He reports from time to time his progress in verse making and comments more or less favorably on his "effusions." This writing of *pottery*—as it pleased him to call it—continued with more serious interest after his graduation, so that in 1840 he was ready to publish a volume of verse entitled "A Year's Life."

The same year was marked by another event of special importance,—his engagement to Maria White, a young woman who was herself a poet and who was deeply interested in all the movements of thought that were making toward freedom and justice before the Civil War. Her influence upon Lowell was to strengthen greatly his confidence in his own best powers as a man and a poet and to help develop in him the broad, kind democratic feeling for his fellow-men that

most endears him to his readers.   This growth
of the poet's character seems the more remarkable when it is considered that his father, a
Unitarian minister, was a man who, though most
generous and well-meaning in his regard for
others, was well enough content with conditions
in his country to feel little sympathy with the
reforms then being urged for securing fuller
liberty and equality.   In his new enthusiasm
Lowell turned away from the influence of his
younger days and became devoted to the cause
of abolition.

In 1842, after abandoning the law, he founded
a magazine, *The Pioneer*, which, however, was
issued only three times.   After this unsuccessful
venture he went back to his poetry, and late in
1843 published a second volume of verse.   In
the following year appeared his first critical
studies in prose, *Conversations on Some of the
Old Poets*.   This work, like most of the first
book of poems, Lowell found in later life to be
unworthy of reprinting.

The income from his writings, though small,
was sufficient for him to marry in 1844; and not
long after this event he became a regular contributor to the *Anti-Slavery Standard*.   In this
appeared the first series of the *Biglow Papers*,
in which, through vigorous prose and verse,
largely in the Yankee dialect of Hosea Biglow,
he protested against the evils that brought on the
Mexican War.   The collected numbers of the
series were published in 1848 and shared the
popularity of two other of Lowell's greatest

works, produced in the same year,—the *Fable for Critics* and *The Vision of Sir Launfal*, a beautiful narrative poem filled with the spirit of Christian brotherhood.

It was not long after this that Lowell began to feel that his work as a writer for the abolitionist cause was narrowing in its effect. For "red-hot" reform he had no liking. It seemed to him that the hope of his cause lay not so much in treating others harshly as in living according to the high principles that the reformers professed. "The longer I live," he wrote, "the more am I convinced that the world must be healed by degrees. I see why Jesus came eating meat and drinking wine and companying with publicans and sinners. He preached the highest doctrine, but he lived the life of other men. . . . Let us sow the best seed we have . . . . and convert other men by our crops, not by drubbing them with our hoes or putting them under our harrows." He decided, then, to take life in a more leisurely way and let the poetic power that he considered his best gift express itself freely.

In 1851, accompanied by his wife and his two children, Lowell visited Europe. The months spent abroad gave him much wished-for opportunities for study and observation, but they were darkened by the death of his son Walter. Close upon this sorrow came the death of Mrs. Lowell in the following year (1853), after the return of the family to Elmwood. From that time for many months the poet could find relief from his

keen sense of loss only in his literary work, and
in the companionship of his daughter Mabel,
the only one of his four children who had
lived.

Some lectures on the English poets given at
the Lowell institute in 1854–55 found so much
favor with the authorities at Harvard College
that soon afterward he was appointed to succeed
Longfellow as professor of foreign languages and
literatures.   After a period of study in Europe,
he assumed charge of classes at Harvard in
1856, and for sixteen years continued in this
work, bringing to it with most remarkable success all the warmth and sincerity and broad scope
of his own interest in the subjects that he taught.
Not many months afterward he was still further
honored by being given the editorship of the
newly founded *Atlantic Monthly*, a position that
he held until 1861.   The year 1857 was made
memorable also by his marriage to Miss Frances
Dunlap, a much-valued friend and the governess
of his daughter.   In 1864 he became joint editor
of the *North American Review*, and in this
magazine continued the second series of the
Biglow Papers, begun in the *Atlantic Monthly*,
the series in which is expressed his finest power
as a poet-patriot.   Of the same excellence is the
famous *Commemoration Ode* written for memorial ceremonies held at Harvard College in honor
of the students who had fallen during the war.
Among other contributions to these periodicals
were numerous studies of poets and poetry—
essays that rank among the best of their kind.

Thus did Lowell prove himself to possess a rare combination of the powers of original composition and of criticism.

So ably had he served the best interests of his country through his writings, that in 1877 he was appointed Minister of the United States to Spain, and served there until 1880, when he was sent as Minister to England. These high trusts, it proved, had not been wrongly placed. Lowell's devotion to the truest American principles, together with his large experience in public affairs, made him a most successful diplomat. He was given high honors by British universities, and he made many friends in England.

After his return to America in 1885 he withdrew gradually from his former active life. Occasionally he wrote and lectured, and several times he made trips to England. It was in his much loved Elmwood that death came to him August 12th, 1891.

Lowell was a man of wide learning, and has a prominent place in American literature for his exceptional critical ability and delightful wit, and for the artistic excellence of both his prose and poetry; but the secret of his power lies not so much in these things as in the sincerity and vigor of thought that rise above all bookishness, and in the warm human feeling that reached out for the love of his fellow-men rather than for fame and distinction. Probably that which most endears him to his countrymen is the quality he attributes to others in these words of admiration: "I am sure that both the President (Hayes) and his wife have in them that excellent new thing we call Americanism, which I suppose is that 'dignity of human nature' which the philosophers of the last century were always seeking and never finding, and which, after all, consists, perhaps, in not thinking yourself either better or worse than your neighbors by reason of any artificial distinction. As I sat behind them at the concert the other night, I was profoundly touched by the feelings of this kingship without mantle and crown from the property-room of the old world. Their dignity was in their very neighborliness, instead of in their distance." Certainly in the realm of American literature, there is no one better entitled than Lowell to this "kingship without mantle and crown."

A CHILD'S THOUGHT OF GOD

ELIZABETH BARRETT BROWNING

They say that God lives very high,
  But if you look above the pines
You cannot see our God, and why?

And if you dig down in the mines
  You never see Him in the gold;
Though, from Him, all that's glory shines.

God is so good, He wears a fold
  Of heaven and earth across His face—
Like secrets kept, for love, untold.

But still I feel that His embrace
  Slides down by thrills, through all things made,
Through sight and sound of every place.

As if my tender mother laid
  On my shut lids, her kisses' pressure,
Half-waking me at night, and said,
    "Who kissed you through the dark, dear
      guesser?"

ELIZABETH BARRETT BROWNING

ROUND the young life of Elizabeth Barrett was so much of illness and dreariness, that we have accustomed ourselves to thinking joy came to her only with her marriage, and we forget, often, that her childhood was not unhappy. Few children, it would seem, were ever born with greater promise of a bright life. Her father was wealthy and generous; she had brothers and sisters near her in age and congenial in tastes, and she was, at least, a fairly strong, active child.

She was born on March 6, 1806, at Coxhoe Hall, in the county of Durham, and when she was but three years old, her father removed to Hope End, in Herfordshire. The estate which he purchased there was a beautiful one, and the house, with its Turkish windows and Oriental-looking decorations, was most picturesque. That the scenery which surrounded her in her youth made on Elizabeth an impression which remained with her all her life is shown clearly in various passages in her poems:

"Green the land is where my daily
   Steps in jocund childhood played,
   Dimpled close with hill and valley,
   Dappled very close with shade;
Summer-snow of apple-blossoms running up
      from glade to glade."

Of all the brothers and sisters, Elizabeth was her father's favorite, and he encouraged her constantly in her precocious studies and in her childish attempts at composition. Long before she was able to read Homer in the original, she came upon Pope's translation of the *Iliad*, and it took a rare hold upon her. She showed its influence and her own bent toward poetry by composing, before she was fourteen, an epic on the "Battle of Marathon," of which her father, to whom it was dedicated, thought so highly that he had it printed and circulated it among his friends. But she also showed the influence of her beloved *Iliad* in a much more childish way, of which she has written delightfully in a poem called *Hector in the Garden*. A great flower bed, roughly shaped like a man and bordered about with turf, was made for her, and this she named after Hector, the Trojan hero and her great favorite.

> "Eyes of gentianellas azure,
>   Staring, winking at the skies;
>   Nose of gillyflowers and box;
>   Scented grasses put for locks,
>   Which a little breeze at pleasure
>   Set a-waving round his eyes."

> "Brazen helm of daffodillies,
>   With a glitter toward the light;
>   Purple violets for the mouth,
>   Breathing perfumes west and south;
>   And a sword of flashing lilies,
>   Holden ready for the fight:

"And a breastplate made of daisies,
  Closely fitting, leaf on leaf;
  Periwinkles interlaced
  Drawn for belt about the waist;
  While the brown bees, humming praises,
  Shot their arrows round the chief."

It was natural enough that Elizabeth should have wanted to begin the study of Greek; and with the help of her father and of Mr. Boyd, a blind friend of her father's, she became a most proficient Greek scholar.

When she was fifteen years old she met with an accident which deprived her in part of the out-of-door life and rambles which she had loved, and threw her more than ever upon her books for company. Impatient because a horse which she desired to ride was not ready just when she wanted it, she went out into the field and attempted to saddle it herself. She fell, with the saddle on top of her; and while this did not leave her the invalid she later became, it weakened her and made her an easy prey to the troubles which afterward came upon her.

That Pope, as well as Homer, left his mark on Miss Barrett was shown by her first published volume, which was brought out when she was about twenty. It was entitled *An Essay on Mind, and Other Poems*, and the poem which gave its name to the book was quite after the manner of Pope. This poem, while remarkable for a girl of Miss Barrett's age, contained little freshness or originality, and she spoke of it afterwards as having been "long repented of as worthy of all repentance."

In 1828 Mrs. Barrett died, and left Elizabeth, the eldest of the ten children, with much of the responsibility of the family. Since her death came before her daughter reached fame or began that voluminous correspondence from which have been gathered most of the facts of her life, little can be known of the mother's character, or of her influence on her daughter. That Miss Barrett was devotedly attached to her mother, however, is to be seen from a sentence in one of her letters. "Her memory," she says, "is more precious to me than any earthly blessing left behind!"

The beloved home at Hope End was sold in 1832, owing, apparently to some fall in the family fortunes, and the Barretts removed to Sidmouth, in Devonshire. The life there was uneventful, as the life at Hope End had been. Miss Barrett, in writing later of herself, declared that "a bird in a cage would have as good a story." But she was by no means idle, for her Greek studies and her writing kept her busy and happy. While at Sidmouth, she brought out a translation of the *Prometheus Bound* of Æschylus, a version with which she was so dissatisfied that she later replaced it, in her collected works, with another.

For three years the Barretts lived at Sidmouth, and their removal to London, in 1835, made important changes in Elizabeth's life. Her health, never good since her fifteenth year,

broke down, and from some date shortly after
the arrival in London she became an apparently
hopeless invalid, confined to her room and often
to her bed. Some compensation for this confinement, however, she found in the new friends,
few, indeed, but devoted and congenial, who
were admitted to her sick room. Chief among
these friends of her earlier London years were
John Kenyon, a distant cousin, and Mary
Russell Mitford, author of *Our Village*. Miss
Mitford made the acquaintance of Miss Barrett
in one of the latter's rare appearances in society,
and she has left an account of the meeting and a
description of Miss Barrett which is famous.

"She was certainly one of the most interesting
persons that I had ever seen. Everybody who
then saw her said the same; so that it is not
merely the impression of my partiality or my
enthusiasm. Of a slight, delicate figure, with a
shower of dark curls falling on either side of a
most expressive face, large tender eyes, richly
fringed by dark eyelashes, a smile like a sun-
beam, and such a look of youthfulness that I had
some difficulty in persuading a friend ... that the
translatress of the *Prometheus* of Æschylus, the
authoress of the *Essay on Mind*, was old enough
to be introduced into company,—in technical
language, was 'out.'"

Although Miss Mitford was nineteen years
older than Miss Barrett, the friendship which
sprang up between them was most close, and
lasted until Miss Mitford's death in 1855. Their
correspondence was constant and voluminous,

as was that, in fact, of Miss Barrett with all of her intimate friends. These letters of hers from her sick room are no more remarkable for number than for brightness and vivacity. Little mention is made of her ailments, except when her friends have specifically demanded news of her health, and the letters deal rather with literary than with other subjects. This was, of course, most natural: the invalid could have little news to communicate from her couch to her friends in the outer world. Her literary activity, too, increased, and she began to contribute to magazines poems of various kinds, which attracted much attention. Not all comment on them was favorable; the people declared that some of them were Sphinx-like—too difficult, if not impossible, of interpretation. But every one realized that here was a real poet, one of striking individuality, and, for a woman, most remarkable learning.

By the autumn of 1838, her health had become so much worse that the doctor ordered removal to a warmer climate, and she was taken to Torquay, where she remained for three years. Her father and her brothers and sisters visited her there from time to time, but her constant companion was her brother Edward, who had all her life been her favorite. What little good Torquay seemed to be doing her was more than overbalanced by a tragedy which occurred in the summer of 1840. Her brother, with two of his friends, went for a sail in a small boat, intending to be absent only until evening. When they did not return, inquiry was set on foot, and it was learned that a small boat had been seen to founder in Babbicombe Bay. The fears caused by this report became certainty three days later, on the recovery of the bodies. The effect on Miss Barrett may be partially imagined. Not only had she lost her best-loved companion, but she was haunted by the morbid feeling that she had caused his death, since he had come to Torquay only to be with her. Twelve years afterward she wrote on this subject—"I have lived heart to heart with my husband these five years. I have never yet spoken out, in a whisper even, what is in me; never yet could find heart or breath; never yet could bear to hear a word of reference from his lips."

Naturally her health suffered greatly from the shock, and it was thought that she could not possibly live more than a few months. Quite unexpectedly, however, she began to improve; it seemed that the desire to quit Torquay, which had grown unendurable to her since the tragedy, gave her strength of body. During the spring and summer of 1841 she was able to resume work on translations, compositions, plans for new poems. Indeed, it was this which saved her, for she wrote some time later to a friend—"I do believe I should be *mad* at this moment, if I had not forced back the current of rushing recollections by work, work, work."

After her return to London in the autumn of 1841, her life went on as before—or rather, stood still as before. From her couch she con-

tinued to send forth the poems which were
bringing her ever-increasing fame, and the
letters which were binding her friends closer to
her.   But an event was drawing nearer, which
was from the first an event and not an episode
in Miss Barrett's life.   In January, 1845, we
find her writing "And I had a letter from Browning the poet last night, which threw me into
ecstasies—Browning, the author of *Paracelsus*,
and the king of mystics;" and a little later she
says, "I am getting deeper and deeper into
correspondence with Robert Browning, poet and
mystic, and we are growing to be the truest of
friends."

Robert Browning had felt and expressed great
admiration for Miss Barrett's poems, and an
allusion to himself in her *Lady Geraldine's
Courtship* gave him an excuse for addressing
her.   Their correspondence flourished, and they
rapidly passed from regarding each other as
mere acquaintances to looking upon each other
as friends.   In fact, there seems to have been
from the very first an almost mystical attraction
between them.   Miss Barrett might have contented herself all her life with this delightfully
personal and literary correspondence, but Browning soon grew impatient and expressed his desire
to see her.   The admission of a new friend to
Miss Barrett's room was at no time a thing to
be undertaken lightly, so hedged about was she
by the care of her family; and in this case she
herself seems to have hesitated long before
allowing Browning to call, for the very feminine

reason that "there is nothing to see in me nor to hear in me." Had she known Browning better, she would have realized that his determination would carry him past all obstacles; and so, indeed, it did.

On May 20, 1845, they met for the first time, and within a short time his friendship for her had ripened into love, and he asked her to marry him. She herself told, in a letter to a friend after her marriage, the story of her courtship.

"He came, and with our personal acquaintance began his attachment for me, a sort of *infatuation* call it, which resisted the various denials which were my plain duty at the beginning, and has persisted past them all. I began with the grave assurance that I was in an exceptional position and saw him just in consequence of it, and that if he ever recurred to that subject again, I never could see him again while I lived; and he believed me and was silent. To my mind, indeed, it was a bare impulse—a generous man of quick sympathies taking up a sudden interest with both hands."

Browning was, as she said, silent, but he was not discouraged, and his letters, his visits, his flowers, at length convinced Miss Barrett that his feeling was something more than a "bare impulse."

"So then," she continued, "I showed him how he was throwing into the ashes his best affections—how the common gifts of youth and cheerfulness were behind me—how I had not strength, even of *heart*, for the ordinary duties of life—everything I told him and showed him. 'Look at this—and this—and this,' throwing down all my disadvantages. To which he did not answer by a single compliment, but simply that he had not then to choose, and that I might be right or he might be right, he was not there to decide; but that he loved me, and should to his last hour. * * * He preferred, he said, of free and deliberate choice, to be allowed to sit only an hour a day by my side, to the fulfilment of the brightest dream which should exclude me, in any possible world."

What Robert Browning wanted so much, it was a foregone conclusion that he would have; and Miss Barrett was at last brought to consent to an engagement. But the difficulties were just begun. Mr. Barrett, adored as he was by his daughter, was more than a little tyrannical, especially with his favorite daughter. His family all well knew that he would never under any circumstances be brought to consent to the marriage of any of his children; and he had, moreover, in the case of Elizabeth, the appearance of reason on his side, in that she was, in the opinion of her family and of most of her medical advisers, a hopeless invalid, unfit to be moved. "A life passed between a bed and a sofa, and avoiding too frequent and abrupt transitions even from one to the other, was the only life she could expect on this earth." Browning believed otherwise, and events showed that he was right.

In the autumn of 1845, the doctors advised that Miss Barrett be taken to Italy, declaring, in fact, that her life depended upon it. Some of her brothers or sisters could easily have accompanied her; there was no lack of money, and the journey was actually planned. For no apparent reason, however, Mr. Barrett refused his consent—said that his daughter should not leave his house. In vain the family argued; in vain a generous friend offered to accompany Miss Barrett, paying all expenses. He was brutally firm. Much hurt by this selfishness and disregard for her life, Miss Barrett promised Browning that if she lived through the winter and were no worse in the following year, she would marry him without her father's consent, for which they knew it was useless to ask. Accordingly, on September 12, 1846, she walked out of her father's house, accompanied only by her maid, was married and returned home. One week later she joined her husband, and they set out for Italy, their future home. Mr. Barrett never forgave his daughter, and his unrelenting anger was a deep sorrow to her, in the midst of her great life happiness.

The Brownings went first to Pisa, and from there to Florence, which they afterward regarded as their home, though they made many excursions and spent seasons elsewhere. Mrs. Browning grew so much better that a friend said to her, "You are not *improved*, you are *transformed*;" and while she was never strong and was often very ill, she never again sank back to the state in which she had been before her marriage. The happiness which shows in her

ELIZABETH BARRETT BROWNING

letters is wonderful. "As for me," she writes, "when I am so good as to let myself be carried upstairs, and so angelical as to sit still on the sofa, and so considerate, moreover, as *not* to put my foot into a puddle, why *my* duty is considered done to a perfection which is worthy of all adoration." And again, "If I could open my heart to you in all seriousness, you would see nothing there but a sort of enduring wonder of happiness."

Mrs. Browning, like her husband, loved Italy, and especially Florence, and many of her poems, notably the *Casa Guidi Windows*, deal with Italian subjects. Of the poems published after her marriage, however, none are more exquisite than the series of *Sonnets from the Portuguese*. These sonnets, which are not translations, and to which the name *From the Portuguese* was given simply as a blind, describe her uncertainty and her joy in the love which was hers.

In 1849 another joy came to her. On March 9th of that year a son, Robert Wiedeman Barrett Browning was born, and from that time on her letters, quite like the letters of any unliterary mother, are full of the wonderful doings of this child. Not that her interest in things literary flagged in the least: she read everything which the libraries of Italy afforded, or which her friends could send to her—novels, for which she confessed to a great liking; poems, political pamphlets, newspapers, all that came to her hand. Her longest and greatest poem, *Aurora Leigh*, was written during her Italian years. While the story of the poem is in no sense autobiographical, the heroine is in her beliefs and her ideals Mrs. Browning's self, and this was the poem by which she felt herself most willing to be judged.

Broken by several trips to England and by excursions to the most beautiful parts of Italy, the years slipped by in uneventful happiness. Friends, many of them Americans, visited the Brownings, and all came away wondering and delighted at the perfect family life they had been allowed to witness. Frail always, Mrs. Browning was spoken of by acquaintances in her later years as seeming "scarce embodied at all."

In June, 1861, Mrs. Browning had an attack of bronchial trouble, not more severe, apparently, than others which had preceded it. But on the night of the twenty-ninth, alone in the room with her husband, she died; and one writer says "none ever saw Browning upon earth again, but only a splendid surface." Mrs. Browning was buried at Florence, the city she had so loved. Upon the wall of Casa Guidi, the building in which she had lived, the citizens, grateful for her love and understanding of them, placed a marble tablet in her memory.

The wonderful thing about Elizabeth Barrett Browning is that from her weakness should have come poems of such strength. There was nothing morbid in the words which came from her hushed, darkened sick room. Indeed, her spirit was never tamed, and she herself confessed that one of her faults was "head-longness;" that she snatched parcels open instead of untying the string, and tore letters instead of cutting them. In Browning's poems, which contain numerous beautiful allusions to her, there is nothing more beautiful and more descriptive than the lines—

"O lyric love, half angel and half bird,
And all a wonder and a wild desire."

DON QUIXOTE

CERVANTES

INTRODUCTORY NOTE

NLIKE many of his class, Miguel de Cervantes Saavedra, the greatest of the old Spanish writers, was born to a changeful and busy life. The year 1547 marked his birth, and during the sixty-nine years of his life he was constantly in action.

He served as a soldier in the war against the Turks, and at the Battle of Lepanto, where he lost the use of his left hand, and in other battles in which he took part, he showed great bravery and won a reputation of the highest kind. While returning in 1575 from Italy to Spain, he was captured by Algerian pirates and was sold in Algiers as a slave. Throughout his five years' captivity, he was constantly threatened with torture, but at no time did his courage fail him. Finally his widowed mother and his sister, helped by some of their friends, none of whom were by any means wealthy, succeeded in getting together sufficient money to ransom him, and immediately on his return to Spain he rejoined his old regiment.

Cervantes had written verses before the beginning of his military career, but had won no name for himself. By 1583, however, he seems to have determined to devote the rest of his life to literature, and in that year he again began writing verses. For a number of years he earned his livelihood by writing for the stage, but few of his plays survive.

In 1605 there appeared the first part of the work which made Cervantes famous, and which has kept his name before the world ever since. This was the inimitable *Don Quixote*, which gives the burlesque adventures of the self-styled "Knight of the Rueful Countenance." This book was not intended to satirize knight-errantry itself, for that had long before died out in Spain. What it did aim to do was to make ridiculous the romances of chivalry over which all Spain at the time of Cervantes seemed to have gone mad. How well Cervantes succeeded in his aim may be known from the fact that after the appearance of his masterpiece, no new romance of chivalry was published in Spain.

The hero of this great work, Don Quixote, is presented as the most courteous and affable of gentlemen, wise on all points except those pertaining to chivalry. It was not only, however, the masterly drawing of the characters of Don Quixote and his squire, Sancho Panza, which made the book popular; the inexhaustible fund of humor has made it to the present day a book which every one delights to read.

The following selections from *Don Quixote* describe some of the typical adventures of the gallant "Knight of the Rueful Countenance," and will serve to give the reader an idea of the book.

DON QUIXOTE PREPARES TO SET OUT ON HIS ADVENTURES

IN a village of La Mancha there lived not long since one of those gentlemen that keep a lance in the lance-rack, an old buckler, a lean hack, and a greyhound for coursing. An olla[1] of rather more beef than mutton, a salad on most nights, scraps on Saturdays, lentils on Fridays, and a pigeon or so extra on Sundays, made away with three-quarters of his income. The rest of it went in a doublet of fine cloth and velvet breeches and shoes to match for holidays, while on week days he made a brave figure in his best homespun. He had in his house a housekeeper past forty, a niece under twenty, and a lad for the field and market-place, who used to saddle the hack as well as handle the bill-hook. The age of this gentleman of ours was bordering on fifty, he was of a hardy habit, spare, gaunt-featured, a very early riser and a great sportsman. They will have it his surname was Quixada or Quesada (for here there is some difference of opinion among the authors who write on the subject), although from reasonable conjectures

---

1. The *olla* is the national dish of Spain, and is a stew composed of beef, bacon, sausage, chick-peas and cabbage, with any other meat or vegetables which may be on hand.

Fly Not, Ye Cowards
and Vile Caitiffs!

it seems plain that he was called Quixana. This, however, is of but little importance to our tale; it will be enough not to stray a hair's breadth from the truth in the telling of it.

You must know, then, that the above-named gentleman whenever he was at leisure (which was mostly all the year round) gave himself up to reading books of chivalry with such ardor and avidity that he almost entirely neglected the pursuit of his field-sports, and even the management of his property; and to such a pitch did his eagerness and infatuation go that he sold many an acre of tillage-land to buy books of chivalry to read, and brought home as many of them as he could get.

* * * * * * * * * *

In short, his wits being quite gone, he hit upon the strangest notion that ever madman in this world hit upon, and that was that he fancied it was right and requisite, as well for the support of his own honor as for the service of his country, that he should make a knight-errant of himself, roaming the world over in full armor and on horseback in quest of adventures, and putting in practice himself all that he had read of as being the usual practices of knights-errant; righting every kind of wrong, and exposing himself to peril and danger from which, in the issue, he was to reap eternal renown and fame. Already the poor man saw himself crowned by the might of his arm Emperor of Trebizond at least; and so, led away by the intense enjoyment he found in these pleasant fancies, he set himself forthwith to put his scheme into execution.

The first thing he did was to clean up some armor that had belonged to his great-grand-father, and had been for ages lying forgotten in a corner eaten with rust and covered with mildew. He scoured and polished it as best he could, but he perceived one great defect in it, that it had no closed helmet, nothing but a simple morion.[2] This deficiency, however, his ingenuity supplied, for he contrived a kind of half-helmet of pasteboard which, fitted on to the morion, looked like a whole one. It is true that, in order to see if it was strong and fit to stand a cut, he drew his sword and gave it a couple of slashes, the first of which undid in an instant what had taken him a week to do. The ease with which he had knocked it to pieces disconcerted him somewhat, and to guard against that danger he set to work again, fixing bars of iron on the inside until he was satisfied with its strength; and then, not caring to try any more experiments with it, he passed it and adopted it as a helmet of the most perfect construction.

He next proceeded to inspect his hack, which surpassed in his eyes the Bucephalus[3] of Alexander or the Babieca of the Cid.[4] Four days were spent in thinking what name to give him, because (as he said to himself) it was not right

---

2. A *morion* is a helmet without visor or beaver for protecting the face.

3. Alexander the Great was so fond of his horse Bucephalus that when it died in India during Alexander's sojourn there, he founded a city which he called Bucephalia, in honor of the steed.

4. The Cid was the greatest of Spanish heroes.

that a horse belonging to a knight so famous, and
one with such merits of his own, should be
without some distinctive name, and he strove to
adapt it so as to indicate what he had been before
belonging to a knight-errant, and what he then
was; for it was only reasonable that, his master
taking a new character, he should take a new
name, and that it should be a distinguished and
full-sounding one, befitting the new order and
calling he was about to follow. And so, after
having composed, struck out, rejected, added
to, unmade, and remade a multitude of names
out of his memory and fancy, he decided upon
calling him Rocinante, a name, to his thinking,
lofty, sonorous, and significant of his condition
as a hack before he became what he was now,
the first and foremost of all the hacks in the
world.[5]

Having got a name for his horse so much to
his taste, he was anxious to get one for himself,
and he was eight days more pondering over this
point, till at last he made up his mind to call
himself Don Quixote, whence, as has been already
said, the authors of this veracious history have
inferred that his name must have been beyond
a doubt Quixada, and not Quesada as others
would have it. Recollecting, however, that the
valiant Amadis[6] was not content to call himself

---

5. *Rocin* is, in Spanish, a horse used for labor, as distinguished from
one kept for pleasure or for personal use; *ante* means *before*. Thus the
name *Rocinante* meant that the horse had formerly been a hack, or
work horse.

6. Amadis de Gaul was the hero of one of the most celebrated
romances of chivalry.

curtly Amadis and nothing more, but added the name of his kingdom and country to make it famous, and called himself Amadis of Gaul, he, like a good knight, resolved to add on the name of his, and to style himself Don Quixote of La Mancha, whereby, he considered, he described accurately his origin and country, and did honor to it in taking his surname from it.

So then, his armor being furbished, his morion turned into a helmet, his hack christened, and he himself confirmed, he came to the conclusion that nothing more was needed now but to look out for a lady to be in love with; for a knight-errant without love was like a tree without leaves or fruit, or a body without a soul. As he said to himself, "If, for my sins, or by my good fortune, I come across some giant hereabouts, a common occurrence with knights-errant, and overthrow him in one onslaught, or cleave him asunder to the waist, or, in short, vanquish and subdue him, will it not be well to have some one I may send him to as a present, that he may come in and fall on his knees before my sweet lady, and in a humble, submissive voice say, 'I am the giant Caraculiambro, lord of the island of Malindrania, vanquished in single combat by the never sufficiently extolled knight Don Quixote of La Mancha, who has commanded me to present myself before your Grace, that your Highness dispose of me at your pleasure'?" Oh, how our good gentleman enjoyed the delivery of this speech, especially when he had thought of some one to call his Lady! There was, so the story goes, in a village near his own a very good-looking farm girl with whom he had been at one time in love, though, so far as is known, she never knew it nor gave a thought to the matter. Her name was Aldonza Lorenzo, and upon her he thought fit to confer the title of Lady of his Thoughts; and after some search for a name which should not be out of harmony with his own, and should suggest and indicate that of a princess and great lady, he decided upon calling her Dulcinea del Toboso — she being of El Toboso—a name, to his mind, musical, uncommon, and significant, like all those he had already bestowed upon himself and the things belonging to him.

THE ADVENTURE OF THE WINDMILLS

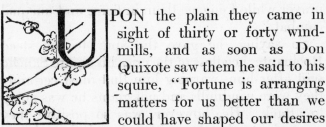 UPON the plain they came in sight of thirty or forty windmills, and as soon as Don Quixote saw them he said to his squire, "Fortune is arranging matters for us better than we could have shaped our desires ourselves, for look there, friend Sancho Panza,[1] where thirty or more monstrous giants present

---

1. When Don Quixote first set out on his quest of adventures, he was unattended. Having been forced, however, to return to his native town, he persuaded a peasant, Sancho Panza by name, to go with him and serve as his squire. While Sancho was a hard-headed, practical man, he was carried away by Don Quixote's promises of reward, and in time, through listening constantly to the Don's conversation, he became almost as mad as his master.

themselves, all of whom I mean to engage in battle and slay, and with whose spoils we shall begin to make our fortunes; for this is righteous warfare, and it is God's good service to sweep so evil a breed from off the face of the earth."

"What giants?" said Sancho Panza.

"Those thou seest there," answered his master, "with the long arms, and some have them nearly two leagues long."

"Look, your worship," said Sancho; "what we see there are not giants but windmills, and what seem to be their arms are the sails that turned by the wind make the millstone go."

"It is easy to see," replied Don Quixote, "that thou art not used to this business of adventures; those are giants; and if thou art afraid, away with thee out of this and betake thyself to prayer while I engage them in fierce and unequal combat."

So saying, he gave the spur to his steed Rocinante, heedless of the cries his squire Sancho sent after him, warning him that most certainly they were windmills and not giants he was going to attack. He, however, was so positive they were giants that he neither heard the cries of Sancho, nor perceived, near as he was, what they were, but made at them shouting, "Fly not, cowards and vile beings, for it is a single knight that attacks you."

A slight breeze at this moment sprang up, and the great sails began to move, seeing which Don Quixote exclaimed, "Though ye flourish more

DON QUIXOTE TILTS WITH THE WINDMILLS

arms than the giant Briareus,[2] ye have to reckon with me."

So saying, and commending himself with all his heart to his lady Dulcinea, imploring her to support him in such a peril, with lance in rest and covered by his buckler, he charged at Rocinante's fullest gallop and fell upon the first mill that stood in front of him; but as he drove his lance-point into the sail the wind whirled it round with such force that it shivered the lance

2. Briareus was a famous giant of ancient mythology, who had fifty heads and one hundred arms.

to pieces, sweeping with it horse and rider, who went rolling over on the plain, in a sorry condition.   Sancho hastened to his assistance as fast as his ass could go, and when he came up found him unable to move, with such a shock had Rocinante fallen with him.

"God bless me!" said Sancho, "did I not tell your worship to mind what you were about, for they were only windmills? and no one could have made any mistake about it but one who had something of the same kind in his head."

"Hush, friend Sancho," replied Don Quixote; "the fortunes of war more than any other are liable to frequent fluctuations; and moreover I think, and it is the truth, that some sage[3] turned these giants into mills in order to rob me of the glory of vanquishing them, such is the enmity he bears me; but in the end his wicked arts will avail but little against my good sword."

"God order it as he may," said Sancho Panza, and helping him to rise got him up again on Rocinante, whose shoulder was half out; and then, discussing the late adventure, they followed the road to Puerto Lápice, for there, said Don Quixote, they could not fail to find adventures, as it was a great thoroughfare.

Finally they passed the night among some trees, from one of which Don Quixote plucked a dry branch to serve him as a lance, and fixed on it the head he had removed from the broken one.

3. By *sage* is here meant an enchanter or magician.

MAMBRINO'S HELMET

•

RAIN fell in gentle drops, and Sancho was for going into the fulling mills,[1] but Don Quixote had taken such a disgust to them on account of the late joke that he would not enter them on any account; so turning aside to the right they came upon another road, different from that which they had taken the night before. Shortly afterwards Don Quixote perceived a man on horseback who wore on his head something that shone like gold, and the moment he saw him he turned to Sancho and said, "I think, Sancho, there is no proverb that is not true, all being maxims drawn from experience itself, the mother of all the sciences, especially that one that says, 'Where one door shuts, another opens.' I say so because if last night fortune shut the door of the adventure we were looking for against us, cheating us with the fulling mills, it now opens wide another one for another better and more certain adventure, and if I do not contrive to enter it, it will be my own fault, and I cannot lay it to my ignorance of fulling mills, or the darkness of the night. I say this because, if I mistake not, there comes toward us one who wears on his head the helmet of Mambrino,[2]

---

1. Don Quixote and Sancho had remained in terror through an entire night, fancying from the noise they heard that they were near some terrible danger. In the morning they found that this noise proceeded from some fulling mills in the neighborhood.

2. Mambrino was a Moorish king, mentioned in some of the romantic poems which *Don Quixote* is intended to burlesque. He possessed an

concerning which I took the oath thou rememberest."

"Mind what you say, your worship, and still more what you do," said Sancho, "for I don't want any more fulling mills to finish off fulling and knocking our senses out."

"The devil take thee, man," said Don Quixote; "what has a helmet to do with fulling mills?"

"I don't know," replied Sancho, "but, faith, if I might speak as I used, perhaps I could give such reasons that your worship would see you were mistaken in what you say."

"How can I be mistaken in what I say, unbelieving traitor?" returned Don Quixote. "Tell me, seest thou not yonder knight coming towards us on a dappled gray steed, who has upon his head a helmet of gold?"

"What I see and make out," answered Sancho, "is only a man on a gray ass like my own, who has something that shines on his head."

"Well, that is the helmet of Mambrino," said Don Quixote; "stand to one side and leave me alone with him; thou shalt see how, without saying a word, to save time, I shall bring this adventure to an issue and possess myself of the helmet I have so longed for."

"I will take care to stand aside," said Sancho; "but God grant, I say once more, that it may not be fulling mills again."

---

enchanted golden helmet which rendered the wearer invulnerable, and which was naturally much sought after by all the knights. Rinaldo finally obtained possession of it. Don Quixote, whose helmet had been destroyed, had sworn that he would lead a life of particular hardship until he had made himself master of the wonderful helmet.

"I have told thee, brother, on no account to mention those fulling mills to me again," said Don Quixote, "or I vow—and I say no more— I'll full the soul out of you."

Sancho held his peace in dread lest his master should carry out the vow he had hurled like a bowl at him.

The fact of the matter as regards the helmet, steed, and knight that Don Quixote saw, was this. In that neighborhood there were two villages, one of them so small that it had neither apothecary's shop, nor barber, which the other that was close to it had; so the barber of the larger served the smaller; and in it there was a sick man who required to be bled and another man who wanted to be shaved, and on this errand the barber was going, carrying with him a brass basin; but as luck would have it, as he was on the way it began to rain, and not to spoil his hat, which probably was a new one, he put the basin on his head, and being clean it glittered at half a league's distance. He rode upon a gray ass, as Sancho said, and this was what made it seem to Don Quixote to be a dapple-gray steed and a knight and a golden helmet; for everything he saw he made to fall in with his crazy chivalry and ill errant notions; and when he saw the poor knight draw near, without entering into any parley with him, at Rocinante's top speed he bore down upon him with the pike pointed low, fully determined to run him through and through, and as he reached him, without checking the fury of his charge, he cried to him, "Defend thyself,

miserable being, or yield me of thine own accord
that which is so reasonably my due."

The barber, who without any expectation or
apprehension of it saw this apparition coming
down upon him, had no other way of saving
himself from the stroke of the lance but to let
himself fall off his ass; and no sooner had he
touched the ground than he sprang up more
nimbly than a deer and sped away across the
plain faster than the wind.

He left the basin on the ground, with which
Don Quixote contented himself, saying that the
pagan had shown his discretion and imitated the
beaver, which finding himself pressed by the
hunters bites and cuts off with its teeth that for
which, by its natural instinct, it knows it is
pursued.

He told Sancho to pick up the helmet, and he,
taking it in his hands, said, "By God the basin
is a good one, and worth a piece of eight[3] if it is
worth a maravedí," and handed it to his master,
who immediately put it on his head, turning it
round, now this way, now that, in search of
the visor. Not finding it he said, "Clearly
the pagan to whose measure this famous head-
piece was first forged must have had a very
large head; but the worst of it is half of it is
wanting."

When Sancho heard him call the basin a head-
piece he was unable to restrain his laughter, but

---

3. The *piece of eight* is equal to about one dollar of American money.
The *maravedi* is a small copper coin, of the value of three mills in American money.

MAMBRINO'S HELMET

remembering his master's wrath he checked himself in the midst of it.

"What art thou laughing at, Sancho?" said Don Quixote.

"I am laughing," said he, "to think of the great head the pagan must have had who owned this helmet, for it looks exactly like a regular barber's basin."

"Dost thou know what I suspect, Sancho?" said Don Quixote; "that this wonderful piece of this enchanted helmet must by some strange accident have come into the hands of some one

who was unable to recognize or realize its value,
and who, not knowing what he did, and seeing
it to be of the purest gold, must have melted
down one half for the sake of what it might be
worth, and of the other made this which is like a
barber's basin, as thou sayest; but be it as it may,
to me who recognize it, its transformation makes
no difference, for I will set it to rights at the first
village where there is a blacksmith, and in such
style that that helmet the god of smithies[4] forged
for the god of battles shall not surpass it or
even come up to it; and in the meantime I will
wear it as well as I can, for something is better
than nothing; all the more as it will be quite
enough to protect me from any chance blow of a
stone."

"Will your worship," said Sancho, "tell me
what are we to do with this dapple-gray steed
that looks like a gray ass, which that Martino[5]
that your worship overthrew has left deserted
here? for, from the way he took to his heels
and bolted, he is not likely ever to come back
for it; and by my beard but the gray is a good
one."

"I have never been in the habit," said Don
Quixote, "of taking spoil of those whom I vanquish, nor is it the practice of chivalry to take
away their horses and leave them to go on foot,
unless indeed it be that the victor have lost his
own in the combat, in which case it is lawful to

---

4. The *god of smithies* was the old Greek and Roman god Hephæstus,
or Vulcan; the *god of battles* was Mars.

5. *Martino* is a blunder of Sancho's for *Mambrino*.

take that of the vanquished as a thing won in
lawful war; therefore, Sancho, leave this horse,
or ass, or whatever thou wilt have it to be; for
when its owner sees us gone hence he will come
back for it."

"God knows I should like to take it," returned
Sancho, "or at least to change it for my own,
which does not seem to me as good a one; verily
the laws of chivalry are strict, since they cannot
be stretched to let one ass be changed for another; I should like to know if I might at least
change trappings."

"On that head I am not quite certain,"
answered Don Quixote, "and the matter being
doubtful, pending better information, I say thou
mayest change them, if so be thou hast urgent
need of them."

"So urgent is it," answered Sancho, "that if
they were for my own person I could not want
them more;" and forthwith, fortified by this
license, he effected the change, and rigged out
his beast to the ninety-nines, making quite another thing of it. This done, they broke their
fast on the remains of the spoils of war plundered
from the sumpter mule, and drank of the brook
that flowed from the fulling mills, without casting
a look in that direction, in such loathing did they
hold them for the alarm they had caused them;
and, all anger and gloom removed, they mounted
and, without taking any fixed road (not to fix
upon any being the proper thing for true knights-
errant), they set out, guided by Rocinante's will,
which carried along with it that of his master,

not to say that of the ass, which always followed him wherever he led, lovingly and sociably; nevertheless they returned to the high road, and pursued it at a venture without any other aim.

DON QUIXOTE'S ENCOUNTER WITH THE LIONS

WHEN the author of this great history came to relate what is set down in this chapter he would have preferred to pass it over in silence, fearing it would not be believed, because here Don Quixote's madness reaches the confines of the greatest that can be conceived, and even goes a couple of bowshots beyond the greatest. But after all, though still under the same fear and apprehension, he has recorded it without adding to the story or leaving out a particle of the truth, and entirely disregarding the charges of falsehood that might be brought against him.

When Don Quixote called Sancho to bring his helmet, Sancho was buying some curds the shepherds agreed to sell him, and flurried by the great haste his master was in did not know what to do with them or what to carry them in; so, not to lose them, for he had already paid for them, he thought it best to throw them into his master's helmet, and acting on this bright idea he went to see what his master wanted with him. He, as he approached, exclaimed to him, "Give me that helmet, my friend, for either I know little of adventures, or what I observe yonder is one that will, and does, call upon me to arm myself."

He of the green gaban,[1] hearing this, looked in all directions, but could perceive nothing, except a cart coming towards them with two or three small flags, which led him to conclude it must be carrying treasure of the King's, and he said so to Don Quixote. He, however, would not believe him, being always persuaded and convinced that all that happened to him must be adventures and still more adventures; so he replied to the gentleman, "He who is prepared has his battle half fought; nothing is lost by my preparing myself, for I know by experience that I have enemies, visible and invisible, and I know not when or where, or at what moment, or in what shapes they will attack me;" and turning to Sancho he called for his helmet; and Sancho, as he had no time to take out the curds, had to give it as it was.

Don Quixote took it, and without perceiving what was in it thrust it down in hot haste upon his head; but as the curds were pressed and squeezed the whey began to run all over his face and beard, whereat he was so startled that he cried out to Sancho, "Sancho, what's this? I think my head is softening, or my brains are melting, or I am sweating from head to foot! If I am sweating it is not indeed from fear. I am convinced beyond a doubt that the adventure which is about to befall me is a terrible one. Give me something to wipe myself

---

1. This was a gentlemanly person whom Don Quixote had met on the road a short time before.

with, if thou hast it, for this profuse sweat is blinding me."

Sancho held his tongue, and gave him a cloth, and gave thanks to God at the same time that his master had not found out what was the matter. Don Quixote then wiped himself, and took off his helmet to see what it was that made his head feel so cool, and seeing all that white mash inside his helmet he put it to his nose, and as soon as he had smelt it he exclaimed, "By the life of my lady Dulcinea del Toboso, but it is curds thou hast put here, thou treacherous, impudent, ill-mannered squire!"

To which, with great composure and pretended innocence, Sancho replied, "If they are curds let me have them, your worship, and I'll eat them; but let the devil eat them, for it must have been he who put them there. I dare to dirty your worship's helmet! You have guessed the offender finely! Faith, sir, by the light God gives me, it seems I must have enchanters too, that persecute me as a creature and limb of your worship, and they must have put that nastiness there in order to provoke your patience to anger, and make you baste my ribs as you are wont to do. Well, this time, indeed, they have missed their aim, for I trust to my master's good sense to see that I have got no curds or milk, or anything of the sort; and that if I had it is in my stomach I would put it and not in the helmet."

"May be so," said Don Quixote. All this the gentleman was observing, and with astonishment, more especially when, after having wiped himself clean, his head, face, beard, and helmet, Don Quixote put it on, and settling himself firmly in his stirrups, easing his sword in the scabbard, and grasping his lance, he cried, "Now come who will, here am I, ready to try conclusions with Satan himself in person!"

By this time the cart with the flags had come up, unattended by any one except the carter on a mule, and a man sitting in front. Don Quixote planted himself before it and said, "Whither are you going, brothers? What cart is this? What have you got in it? What flags are those?"

To this the carter replied, "The cart is mine; what is in it is a pair of fine caged lions, which the governor of Oran is sending to court as a present to his Majesty; and the flags are our lord the King's, to show that what is here is his property."

"And are the lions large?" asked Don Quixote.

"So large," replied the man who sat at the door of the cart, "that larger, or as large, have never crossed from Africa to Spain; I am the keeper, and I have brought over others, but never any like these. They are male and female; the male is in that first cage and the female in the one behind, and they are hungry now, for they have eaten nothing to-day, so let your worship stand aside, for we must make haste to the place where we are to feed them."

Hereupon, smiling slightly, Don Quixote exclaimed, "Lion-whelps to me! to me whelps of lions, and at such a time! Then, by God! those gentlemen who send them here shall see if I am a man to be frightened by lions. Get down, my good fellow, and as you are the keeper open the cages, and turn me out those beasts, and in the midst of this plain I will let them know who Don Quixote of La Mancha is, in spite and in the teeth of the enchanters who send them to me."

"So, so," said the gentleman to himself at this; "our worthy knight has shown of what sort he is; the curds, no doubt, have softened his skull and brought his brains to a head."

At this instant Sancho came up to him, saying, "Señor, for God's sake do something to keep my master, Don Quixote, from tackling these lions; for if he does they'll tear us all to pieces here."

"Is your master then so mad," asked the gentleman, "that you believe and are afraid he will engage such fierce animals?"

"He is not mad," said Sancho, "but he is venturesome."

"I will prevent it," said the gentleman; and going over to Don Quixote, who was insisting upon the keeper's opening the cages, he said to him, "Sir knight, knights-errant should attempt adventures which encourage the hope of a successful issue, not those which entirely withhold it; for valor that trenches upon temerity savors rather of madness than of courage; moreover, these lions do not come to oppose you, nor do they dream of such a thing; they are going as presents to his Majesty, and it will not be right to stop them or delay their journey."

"Gentle sir," replied Don Quixote, "you go

and mind your tame partridge and your bold
ferret, and leave every one to manage his own
business; this is mine, and I know whether these
gentlemen the lions come to me or not;" and then
turning to the keeper he exclaimed, "By all that's
good, sir scoundrel, if you don't open the cages
this very instant, I'll pin you to the cart with
this lance."

The carter, seeing the determination of this
apparition in armor, said to him, "Please your
worship, for charity's sake, señor, let me unyoke
the mules and place myself in safety along with
them before the lions are turned out; for if they
kill them on me I am ruined for life, for all I
possess is this cart and mules."

"O man of little faith," replied Don Quixote,
"get down and unyoke; you will soon see that
you are exerting yourself for nothing, and that
you might have spared yourself the trouble."

The carter got down and with all speed un-
yoked the mules, and the keeper called out at the
top of his voice, "I call all here to witness that
against my will and under compulsion I open
the cages and let the lions loose, and that I warn
this gentleman that he will be accountable for all
the harm and mischief which these beasts may
do, and for my salary and dues as well. You,
gentlemen, place yourselves in safety before I
open, for I know they will do me no harm."

Once more the gentleman strove to persuade
Don Quixote not to do such a mad thing, as it
was tempting God to engage in such a piece of
folly. To this, Don Quixote replied that he

knew what he was about. The gentleman in return entreated him to reflect, for he knew he was under a delusion.

"Well, señor," answered Don Quixote, "if you do not like to be a spectator of this tragedy, as in your opinion it will be, spur your flea-bitten mare and place yourself in safety."

Hearing this, Sancho with tears in his eyes entreated him to give up an enterprise compared with which the one of the windmills, and the awful one of the fulling mills, and, in fact, all the feats he had attempted in the whole course of his life, were cakes and fancy bread. "Look ye, señor," said Sancho, "there's no enchantment here, nor anything of the sort, for between the bars and chinks of the cage I have seen the paw of a real lion, and judging by that I reckon the lion such a paw could belong to must be bigger than a mountain."

"Fear, at any rate," replied Don Quixote, "will make him look bigger to thee than half the world. Retire, Sancho, and leave me; and if I die here thou knowest our old compact; thou wilt repair to Dulcinea—I say no more." To these he added some further words that banished all hope of his giving up his insane project. He of the green gaban would have offered resistance, but he found himself ill-matched as to arms, and did not think it prudent to come to blows with a madman, for such Don Quixote had shown himself to be in every respect; and the latter, renewing his commands to the keeper and repeating his threats, gave warning to the gentleman to spur his mare, Sancho his Dapple, and the carter his mules, all striving to get away from the cart as far as they could before the lions broke loose. Sancho was weeping over his master's death, for this time he firmly believed it was in store for him from the claws of the lions; and he cursed his fate and called it an unlucky hour when he thought of taking service with him again; but with all his tears and lamentations he did not forget to thrash Dapple so as to put a good space between himself and the cart. The keeper, seeing that the fugitives were now some distance off, once more entreated and warned Don Quixote as he had entreated and warned him before; but he replied that he heard him, and that he need not trouble himself with any further warnings or entreaties, as they would be fruitless, and bade him make haste.

During the delay that occurred while the keeper was opening the first cage, Don Quixote was considering whether it would not be well to do battle on foot, instead of on horseback, and finally resolved to fight on foot, fearing that Rocinante might take fright at the sight of the lions; he therefore sprang off his horse, flung his lance aside, braced his buckler on his arm, and drawing his sword, advanced slowly with marvelous intrepidity and resolute courage, to plant himself in front of the cart, commending himself with all his heart, first to God, and then to his lady Dulcinea.

The keeper, seeing that Don Quixote had taken up his position, and that it was impossible

for him to avoid letting out the male without in-
curring the enmity of the fiery and daring knight,
flung open the doors of the first cage, containing,
as has been said, the lion, which was now seen to
be of enormous size, and grim and hideous mien.
The first thing he did was to turn round in the
cage in which he lay, and protrude his claws, and
stretch himself thoroughly; he next opened his
mouth, and yawned very leisurely, and with near

HE PUT HIS HEAD OUT OF THE CAGE

two palms'-length of tongue that he had thrust
forth, he licked the dust out of his eyes and
washed his face; having done this, he put his
head out of the cage and looked all round with
eyes like glowing coals, a spectacle and demeanor
to strike terror into temerity itself.   Don Quixote
merely observed him steadily, longing for him
to leap from the cart and come to close quarters
with him, when he hoped to hew him in pieces.
    So far did his unparalleled madness go; but
the noble lion, more courteous than arrogant, not
troubling himself about silly bravado, after hav-

ing looked all round, as has been said, turned about and presented his hind-quarters to Don Quixote, and very coolly and tranquilly lay down again in the cage. Seeing this, Don Quixote ordered the keeper to take a stick to him and provoke him to make him come out.

"That I won't," said the keeper; "for if I anger him, the first he'll tear to pieces will be myself. Be satisfied, sir knight, with what you have done, which leaves nothing more to be said on the score of courage, and do not seek to tempt fortune a second time. The lion has the door open; he is free to come out or not to come out; but as he has not come out so far, he will not come out to-day. The greatness of your worship's courage has been fully manifested already; no brave champion, so it strikes me, is bound to do more than challenge his enemy and wait for him on the field; if his adversary does not come, on him lies the disgrace, and he who waits for him carries off the crown of victory."

"That is true," said Don Quixote; "close the door, my friend, and let me have, in the best form thou canst, what thou hast seen me do, by way of certificate; to wit, that thou didst open for the lion, that I waited for him, that he did not come out, that I still waited for him, and that still he did not come out, and lay down again. I am not bound to do more; enchantments avaunt, and God uphold the right, the truth, and true chivalry! Close the door as I bade thee, while I make signals to the fugitives that have left us, that they may learn this exploit from my lips."

The keeper obeyed, and Don Quixote, fixing
on the point of his lance the cloth he had wiped
his face with after the deluge of curds, proceeded
to recall the others, who still continued to fly,
looking back at every step, all in a body, the gentleman bringing up the rear.   Sancho, however,
happening to observe the signal of the white
cloth, exclaimed, "May I die, if my master has
not overcome the wild beasts, for he is calling to
us."

They all stopped, and perceived that it was
Don Quixote who was making signals, and shaking off their fears to some extent, they approached
slowly until they were near enough to hear distinctly Don Quixote's voice calling to them.
They returned at length to the cart, and as they
came up, Don Quixote said to the carter, "Put
your mules to once more, brother, and continue
your journey; and do thou, Sancho, give him
two gold crowns for himself and the keeper, to
compensate for the delay they have incurred
through me."

"That will I give with all my heart," said
Sancho; "but what has become of the lions?
Are they dead or alive?"

The keeper, then, in full detail, and bit by bit,
described the end of the contest, exalting to the
best of his power and ability the valor of Don
Quixote, at the sight of whom the lion quailed,
and would not and dared not come out of the
cage, although he had held the door open ever so
long; and showing how, in consequence of his
having represented to the knight that it was

tempting God to provoke the lion in order to force him out, which he wished to have done, he very reluctantly, and altogether against his will, had allowed the door to be closed.

"What dost thou think of this, Sancho?" said Don Quixote. "Are there any enchantments that can prevail against true valor? The enchanters may be able to rob me of good fortune, but of fortitude and courage they can not."

Sancho paid the crowns, the carter put to, the keeper kissed Don Quixote's hands for the bounty bestowed upon him, and promised to give an account of the valiant exploit to the King himself, as soon as he saw him at court.

"Then," said Don Quixote, "if his Majesty should happen to ask who performed it, you must say The Knight of the Lions; for it is my desire that into this the name I have hitherto borne of Knight of the Rueful Countenance be from this time forward changed, altered, transformed, and turned."

THE ADVENTURE OF THE ENCHANTED BARK

UPON proceeding with their journey, they discovered a small boat, without oars or any other gear, that lay at the water's edge tied to the stem of a tree growing on the bank. Don Quixote looked all round, and seeing nobody, at once, without more ado, dismounted from Rocinante and bade Sancho get down from Dapple

and tie both beasts securely to the trunk of a
poplar or willow that stood there. Sancho asked
him the reason of this sudden dismounting and
tying. Don Quixote made answer, "Thou must
know, Sancho, that this bark here is plainly, and
without the possibility of any alternative, calling
and inviting me to enter it, and in it go to give aid
to some knight or other person of distinction in
need of it, who is no doubt in some sore strait;
for this is the way of the books of chivalry and of
the enchanters who figure and speak in them.
When a knight is involved in some difficulty from
which he cannot be delivered save by the hand
of another knight, though they may be at a distance of two or three thousand leagues or more
one from the other, they either take him up on a
cloud, or they provide a bark for him to get into,
and in less than the twinkling of an eye they carry
him where they will and where his help is required; and so, Sancho, this bark is placed here
for the same purpose; this is as true as that it is
now day, and ere this one passes tie Dapple and
Rocinante together, and then in God's hand be
it to guide us; for I would not hold back from
embarking, though bare-footed friars were to
beg me."

"As that's the case," said Sancho, "and your
worship chooses to give in to these—I don't
know if I may call them absurdities—at every
turn, there's nothing for it but to obey and bow
the head, bearing in mind the problem, 'Do as
thy master bids thee, and sit down to table with
him;' but for all that, for the sake of easing my

conscience, I want to warn your worship that it is my opinion this bark is no enchanted one, but belongs to some of the fishermen of the river, for they catch the best shad in the world here."

As Sancho said this, he tied the beasts, leaving them to the care and protection of the enchanters with sorrow enough in his heart. Don Quixote bade him not be uneasy about deserting the animals, for he who would carry themselves over such longinquous roads and regions would take care to feed them.

"I don't understand that logiquous," said Sancho, "nor have I ever heard the word all the days of my life."

"Longinquous," replied Don Quixote, "means far off; but it is no wonder thou dost not understand it, for thou art not bound to know Latin, like some who pretend to know it and don't."

"Now they are tied," said Sancho; "what are we to do next?"

"What?" said Don Quixote, "cross ourselves and weigh anchor; I mean, embark and cut the moorings by which the bark is held;" and jumping into it, followed by Sancho, he cut the rope, and the bark began to drift away slowly from the bank. But when Sancho saw himself somewhere about two yards out in the river, he began to tremble and give himself up for lost; but nothing distressed him more than hearing Dapple bray and seeing Rocinante struggling to get loose, and said he to his master, "Dapple is braying in grief at our leaving him, and Rocinante is trying to escape and plunge in after us. O dear friends,

THE ENCHANTED BARK

peace be with you, and may this madness that is taking us away from you, turned into sober sense, bring us back to you." And with this he fell weeping so bitterly, that Don Quixote said to him, sharply and angrily, "What art thou afraid of, cowardly creature? What art thou weeping at, heart of butter-paste? Who pursues or molests thee, thou soul of a tame mouse? What dost thou want, unsatisfied in the very heart of abundance? Art thou, perchance, tramping barefoot over the mountains, instead of being seated on a bench like an archduke on the tranquil stream of this pleasant river, from which in a short space we shall come out upon the broad sea? But we must have already emerged and gone seven hundred or eight hundred leagues; and if I had here an astrolabe to take the altitude of the pole, I could tell thee how many we have travelled, though either I know little, or we have already crossed or shall shortly cross the equinoctial line which parts the two opposite poles midway."

"And when we come to that lane your worship speaks of," said Sancho, "how far shall we have gone?"

"Very far," said Don Quixote, "for of the three hundred and sixty degrees that this terraqueous globe contains, as computed by Ptolemy, the greatest cosmographer known, we shall have travelled one-half when we come to the line I spoke of."

"By God," said Sancho, "your worship gives me a nice authority for what you say, putrid Dolly something transmogrified, or whatever it is."

Don Quixote laughed at the interpretation Sancho put upon "computed," and the name of the cosmographer Ptolemy.

* * * * * * *

"I can see with my own eyes," said Sancho, "that we have not moved five yards away from the bank, or shifted two yards from where the animals stand, for there are Rocinante and Dapple in the very same place where we left them; and watching a point, as I do now, I swear by all that's good, we are not stirring or moving at the pace of an ant."

They now came in sight of some large water mills that stood in the middle of the river,[1] and the instant Don Quixote saw them he cried out to Sancho, "Seest thou there, my friend? there stands the city, castle, or fortress, where there is, no doubt, some knight in durance, or ill-used queen, or infanta, or princess, in aid of whom I am brought hither."

"What the devil city, fortress, or castle is your worship talking about, señor?" said Sancho; "don't you see that those are mills that stand in the river to grind corn?"

"Hold thy peace, Sancho," said Don Quixote; "though they look like mills they are not so; I have already told thee that enchantments transform things and change their proper shapes; I do not mean to say they really change them from one form into another, but that it seems as though they did, as experience proved in the transformation of Dulcinea, sole refuge of my hopes."

By this time, the boat, having reached the middle of the stream, began to move less slowly than hitherto. The millers belonging to the mills, when they saw the boat coming down the river, and on the point of being sucked in by the

---

1. In certain rivers of Spain, floating mills, moored in mid-stream, were common.

draught of the wheels, ran out in haste, several of them, with long poles to stop it, and being all mealy, with faces and garments covered with flour, they presented a sinister appearance. They raised loud shouts, crying, "Devils of men, where are you going to? Are you mad? Do you want to drown yourselves, or dash yourselves to pieces among these wheels?"

"Did I not tell thee, Sancho," said Don Quixote at this, "that we had reached the place where I am to show what the might of my arm can do? See what ruffians and villains come out against me; see what monsters oppose me; see what hideous countenances come to frighten us! You shall soon see, scoundrels!" And then standing up in the boat he began in a loud voice to hurl threats at the millers, exclaiming, "Ill-conditioned and worse-counselled rabble, restore to liberty and freedom the person ye hold in durance in this your fortress or prison, high or low or of whatever rank or quality he be, for I am Don Quixote of La Mancha, otherwise called the Knight of the Lions, for whom, by the disposition of Heaven above, it is reserved to give a happy issue to this adventure;" and so saying he drew his sword and began making passes in the air at the millers, who, hearing but not understanding all this nonsense, strove to stop the boat, which was now getting into the rushing channel of the wheels.

Sancho, in very real despair, fell upon his knees devoutly appealing to Heaven to deliver him from such imminent peril; which it did by

the activity and quickness of the millers, who,
pushing against the boat with their poles,
stopped it, not, however, without upsetting it
and throwing Don Quixote and Sancho into the
water; and lucky it was for Don Quixote that
he could swim like a goose, though the weight of
his armor carried him twice to the bottom; and
had it not been for the millers, who plunged in
and hoisted them both out, it would have been
Troy town with the pair of them. As soon as,
more drenched than thirsty, they were landed,
Sancho went down on his knees and with clasped
hands and eyes raised to heaven, prayed a long
and fervent prayer to God to deliver him evermore from the rash projects and attempts of his
master.

The surprised fishermen, the owners of the
boat, which the mill-wheels had knocked to pieces,
now came up, and seeing it smashed they proceeded to strip Sancho and to demand payment
for it from Don Quixote; but he with great
calmness, just as if nothing had happened to
him, told the millers and fishermen that he
would pay for the bark most cheerfully, on condition that they delivered up to him, free and
unhurt, the person or persons that were in
durance in that castle of theirs.

"What persons or what castle art thou talking
of, madman ?" said one of the millers; "art thou
for carrying off the people who come to grind
corn in these mills ?"

"That's enough," said Don Quixote to himself, "it would be preaching in the desert to

attempt by entreaties to induce this rabble to do any virtuous action. In this adventure two mighty enchanters must have encountered one another, and one frustrates what the other attempts; one provided a bark for me, and the other upset me; God help us, this world is all machinations and schemes at cross purposes one with the other. I can do no more." And then turning towards the mills he said aloud, "Friends, whoe'er ye be that are immured in that prison, forgive me that, to my misfortune and yours, I cannot deliver you from your misery; this adventure is doubtless reserved and destined for some other knight."

So saying he settled with the fishermen, and paid fifty reals for the boat, which Sancho handed to them very much against the grain, saying, "With a couple more bark businesses like this we shall have sunk our whole capital, which is none too large."

The fishermen and the millers stood staring in amazement at the two figures, so very different to all appearance from ordinary men, and were wholly unable to make out the drift of the observations and questions Don Quixote addressed to them; and coming to the conclusion that they were madmen, they left them and betook themselves, the millers to their mills, and the fishermen to their huts.

In low spirits and bad humor, Don Quixote and Sancho returned to their beasts, and to their life of beasts, and this was the end of the adventure of the enchanted bark.

THE ADVENTURE OF THE WOODEN HORSE

NOTE,—Don Quixote and Sancho his squire, having encountered in a forest a certain duke and his duchess, had been invited to pass some time in the ducal palace. The duke and his friends, bent on amusement, persuaded Don Quixote that a vile enchanter, angered at some ladies, had for punishment caused heavy beards to grow on their faces. They even showed him the ladies, impersonated, of course, by men; and they persuaded him that the beards would be removed if he, with his squire, would take a long ride on a famous wooden horse, Clavileño.

 AND now night came, and with it the appointed time for the arrival of the famous horse Clavileño, the non-appearance of which was already beginning to make Don Quixote uneasy, for it struck him that, as Malambruno[1] was so long about sending it, either he himself was not the knight for whom the adventure was reserved, or else Malambruno did not dare to meet him in single combat. But lo! suddenly there came into the garden four wildmen all clad in green ivy bearing on their shoulders a great wooden horse. They placed it on its feet on the ground, and one of the wild-

------

[1]. This was the wicked enchanter who had caused the beards to grow.

men said, "Let the knight who has heart for it mount this machine."

Here Sancho exclaimed, "I don't mount, for neither have I the heart nor am I a knight."

"And let the squire, if he has one," continued the wild-man, "take his seat on the croup, and let him trust the valiant Malambruno; for by no sword save his, nor by the malice of any other, shall he be assailed. It is but to turn this peg the horse has in his neck, and he will bear them through the air to where Malambruno awaits them; but lest the vast elevation of their course should make them giddy, their eyes must be covered until the horse neighs, which will be the sign of their having completed their journey."

With these words, leaving Clavileño behind them, they retired with easy dignity the way they came. As soon as the Distressed One[2] saw the horse, almost in tears she exclaimed to Don Quixote, "Valiant knight, the promise of Malambruno has proved trustworthy; the horse has come, our beards are growing, and by every hair in them we all of us implore thee to shave and shear us, as it is only mounting him with thy squire and making a happy beginning with your new journey."

"That I will, Señora Countess Trifaldi," said Don Quixote, "most gladly and with right good will, without stopping to take a cushion or put on my spurs, so as not to lose time, such is my desire to see you, señora, and all these duennas shaved clean."

---

2. This was the leader of the sorrowful bearded ladies.

"That I won't," said Sancho, "with good will
or bad will, or any way at all; and if this shaving
can't be done without my mounting on the croup,
my master had better look out for another squire
to go with him, and these ladies for some other
way of making their faces smooth; I'm no witch
to have a taste for travelling through the air.
What would my islanders say when they heard
their governor was going strolling about on the
winds ?"[3]

"Friend Sancho," said the duke at this, "the
island that I have promised you is not a moving
one, or one that will run away; it has roots so
deeply buried in the bowels of the earth that it
will be no easy matter to pluck it up or shift it
from where it is; you know as well as I do that
there is no sort of office of any importance that
is not obtained by a bribe of some kind, great or
small; well, then, that which I look to receive for
this government is that you go with your master
Don Quixote, and bring this memorable adventure to a conclusion; and whether you return
on Clavileño as quickly as his speed seems to
promise, or adverse fortune brings you back on
foot travelling as a pilgrim from hostel to hostel
and from inn to inn, you will always find your
island on your return where you left it, and your
islanders with the same eagerness they have
always had to receive you as their governor, and
my good will will remain the same; doubt not
the truth of this, Señor Sancho, for that would

3. The duke had promised to bestow on Sancho the government
of an island.

be grievously wronging my disposition to serve you."

"Say no more, señor," said Sancho; "I am a poor squire and not equal to carrying so much courtesy; let my master mount; bandage my eyes and commit me to God's care, and tell me if I may commend myself to our Lord or call upon the angels to protect me when we go towering up there."

To this the Trifaldi[4] made answer, "Sancho, you may freely commend yourself to God or whom you will; for Malambruno, though an enchanter, is a Christian, and works his enchantments with great circumspection, taking very good care not to fall out with any one."

"Well then," said Sancho, "God and the most holy Trinity give me help!"

"Cover thine eyes, Sancho," said Don Quixote, "and mount; for one who sends for us from lands so far distant cannot mean to deceive us for the sake of the paltry glory to be derived from deceiving persons who trust in him; though all should turn out the contrary of what I hope, no malice will be able to dim the glory of having undertaken this exploit."

"Let us be off, señor," said Sancho, "for I have taken the beards and tears of the ladies deeply to heart, and I shan't eat a bite to relish it until I have seen them restored to their former smoothness. Mount, your worship, and blind-fold yourself, for if I am to go on the croup, it is plain the rider in the saddle must mount first."

---

4. The name of the "Distressed One."

"That is true," said Don Quixote, and, taking a handkerchief out of his pocket, he begged the Distressed One to bandage his eyes very carefully; but after having them bandaged he uncovered them again, saying, "If my memory does not deceive me, I have read in Virgil of the Palladium of Troy, a wooden horse the Greeks offered to the goddess Pallas, which was big with armed knights, who were afterwards the destruction of Troy; so it would be as well to see, first of all, what Clavileño has in his stomach."

"There is no occasion," said the Distressed One; "I will be bail for him, and I know that Malambruno has nothing tricky or treacherous about him; you may mount without any fear, Señor Don Quixote; on my head be it if any harm befalls you."

Don Quixote thought that to say anything further with regard to his safety would be putting his courage in an unfavorable light; and so, without more words, he mounted Clavileño, and tried the peg, which turned easily; and as he had no stirrups and his legs hung down, he looked like nothing so much as a figure in some Roman triumph painted or embroidered on a Flemish tapestry.

Much against the grain, and very slowly, Sancho proceeded to mount, and, after settling himself as well as he could on the croup, found it rather hard and not at all soft, and asked the duke if it would be possible to oblige him with a pad of some kind, or a cushion; even if it were off the couch of his lady the duchess, or the bed of one of the pages; as the haunches of that horse were more like marble than wood. On this the Trifaldi observed that Clavileño would not bear any kind of harness or trappings, and that his best plan would be to sit sideways like a woman, as in that way he would not feel the hardness so much.

Sancho did so, and bidding them farewell, allowed his eyes to be bandaged, but immediately

THEY WERE BLINDFOLDED

afterwards uncovered them again, and looking tenderly and tearfully on those in the garden, bade them help him in his present strait with plenty of Paternosters and Ave Marias, that God might provide some one to say as many for them, whenever they found themselves in a similar emergency.

At this Don Quixote exclaimed, "Art thou on the gallows, thief, or at thy last moment, to use pitiful entreaties of that sort? Cover thine eyes,

cover thine eyes, abject animal, and let not thy
fear escape thy lips, at least, in my presence."

"Let them blindfold me," said Sancho; "as
you won't let me commend myself or be com-
mended to God, is it any wonder if I am afraid
there is a region of devils about here that will
carry us off?"

They were then blindfolded, and Don Quixote,
finding himself settled to his satisfaction, felt for
the peg, and the instant he placed his fingers on
it, all the duennas and all who stood by lifted up
their voices exclaiming, "God guide thee, valiant
knight! God be with thee, intrepid squire!
Now, now ye go cleaving the air more swiftly
than an arrow! Now ye begin to amaze and
astonish all who are gazing at you from the
earth! Take care not to wobble about, valiant
Sancho! Mind thou fall not, for thy fall will be
worse than that rash youth's who tried to steer
the chariot of his father the Sun!"[5]

As Sancho heard the voices, clinging tightly
to his master and winding his arms round him,
he said, "Señor, how do they make out we are
going up so high, if their voices reach us here and
they seem to be speaking quite close to us?"

"Don't mind that, Sancho," said Don Quixote; "for as affairs of this sort and flights like
this are out of the common course of things, you
can see and hear as much as you like a thousand
leagues off; but don't squeeze me so tight or thou
wilt upset me; and really I know not what thou
hast to be uneasy or frightened at, for I can

5. This was Phaethon, whose story is told in Volume II.

safely swear I never mounted a smoother-going steed all the days of my life; one would fancy we never stirred from one place. Banish fear, my friend, for indeed everything is going as it ought, and we have the wind astern."

"That's true," said Sancho, "for such a strong wind comes against me on this side, that it seems as if people were blowing on me with a thousand pair of bellows;" which was the case; they were puffing at him with a great pair of bellows; for the whole adventure was so well planned by the duke, the duchess, and their majordomo, that nothing was omitted to make it perfectly successful.

Don Quixote now, feeling the blast, said, "Beyond a doubt, Sancho, we must have already reached the second region of the air, where the hail and snow are generated; the thunder, the lightning, and the thunderbolts are engendered in the third region, and if we go on ascending at this rate, we shall shortly plunge into the region of fire, and I know not how to regulate this peg, so as not to mount up where we shall be burned."

And now they began to warm their faces, from a distance, with tow that could be easily set on fire and extinguished again, fixed on the end of a cane. On feeling the heat Sancho said, "May I die if we are not already in that fire place, or very near it, for a good part of my beard has been singed, and I have a mind, señor, to uncover and see whereabouts we are."

"Do nothing of the kind," said Don Quixote; "remember the true story of the licentiate

Torralva that the devils carried flying through
the air riding on a stick with his eyes shut; who
in twelve hours reached Rome and dismounted
at Torre di Nona, which is a street of the city,
and saw the whole sack and storming and the
death of Bourbon, and was back in Madrid the
next morning, where he gave an account of all
he had seen; and he said moreover that as he was
going through the air, the devil bade him open
his eyes, and he did so, and saw himself so near
the body of the moon, so it seemed to him, that
he could have laid hold of it with his hand, and
that he did not dare to look at the earth lest he
should be seized with giddiness.   So that, Sancho, it will not do for us to uncover ourselves, for
he who has us in charge will be responsible for us;
and perhaps we are gaining an altitude and
mounting up to enable us to descend at one swoop
on the Kingdom of Kandy, as the saker or
falcon does on the heron, so as to seize it however
high it may soar; and though it seems to us not
half an hour since we left the garden, believe me
we must have travelled a great distance."

The duke, the duchess, and all in the garden
were listening to the conversation of the two
heroes, and were beyond measure amused by it;
and now, desirous of putting a finishing touch
to this rare and well-contrived adventure, they
applied a light to Clavileño's tail with some tow,
and the horse, being full of squibs and crackers,
immediately blew up with a prodigious noise,
and brought Don Quixote and Sancho Panza to
the ground half singed.   By this time the bearded

band of duennas, the Trifaldi and all, had
vanished from the garden, and those that remained lay stretched on the ground as if in a
swoon. Don Quixote and Sancho got up rather
shaken, and, looking about them, were filled with
amazement at finding themselves in the same
garden from which they had started, and seeing
such a number of people stretched on the ground;
and their astonishment was increased when at
one side of the garden they perceived a tall lance
planted in the ground, and hanging from it by
two cords of green silk a smooth, white parchment on which there was the following inscription
in large gold letters: "The illustrious Don
Quixote of La Mancha has, by merely attempting it, finished and concluded the adventure of
the Countess Trifaldi, otherwise called the
Distressed Duenna; Malambruno is now satisfied
on every point, the chins of the duennas are now
smooth and clean, and when the squirely flagella-
tion shall have been completed, the white dove
shall find herself delivered from the pestiferous
hawks that persecute her,[6] and in the arms of her
beloved mate; for such is the decree of the sage
Merlin, arch-enchanter of enchanters."

As soon as Don Quixote had read the inscription on the parchment he perceived clearly that it
referred to the disenchantment of Dulcinea, and
returning hearty thanks to Heaven that he had

6. Don Quixote and Sancho Panza had been persuaded that Dulcinea del Toboso, Don Quixote's lady, was under enchantment, from
which she could not be released until Sancho had given himself three
thousand three hundred lashes.

with so little danger achieved so grand an
exploit as to restore to their former complexion
the countenances of those venerable duennas,
now no longer visible, he advanced towards the
duke and duchess, who had not yet come to
themselves, and taking the duke by the hand he
said, "Be of good cheer, worthy sir, be of good
cheer; it's nothing at all; the adventure is now
over and without any harm done, as the inscription fixed on this post shows plainly."

The duke came to himself slowly and like one
recovering consciousness after a heavy sleep,
and the duchess and all who had fallen prostrate
about the garden did the same, with such demon-
strations of wonder and amazement that they
would have almost persuaded one that what they
pretended so adroitly in jest had happened to
them in reality. The duke read the placard
with half-shut eyes, and then ran to embrace
Don Quixote with open arms, declaring him to
be the best knight that had ever been seen in any
age. Sancho kept looking about for the Distressed One, to see what her face was like without
the beard, and if she was as fair as her elegant
person promised; but they told him that, the
instant Clavileño descended flaming through
the air and came to the ground, the whole band
of duennas with the Trifaldi vanished, and that
they were already shaved and without a stump
left.

The duchess asked Sancho how he had fared
on that long journey, to which Sancho replied,
"I felt, señora, that we were flying through the

region of fire, as my master told me, and I wanted
to uncover my eyes for a bit; but my master, when
I asked leave to uncover myself, would not let
me; but as I have a little bit of curiosity about
me, and a desire to know what is forbidden and
kept from me, quietly and without any one
seeing me I drew aside the handkerchief covering
my eyes ever so little, close to my nose, and from
underneath looked towards the earth, and it
seemed to me that it was altogether no bigger
than a grain of mustard seed, and that the men
walking on it were little bigger than hazel nuts;
so you may see how high we must have got to
them."

To this the duchess said, "Sancho, my friend,
mind what you are saying; it seems you could
not have seen the earth, but only the men walking
on it; it is plain that if the earth looked to you
like a grain of mustard seed, and each man like
a hazel nut, one man alone would have covered
the whole earth."

"That is true," said Sancho, "but for all that
I got a glimpse of a bit of one side of it, and saw
it all."

"Take care, Sancho," said the duchess; "with
a bit of one side one does not see the whole of
what one looks at."

"I don't understand that way of looking at
things," said Sancho; "I only know that your
ladyship will do well to bear in mind that as we
were flying by enchantment so I might have
seen the whole earth and all the men by enchantment, whatever way I looked; and if you won't

believe this, no more will you believe that, un-
covering myself nearly to the eyebrows, I saw
myself so close to the sky that there was not a
palm and a half between me and it; and by
everything that I can swear by, señora, it is
mighty great! And it so happened we came by
where the seven she-goats are,[7] and by God and
upon my soul, as in my youth I was a goatherd
in my own country, as soon as I saw them I felt
a longing to be among them for a little, and if I
had not given way to it I think I'd have burst.
So I come and take, and what do I do? without
saying anything to anybody, not even to my
master, softly and quietly I got down from
Clavileño and amused myself with the goats—
which are like violets, like flowers—for nigh
three-quarters of an hour; and Clavileño never
stirred or moved from one spot."

"And while the good Sancho was amusing
himself with the goats," said the duke, "how
did Señor Don Quixote amuse himself?"

To which Don Quixote replied, "As all these
things and such like occurrences are out of the
ordinary course of nature, it is no wonder that
Sancho says what he does; for my own part I can
only say that I did not uncover my eyes either
above or below, nor did I see sky or earth or sea
or shore. It is true I felt that I was passing
through the region of the air, and even that I
touched that of fire; but that we passed farther
I cannot believe; for the region of fire being between the heaven of the moon and the last region

7. The "seven she-goats" were the Pleiades.

of the air, we could not have reached that heaven where the seven she-goats Sancho speaks of are without being burned; and as we were not burned, either Sancho is lying or Sancho is dreaming."

"I am neither lying nor dreaming," said Sancho; "only ask me the tokens of those same goats, and you'll see by that whether I'm telling the truth or not."

"Tell us them then, Sancho," said the duchess.

"Two of them," said Sancho, "are green, two blood-red, two blue, and one a mixture of all colors."

"An odd sort of goat, that," said the duke; "in this earthly region of ours we have no such colors; I mean goats of such colors."

"That's very plain," said Sancho; "of course there must be a difference between the goats of heaven and the goats of the earth."

"Tell me, Sancho," said the duke, "did you see any he-goat among those she-goats?"

"No, señor," said Sancho; "but I have heard say that none ever passed the horns of the moon."

They did not care to ask him anything more about his journey, for they saw he was in the vein to go rambling all over the heavens giving an account of everything that went on there, without having ever stirred from the garden. Such, in short, was the end of the adventure of the Distressed Duenna, which gave the duke and duchess laughing matter not only for the time being, but for all their lives, and Sancho something to talk about for ages, if he lived so long.

THE STORY OF THE LASHES

NOTE,—It had been prophesied, by a pretended enchanter, that the Lady Dulcinea del
Toboso could be freed from the enchantment
under which a wicked magician had placed
her, if Sancho would of his own free will give
himself three thousand three hundred lashes.

———————

SANCHO went along anything but
cheerful, and finally he said to his
master, "Surely, señor, I'm the most
unlucky doctor in the world; there's
many a physician that, after killing
the sick man he had to cure, requires
to be paid for his work, though it is
only signing a bit of a list of medicines, that the
apothecary and not he makes up, and, there, his
labor is over; but with me, though to cure somebody else costs me drops of blood, smacks,
pinches, pin-proddings, and whippings, nobody
gives me a farthing."

"Thou art right, Sancho my friend," said Don
Quixote, "and I can say for myself that if thou
wouldst have payment for the lashes on account
of the disenchantment of Dulcinea, I would have
given it to thee freely ere this. I am not sure,
however, whether payment will comport with
the cure, and I would not have the reward
interfere with the medicine. Still, I think
there will be nothing lost by trying it; consider how much thou wouldst have, Sancho,
and whip thyself at once, and pay thyself

down with thine own hand, as thou hast money of mine."

At this proposal Sancho opened his eyes and his ears a palm's breadth wide, and in his heart very readily acquiesced in whipping himself, and said he to his master, "Very well then, señor, I'll hold myself in readiness to gratify your worship's wishes if I'm to profit by it; for the love of my wife and children forces me to seem grasping. Let your worship say how much you will pay me for each lash I give myself."

"If, Sancho," replied Don Quixote, "I were to requite thee as the importance and nature of the cure deserves, the treasures of Venice, the mines of Potosi, would be insufficient to pay thee. See what thou hast of mine, and put a price on each lash."

"Of them," said Sancho, "there are three thousand three hundred and odd; of these I have given myself five, the rest remain; let the five go for the odd ones, and let us take the three thousand three hundred, which at a quarter real apiece (for I will not take less though the whole world should bid me) make three thousand three hundred quarter reals; the three thousand are one thousand five hundred half reals, which make seven hundred and fifty reals; and the three hundred make a hundred and fifty half reals, which come to seventy-five reals, which added to the seven hundred and fifty make eight hundred and twenty-five reals in all. These I will stop out of what I have belonging to your worship, and I'll return home rich and content, though well whipped."

"O blessed Sancho! O dear Sancho!" said Don Quixote; "how we shall be bound to serve thee, Dulcinea and I, all the days of our lives that Heaven may grant us! If she returns to her lost shape (and it cannot be but that she will) her misfortune will have been good fortune, and my defeat a most happy triumph. But look here, Sancho; when wilt thou begin the scourging? For if thou wilt make short work of it, I will give thee a hundred reals over and above."

"When?" said Sancho; "this night without fail. Let your worship order it so that we pass it out of doors and in the open air, and I'll scarify myself."

Night, longed for by Don Quixote with the greatest anxiety in the world, came at last, though it seemed to him that the wheels of Apollo's car had broken down, and that the day was drawing itself out longer than usual, just as is the case with lovers, who never make the reckoning of their desires agree with time. They made their way at length in among some pleasant trees that stood a little distance from the road, and there vacating Rocinante's saddle and Dapple's pack-saddle, they stretched themselves on the green grass and made their supper off Sancho's stores, and he, making a powerful and flexible whip out of Dapple's halter and head-stall, retreated about twenty paces from his master among some beech trees. Don Quixote, seeing him march off with such resolution and spirit,

said to him, "Take care, my friend, not to cut
thyself to pieces; allow the lashes to wait for one
another, and do not be in so great a hurry as to
run thyself out of breath midway; I mean, do not
lay on so strenuously as to make thy life fail thee
before thou hast reached the desired number;
and that thou mayest not lose by a card too much
or too little, I will station myself apart and count

SANCHO PREPARES TO LASH HIMSELF

on my rosary here the lashes thou givest thyself.
May Heaven help thee as thy good intention
deserves."

" 'Pledges don't distress a good paymaster,' "
said Sancho; "I mean to lay on in such a way
as without killing myself to hurt myself, for in
that, no doubt, lies the essence of this miracle."

He then stripped himself from the waist
upwards, and snatching up the rope he began to
lay on and Don Quixote to count the lashes.   He

might have given himself six or eight when he
began to think the joke no trifle, and its price
very low; and holding his hand for a moment, he
told his master that he cried off on the score of a
blind bargain, for each of those lashes ought to
be paid for at the rate of half a real instead of a
quarter.

"Go on, Sancho my friend, and be not disheartened," said Don Quixote; "for I double
the stakes as to price."

"In that case," said Sancho, "in God's hand
be it, and let it rain lashes." But the rogue no
longer laid them on his shoulders, but laid on to
the trees, with such groans every now and then,
that one would have thought at each of them his
soul was being plucked up by the roots. Don
Quixote, touched to the heart, and fearing he
might make an end of himself, and that through
Sancho's imprudence he might miss his own
object, said to him, "As thou livest, my friend,
let the matter rest where it is, for the remedy
seems to me a very rough one, and it will be
well to have patience; Rome was not built in a
day. If I have not reckoned wrong thou hast
given thyself over a thousand lashes; that is
enough for the present; for the ass, to put it in
homely phrase, bears the load, but not the over-
load."

"No, no, señor," replied Sancho; "it shall
never be said of me, 'The money paid, the arms
broken;' go back a little further, your worship,
and let me give myself at any rate a thousand
lashes more; for in a couple of bouts like this we

shall have finished off the lot, and there will be even cloth to spare."

"As thou art in such a willing mood," said Don Quixote, "may heaven aid thee; lay on and I'll retire."

Sancho returned to his task with so much resolution that he soon had the bark stripped off several trees, such was the severity with which he whipped himself; and one time, raising his voice, and giving a beech a tremendous lash, he cried out, "Here dies Samson, and all with him!"

At the sound of his piteous cry and of the stroke of the cruel lash, Don Quixote ran to him at once, and seizing the twisted halter that served him for a lash, said to him, "Heaven forbid, Sancho my friend, that to please me thou shouldst lose thy life, which is needed for the support of thy wife and children; let Dulcinea wait for a better opportunity, and I will content myself with a hope soon to be realized, and have patience until thou hast gained fresh strength so as to finish off this business to the satisfaction of everybody."

"As your worship will have it so, señor," said Sancho, "so be it; but throw your cloak over my shoulders, for I'm sweating and I don't want to take cold; it's a risk that novice disciplinants run."

Don Quixote obeyed, and stripping himself covered Sancho, who slept until the sun woke him; they then resumed their journey, which for the time being they brought to an end at a village that lay three leagues farther on.

RINGROSE AND HIS BUCCANEERS[1]

UST two days after we took possession of the town of Santa Maria, we departed thence, on Saturday, April 17th, 1680. We all embarked in thirty-five canoes which we had taken while lying at anchor at the front of the town. Thus we sailed, or rather rowed, down the river in quest of the South Sea upon which Panama is seated. Our prisoners, the Spaniards, begged very earnestly that they might be permitted to go with us and not be left to the mercy of the Indians, who would show them no favor and whose cruelty they so much feared, but we had such difficulty in finding boats for ourselves that we could assist them little. However, they found soon after either logs or old canoes, so that they were able to come along with us.

---

1. This selection is taken from *The Dangerous Voyage and Bold Attempts of Captain Bartholomew Sharp and Others*, an account written in 1685 by Basil Ringrose, one of the pirates who sailed with Captain Sharp.

The expedition was organized with a general design to pillage and plunder on the Isthmus of Darien and the continent of South America. At the original rendezvous there were seven ships containing four hundred and seventy-seven men under the command of experienced pirate captains. The natural leaders were Captains Coxon, Sawkins and Sharp. At first the expedition met with comparatively little opposition, and they captured the town of Santa Maria, but the plunder was so small here that they were dissatisfied with what they were doing and decided again to take and plunder Panama. It is at this point that we take up the narrative of Ringrose.

Where the account appears in the first person, it is practically as it came from the pen of Ringrose, though omissions have been made and occasionally the phraseology has been changed.

It was my misfortune to have a canoe which was very heavy and consequently sluggish. Because of this we were left behind the rest a little way, there being only four men beside myself in the boat. As the tide fell it left several shoals of sand naked, and hence we, not knowing the location of the channel amongst such a variety of streams, steered for over two miles into a shoal where we were forced to lie by until high water came. As soon as the tide began to turn, we rowed away, but in spite of all our endeavors we could neither find nor overtake our companions. At ten o'clock, when the tide became low, we stuck an oar in the sands and by turns slept in our canoe, where we were pierced to the skin by the showers that fell in the night.

The next morning, as soon as the day had come, we rowed away down the river in pursuit of our people, and after going about two leagues we were so fortunate as to overtake them at an Indian landing place, where they had been taking in water. They told us that we would not find water again for six days, and that we must without fail fill our jars. Although we made what haste we could, by the time our jars were filled our friends had all departed and were already out of sight. Such is the nature of the pirates; they care not in the least whom they lose or leave behind.

We rowed after them as fast as we possibly could, but all in vain, for here in the mouth of the river the islands were so numerous that it was very easy for us to lose them a second time.

After much trouble and toil we did at last find
the mouth of the river, but here the tide was again
coming in, so that though we were within a
stone's throw from the mouth of the river we
could not go through it, but were forced to put
ashore and wait for better water. Accordingly
we hauled our canoe close by the bushes and
fastened it to a tree which the tide had almost
covered.

As soon as the tide began to turn, we rowed
away again, crossing the Gulf of Miguel. Here
we had a very hard time fighting the waves, which
dashed against our canoe and might easily have
filled and overwhelmed it, for the boat was nearly
twenty feet long and not over one and a half
broad where it was widest. At dark we landed
on an island where we had the most sorrowful
resting place I ever experienced in my whole
life. It rained impetuously all night long, in so
much that we were wet from head to foot and
had not one dry thread about us; and so violent
was the rain that we could not keep any fire
going to warm or dry ourselves. Not one minute's sleep did we get during the whole night,
and our plight was indeed an awful one, remote
from our companions and wholly destitute of all
human comfort. As morning broke, our plight
was little relieved, for a vast sea surrounded us on
one side, and on the other we could see nothing
but high mountains and rocks. Our boat was
but an eggshell, and we had few clothes to defend
us from the weather. In fact, not one of us
at that time had a shoe to his foot.

WE MANAGED TO GET TO SHORE

Wet and cold as we were, however, we put forth to sea and rowed away, passing several islands. In the open sea the smallness of our vessel put us again in deadly peril, and it always required one man and sometimes two to bail out the water that came over the sides of the boat. When we had struggled for some time with these difficulties, and when we were near one of the smaller islands, a huge wave overturned our boat and we were all forced to swim for our lives, but did manage to get to shore, where soon our

canoe was thrown after us. All our bread and
fresh water were spoiled, but as our guns were
lashed to the boat and were kept in waxed cases,
we lost none of them. Our first business was
to take them out and clean them.

Scarcely had this been done when we saw
another boat suffering the same misfortune at
a little distance from us. The persons thus cast
ashore proved to be six Spaniards from the
garrison at Santa Maria who had followed us to
escape the Indians. Presently they joined us,
and we built a fire, broiled our meat on the coals,
and all ate amicably together. We were suffering terribly for water, as we had none to drink
and knew not where to get any. Fortunately
our canoe was thrown on edge and very little
injured, but the one on which the Spaniards
came split itself against the rocks, being old and
slender, and was broken into a hundred pieces.

My company was now much discouraged and
wished to return, but after much persuasion
I induced them to go forward at least one day
longer, saying I would then be willing to do whatever they saw fit. About the time they concluded
to follow me, our watchman espied an Indian,
who as soon as he knew he had been seen ran
hastily to the woods. Immediately I sent two
of my companions after him. Finding he was
one of our friendly Indians they followed him
along the shore to where seven more of his companions with a great canoe were resting on the
seashore. By means of signs I asked him what
had become of my companions, and the Indians

assured us that if we would take their boat
instead of our own, we would overtake our
friends before morning.

We were rejoicing over this news when the
Indians noticed that six of the men of our company did not seem to be of the same language
and kind as ourselves. We told them they were
Wankers, which is the name the Indians commonly give to the Spaniards. Their next question was "May we kill those Spaniards?" I
answered them, "By no means; I will not consent to have it done." To this the Indians
seemed to consent, but after a little while, when
my back was turned, some of my company, thinking to oblige the Indians, beckoned to them to
kill the Spaniards. Perceiving their danger,
the Spaniards made a great outcry, which I
heard, and I turned around in time to save
their lives. Although I was able to accomplish
this, I could not prevent them, however, from
taking one of the Spaniards as a slave. To the
others, however, I gave the canoe in which I
came and bade them to get away as speedily as
possible in order to save their lives from the
Indians.

Then joining company with the Indians we
entered a very large canoe which was able to
carry at least twenty men more easily than our
canoe could carry five. Moreover the Indians
had also fitted a good sail to the canoe, so that,
having a fresh breeze, we set sail and moved
rapidly away, to the infinite joy and comfort
of our hearts. In one place we ran into a heavy

sea which was caused by a strong current and the
heavy winds, and many times our boat was filled
with spray. Again at night it rained heavily
for several hours and was very dark.

About nine o'clock we discovered two fires
on the shore of the mainland. The Indians
began to shout and to cry out joyously that these
fires were made by their companions. Accordingly we made for the shore as fast as we could
drive, but as soon as we had reached it about
sixty Spaniards armed with clubs and other
arms rushed out into the breakers, laid hold of
our canoe on both sides and pulled it out of the
water. Thus were we all taken and made prisoners. I laid hold of my gun, thinking to defend
myself, but it was all in vain, for four or five of
them stopped and overpowered me. The Indians leaped overboard and got away very nimbly
into the woods, though my companions were too
much amazed to make any attempt to escape.

Our captors could speak neither French nor
English, but I was able to talk, in Latin, with
one of them who seemed more intelligent than
the rest, and from him I learned that these were
Spaniards who had been put ashore by our other
boats for fear that some of them might escape
and warn Panama that we were on our way to
capture it. For this reason the Spaniards were
much rejoiced at taking us, and they designed
to treat us very severely for plundering their
town of Santa Maria.

But even while the Spaniard was talking
to me, there came in a poor wretch that I had

saved from the Indians. When he reported how
kindly I had treated him and the rest of his companions, the captain rose from his seat and embraced me, saying, "You Englishmen are very
friendly enemies and good people, but the Indians are rogues and a treacherous nation.
Come and sit by me and eat of the victuals
which your companions left us when they turned
from shore." For the kindness I had shown
their countrymen, the Spaniards agreed to give
us our lives and liberty, but it was only after long
persuasion that I could induce them to spare the
lives of the Indians. However, I accomplished
this and was bidden to take my canoe and go in
God's name, with the wish that we might be as
fortunate as we had been generous.

Having found the Indians, we took our departure soon after, although the Spaniards invited us to stay with them longer. All that night
it rained very hard and we found no place where
we could land. About ten o'clock the next
morning, however, after a night of rowing and
paddling, we espied a canoe coming toward us
at great speed. The men in it proved to be of
our old English company, who supposed us to be
Spaniards and were coming to attack us. They
had given me and my companions up for lost,
but now we were all mutually rejoiced, and were
soon reunited on the shore of a deep bay which
lay concealed behind a point of rocks.

On the morning of the second day after, that
is, on the twenty-third of April, the day sacred
to Saint George, our patron of England, we

came before sunrise within view of the city of
Panama, which makes a pleasant show to vessels
that are at sea. At that time there lay at anchor
near the Island of Perico, which is distant
about two leagues from Panama, five great ships
and three smaller men-of-war called *The Little
Fleet.* The latter, it appeared, had been suddenly manned with a design to fight us and prevent us from making any further attempts upon
the city or seacoast.

Accordingly, as soon as they spied us, they instantly weighed anchor and came directly to meet
us. Two of our boats were very heavy and could
not row as fast as the canoes, and accordingly
we were already far in advance. There were
five canoes in this company, and among them
only thirty-six men in a very unfit condition to
fight, being tired and worn with so much rowing. The enemy sailed toward us directly before
the wind, and we feared greatly lest they should
run us down. So we rowed straight up into the
"wind's eye" as the sailors say, and got close
to windward of them. While we were doing
this, other of our boats in which were thirty-
two more men overtook us, so that altogether
we were sixty-eight men engaged in the fight
that day.

In the three vessels of the Little Fleet that op-
posed us were altogether two hundred and seven-
ty-eight men, of whom more than two hundred
were native Spaniards, the rest being Indians
or Mulattoes. The commanders of these ships
had issued orders that no quarter was to be given

to any of the buccaneers. But such bloody commands as these seldom or never prosper.

The canoe of Captain Sawkins and that wherein I was were much to the leeward of the rest. The third of the Spanish ships came between us two and fired on me to the windward and on Captain Sawkins to the leeward, wounding with these broadsides four men in the Captain's canoe and one in mine. Nevertheless, he paid so dear for his passage between us that he was not very quick in coming about again and trying it a second time; for with our first volley we killed several of his men upon the decks. Thus we got to the windward of the enemy as our other canoes had already done.

At this moment the Admiral of the Little Fleet came up with us suddenly, scarcely giving us time to charge, and thinking to pass by us with as little damage as the first of his ships had received, or even less. But it fell out much worse for him, for we were so fortunate as to kill the man at the helm, so that his ship ran into the wind and her sails lay "a-back" as the mariners say. This gave us time to come up under the stern of his vessel, and firing continually into the vessel we killed as many as came to the helm, and cut in two his mainsail and brace.

At this time the third Spanish vessel was seen coming up to the aid of the Admiral's ship. Captain Sawkins left the latter to our four canoes and rowed away to meet the oncoming Spaniards. The dispute or fight between them was very hot, as they lay close together, and fought from one side of the deck to the other, both giving and receiving death as fast as they could charge. Meanwhile the first ship tacked about and came up to relieve the Admiral. We determined to prevent this design, and two of our canoes, Captain Springer's and my own, stood out to meet the new arrival, who made direct upon the Admiral, who stood upon the quarter-deck waving at him with a handkerchief what to do. But we met him in the middle of his way, and came so close to him that if he had not turned his course, we should have been on board him. As it was, we killed so many of his crew that the vessel had scarcely men enough left alive and unwounded to carry her off. Fortunately for them, the wind sprang up fresh, and they were able to sail away and save their lives.

Having put to flight the vessel which was to relieve the Admiral, we turned about and with a loud halloo joined our friends in the other boat, and came so close under the stern of the Admiral's ship that we wedged up the rudder and at the same time killed both the Admiral and the chief pilot. Seeing how disabled their ship was, and disheartened by the slaughter, for at least two-thirds of their men had been killed and many others wounded, they cried for quarter, which had several times been offered them, but had been always stoutly denied. So we took possession of the Admiral's ship and put on board all our wounded men, including Captain Harris, who had been shot through both his legs. As soon as this was done, we instantly sent some of our ships to go and aid Captain Sawkins, who had been fighting against the second Spanish ship.   Indeed, to give our enemies their due, no men in the world ever fought more bravely than these same Spaniards.

Coming up close under the Spaniard's side, we gave him a full volley of shot and expected to have a like return from him, but of a sudden we saw his men that were abaft the mast, blown up in the air, some of them falling into the deck and others into the sea.   This disaster was no sooner seen ·by their valiant Captain than he leapt overboard, and in spite of all our shot succeeded in rescuing some of his men, although he was much burned in both his hands himself. But as misfortune seldom comes alone, while he was rescuing these men to reinforce the ship and renew the fight, another jar of powder took fire and blew up several others upon the forecastle.

Under cover of the smoke from these explosions, Captain Sawkins led his men on board and took the ship.   Soon after I went on board myself, and indeed, such a miserable sight I never saw in my life.   For not one man was to be found but was either killed, desperately wounded or horribly burned with powder, in so much that their black skins were turned white in several places where the powder had torn it from their flesh and bones.

Having compassionated their misery, I afterwards went on board the Admiral's ship, and here what I saw did much astonish me, and would scarcely be believed by others than ourselves who saw it. There were found on this ship only twenty-five men alive, where before the fight there were four-score and six. And out of these twenty-five men, only eight were able to bear arms, all the rest being desperately wounded, and by their wounds totally unable to make any resistance or to defend themselves. Their blood ran down the decks in whole streams, and scarcely one place in the ship was free from blood.

Having once possessed ourselves of two vessels of the little fleet, Captain Sawkins asked the prisoners how many men there were on the largest ship that we could see lying in the harbor of Perico, and also how many were upon the smaller ships. Peralta, the heroic captain of the second vessel, tried to dissuade Sawkins from attacking the Spanish vessels at anchor, saying in the biggest one alone there were three hundred and fifty men, and that all the other vessels would be found too well provided for defense against the small number of the buccaneers. One of the Spaniards, however, who lay dying on the deck, told Captain Sawkins that there was not a single man on board any one of the great ships in the harbor, for they had all been drawn away to fight on the ships of the Little Fleet. Believing the dying man's story, we sailed into the harbor and went on board the ships, finding, as we had been told, not one person there. They had set on fire the biggest ship and made a hole in her hull, but we put out the flames and stopped the leak. All our wounded were then placed on this ship, which for a time became our hospital.

Having counted up our own loss and damages, we found eighteen of our men killed and twenty-two wounded.

The three captains against whom we fought were esteemed by the Spaniards as the bravest in the South Seas, nor was this reputation undeserved by them, as may easily be seen from the story of this bloody battle. We began the fight about a half hour after sunrise, and by noon had finished the battle. While Captain Peralta was our prisoner, he would often break out and say: "Surely you Englishmen are the valiantest in the whole world, and always design to fight in the open; while all other nations have invented all kinds of ways to barricade themselves and fight as close as possible;" and yet notwithstanding, we killed more of the enemy than they have of us.

The journal of Basil Ringrose is a very interesting document, and we should enjoy following it to the end if we had the space and if it were not for the fact that he devotes so much space to information that is valuable chiefly to a sailor. Accordingly it seems best to give a brief summary of his journal in our own words:

Captain Peter Harris, whom Ringrose calls "a brave and stout soldier and a valiant Englishman, born in the county of Kent," died of his wounds, and they buried him with the usual honors of war—a volley from all their guns.

The buccaneers captured the five ships that lay near the Island of Perico and divided the spoils among themselves. Within the next two or three days, however, dissensions arose among them, and Captain Coxon, taking with him a large number of men together with most of the Indian allies, deserted the expedition and returned. During this time Captain Sharp was absent, and after the departure of Coxon, Captain Sawkins was chosen to command. For some weeks the buccaneers remained in the Bay of Panama, capturing vessels that came toward that port, and ravaging the numerous settlements on the adjacent islands.

While they were at Taboga, the governor of Panama sent a message to Captain Sawkins inquiring why he came to this locality. Captain Sawkins replied, "We came to assist the Indian King of Darien, who is the true lord of Panama and all the country round about. Since we came so far, there seems to be no reason why we should not have some satisfaction. Accordingly, if you will send us five hundred pieces of eight for each man and a thousand for each commander and will promise no longer to annoy the Indians or deprive them of their liberty, we will go away peaceably: otherwise, we will stay here, get what we can and cause all the damage possible to you."

In answer to this, the governor inquired by messenger—"From whom do you have your commission and to whom shall I complain for the damages which you have already done?"

SAWKINS WAS KILLED AT THE HEAD OF HIS MEN

The reply of Captain Sawkins to this message was prompt and decisive, for he said, "All my company have not yet arrived, but as soon as they come, we will visit you at Panama and bring our commissions on the muzzles of our guns, at which time you may read them as plain as the flame of gunpowder can make them."

On the 22nd of May, Captains Sawkins and Sharp took with them about sixty men and attacked the town of Pueblo Nueva. The buccaneers found that the inhabitants of this town

were well prepared for the defense. They had
cut down great trees and laid them across the
narrow river which led to their town in such a
way as to prevent the ascent of any boats.
Sawkins and his followers landed at the mouth
of the river and made their way by land until
they reached some heavy breastworks which had
been thrown up by the Spaniards. With undaunted courage, Sawkins stormed the defenses,
and was killed at the head of his men. His
loss was a sad one to the pirates, because
they regarded him as their most valiant
leader, and because, next to Captain Sharp, he
was best beloved by them. In fact, his loss
meant the desertion of a number more of the
buccaneers, who left their companions and returned over land, as Captain Coxon and his
officers had done.

Thus all the adventurers who wished to remain in the South Seas and still further ravage
the coast of South America, elected Captain
Sharp commander-in-chief, and vowed themselves to be faithful to him in all things. A large
number, however, of the pirates deserted, preferring the dangers of land travel in rainy season
to continued adventure in the South Seas.

Basil Ringrose was among those who were
tired of the expedition and wished to return
home, but he finally decided to remain with Captain Sharp because of the great difficulties he
foresaw in returning by the shorter way.

It was the last day of May when the mutineers
departed, and it was on the sixth of June, a dark

and rainy day, that they set sail on the long and
adventurous voyage. Almost from the start
they met with most vexatious delays which gave
an opportunity for the Spanish on shore to send
ahead news of their coming. In consequence
of this, they were almost everywhere expected,
and most of the towns which were unable to defend themselves succeeded in concealing their
wealth, provisions and supplies so that the buccaneers were unable to seize treasures of any
great value. As a whole, the voyage was a disappointment, but from time to time the adventurers succeeded in taking sufficient food and
occasionally gold and silver in such quantities
that the voyage was somewhat profitable to those
who survived.

The journal of Ringrose is full of interesting
little details, which show how exciting the trip
must have been, and how great were the perils
and privations of its followers.

In one place we find them anchored for four
or five days, trying to dry their sails so that they
could be able to take them down and repair the
hull of their ship, yet all the time the rain fell in
such torrents that they were unable to work.
At another place he tells of killing a snake which
was fourteen inches in circumference and eleven
feet in length. On this part of the coast they
saw every day whales and grampuses, which
often came and dove under the ship, and although the men fired at them several times, the
bullets rebounded from their tough skins. At
this place, too, the best food consisted of Indian

conies, snakes, oysters, periwinkles, a few small
turtles and a variety of small fish.

Again, we find some of the most valuable of
the men dying from malignant fevers, and all
suffering from want of provisions. For a long
time they had nothing but flour and water, and
then again they were able to revel in small par-
ticles of meat, with a good supply of sugar which
they took from some of the mills along the coast.
Now and then they seized a flock of goats, and
then for days the feasting was continuous, while
the surplus flesh was salted and stored away for
future use.

On the 24th of August they discovered a vessel
some distance from them, and because of the
darkness, ran very close to it before they were
discovered. When they were within hail, they
called in Spanish to the ship and commanded it
to lower its sails. "Not we," replied the Spaniards; "we will soon make you lower your own."
The pirates immediately fired upon them, and
they responded at a lively rate from their own
guns. For half an hour or more the fight was
very brisk, and undoubtedly would have lasted
much longer had not the buccaneers been fortunate enough to kill the man at the helm, after
which no one of the Spaniards dared to take his
place, and the ship drifted aimlessly. About
the same time another lucky shot tore off the
mainsail, and seeing their helpless condition the
Spaniards begged for quarter and gave up their
ship. Afterwards they declared that they fought
the pirates only out of bravado, for they had

agreed on a wager before they left shore to do so
in case they met with Captain Sharp.   Although
the fight was short, the pirates themselves had
suffered considerable damage to their ship, and
several of their men were sadly wounded.

The captain of the captured vessel gave the
buccaneers a great deal of information as to what
had happened after they left Panama, and also
as to the preparations which were being made
to defend the towns against the adventurers, and
to capture the vessel if possible whenever it appeared.

At Tumbes they heard that this was the first
settlement made by the Spanish after Panama,
and that at the time of the settlement a priest
went ashore with a cross in his hand, while ten
thousand Indians gathered on the hillsides and
stood watching him.   As he landed, two lions
came out of the woods toward him, but when he
laid the cross gently over their backs, they fell
down and worshiped him; moreover, two tigers
following did the same thing.   The Indians seeing these wonderful things recognized the power
of the Christian religion and at once embraced it.

By the end of October they were near the Fort
of Hilo on the coast of Peru, far south of the
equator.   Here at night they anchored about
two miles from the village, while they sent four
canoes with fifty men in them to seize and plunder the town.   In the morning they discovered
by the flags which the men had put out, that the
town was in the hands of the English.   Accordingly, all the men that could be spared from the

ship landed and learned that the enemy had
been put to flight after a few volleys had been ex-
changed. In the town they secured great quantities of pitch and tar, besides oil, wine, flour and
several other kinds of provisions. Most of the
Spaniards had fled to the hills, and the pirates
were afraid that at any moment they might be
attacked. The second day about sixty of the
men were sent out with orders to search the valley and the country round about the town. The
whole region was found to be very pleasing,
thickly set with groves of figs, olives, oranges,
lemons and other fruits. About four miles up
the valley appeared a great sugar factory, where
sugar, oil and molasses were found in abundance.
The mill was deserted, and the pirates were unable to capture any of the inhabitants, though
from time to time the Spaniards were seen marching along the hilltops whence they tumbled down
great stones and fired at random among the
buccaneers.

At the sugar factory, under a flag of truce, the
Spaniards promised to deliver eighty beef cattle
at the port the next day by noon as a ransom for
the building. Captain Sharp accordingly sent
word that no violence was to be offered to those
who brought the beeves down to the ship.

The next morning the Spaniards, bearing a
flag of truce, came to Captain Sharp and told
him that sixteen of the cattle were already at the
port, and the rest would be there the next morning. Accordingly, the raiders began their retreat to the sea, expecting to reëmbark on the

ship. Ringrose thought that at least twenty
men should be left behind at the sugar house for
a lookout to keep watch of the Spaniards, but he
was overruled on this and all went on to the port,
where, however, no cattle were found, nor was
there evidence that any effort had been made to
bring them. The next morning Captain Sharp
went again to the hills and met the Spaniards,
who promised that the cattle would certainly be
there by night, and accordingly it was decided
to wait one day more. The next morning the
experience was repeated, but that day passed
without any of the beeves appearing, and on the
following morning the pirates marched up the
village and burned not only the sugar mill but
all of the buildings round about, breaking the
machinery and destroying all of the oil and other
provisions which they could not carry away.

This done, they returned to the port by a new
route over the mountains, and in doing so escaped an ambuscade which would inevitably
have destroyed them all. As it was, they reached
the shore only to find more than three hundred
cavalrymen charging upon them from the north.
As quickly as possible the buccaneers threw
themselves into a posture of defense and charged
to meet the advancing horsemen. The horsemen retreated as the pirates advanced, with the
intention of leading the latter away from the village and the rocks near the port. Detecting the
stratagem, the pirates returned to the port, and
a battle at long range commenced, which lasted
the entire day. Meanwhile the Spaniards had

been receiving continuous reinforcements, and
appeared in numbers on the hills on all sides, so
that the pirates, fearing they would be overpowered by force of numbers, resolved that night
to escape and sail away from the coast which had
brought them so much trouble. Nevertheless,
they had gathered a great quantity of provisions,
which were very acceptable under the circumstances.

Early in December the buccaneers had another
series of exciting experiences at the town of La
Serena. Here a force was landed and sent
toward the city, but it quickly discovered that the
inhabitants had been warned of the approach of
the pirates and were rallying to defend themselves, led by a troop of a hundred Spanish horse.
The advance guard of the buccaneers, however,
was able to rout the Spaniards and drive them
from the town. At a short distance away, however, the cavalry rallied, and appeared ready to
offer battle in a more favorable place, but the
pirates brought up their reinforcements, and
when they offered to attack the Spaniards, the
latter fled again. A third time they formed and
a third time retreated. This method of fighting
they continued until the English were drawn far
away from the town, which was evidently the
plan of the Spaniards, although they lost three
of their officers and several horses. The buccaneers, abandoning the chase, crossed the green
fields and waded the irrigating streams which
enclosed them, finding here and there a house,
but all destitute of both inhabitants and provi-

sions. The Spaniards had taken good care that
little should be left for the pirates. Near the
town they found fine fruit orchards and gardens,
and regaled themselves with strawberries, which
are described as being big as walnuts and very
delicious to the taste. In fact, everything about
the place pleased them, excepting the fact that
most of the valuables had been transported and
hidden. It appeared, too, that the Spaniards,
fearing a revolt among their Chilian slaves, had
killed nearly all of them. Nevertheless a few
were found who served as guides and showed the
pirates where much plate and many kinds of
valuable goods had been stored away.

The buccaneers spent that night in the village,
and the next morning the Spaniards came bearing a flag of truce and offered to treat with their
conquerors. The buccaneers finally agreed to
depart, providing a ransom of ninety-five thousand pieces of eight was paid. This was promised by the inhabitants, and it was agreed that
it should be paid the next day.

That night an earthquake shook the surrounding country and badly frightened the pirates,
who were sleeping in one of the largest churches.
Moreover, during the night the Spaniards turned
the mountain streams through the streets of the
town, apparently hoping to drive out the buccaneers, or at least to prevent the burning of the
town.

Until noon the next day the pirates waited for
the ransom, but when it did not appear they were
satisfied that the Spaniards had never intended

to pay it, and accordingly the buccaneers burned
the town and retreated to the coast. Here they
found that the Spaniards had tried to burn the
ship by rather an extraordinary stratagem. They
took the hide of a horse, blew it up till it floated
like a great bladder, and upon it put a man who
paddled himself under the stern of the ship.
Here he crammed oakum, brimstone and other
combustibles between the rudder and the stern-
post, and set the whole on fire. In a few moments the vessel was covered with smoke, and in
the confusion the Spaniard escaped. However,
his plot was not successful, for the pirates had
the good fortune to discover the cause of the fire
and put it out before any serious damage was
done.

Three weeks later, the pirates visited the island
of Juan Fernandez, where they spent several
days and where they celebrated their Christmas
holiday by firing three volleys of shot. They
found an abundance of goats on the island and
were able to replenish their larder. The water
supply was excellent, but at one time when Ringrose with nine of his companions in two canoes
had landed to fill their jars, a storm came up
which prevented them from returning to the
ship. The wind grew so violent that the ship
itself was forced to sail out into the open sea.
About noon, Ringrose and his companions tried
to follow the ship, but were driven back upon the
shore by a raging sea. Early in the evening
they tried a second time, and got some little distance from land, but the waves were so violent

that they were forced to throw overboard all their jars of water to lighten their boats. Even then they were unable to reach their ship, but went ashore in the darkness and hauled up their canoes. They were unable to rest where they landed because of the great numbers of noisy seals that troubled them exceedingly. Therefore they went higher up into the islands, kindled a fire and spent a wet, hungry and uncomfortable night. All about them were the nests and roosting places of a multitude of birds, one of which fell down into their fire and was killed. Early the next morning they put to sea again, and finally found their ship half a league from them at anchor in a bay which furnished them a better anchorage than any they had previously discovered. More days were spent in taking on water, chopping wood, catching fish and killing goats. Terrible storms struck them, and the death of one of their mates made the stay an unhappy one.

Here they were told the story of a man who was cast upon this island, the only one saved from a large ship, and who lived five years there before any one came to carry him off. This was probably Alexander Selkirk, from whose adventures on the island Defoe wrote his *Robinson Crusoe*. Ringrose tells us that he on a trip into the island one day found cut in the bark of a tree a cross with several letters beside it, and that on the same tree he cut his own name with a cross above it. On the twelfth of January, seeing three ships which appeared to be men-of-war sailing toward them, they hurriedly left the

RINGROSE CUT HIS NAME

island, abandoning there one of their Indian
allies because he could not be found in time.
Thus a second Man Friday was deposited upon
Robinson Crusoe's island.

While at the island, some of the buccaneers
mutinied, deposed Captain Sharp, and chose
Watling to be their commander. When they
left the island they went directly to the coast and
made a second attempt upon the town of Arica,
but they were beaten off with great loss of men,

among the killed being Captain Watling. After their return to the ship, Sharp was again chosen captain, and remained as such until the end of the voyage.

It seems that about the first of February Ringrose was taken sick, and that thereafter he was unable to keep a constant diary, so that our accounts of the remainder of the voyage are brief and broken.

In March, sick and discouraged by the misfortunes they had met, the buccaneers decided not to continue the voyage, but to land, abandon their ship and return home across the continent. For one reason and another, however, they delayed leaving the ship, and continued to work their way north until about the middle of April. Forty-seven of the men who had been discontented all along were then put ashore, while the rest of the party decided to remain loyal to Captain Sharp, and to go home around the southern part of the continent. Before the mutineers were put ashore, the ship had come north almost to the equator, so that the journey of the deserters was materially lessened. Two of the mutineers reached the Isthmus, crossed it and subsequently published some brief accounts of their experiences.

Sharp's vessel cruised about in the vicinity of the equator, raiding small towns and capturing Spanish vessels, and piling up a large amount of treasure, until the end of August, when the buccaneers turned south with a determination to make the voyage home as quickly as possible.

About the twentieth of September they passed the Tropic of Capricorn, and by the middle of October they were almost opposite the Straits of Magellan. On this voyage they had kept most of the time far away from the coast, and had landed only when necessary to re-stock their ship with water and provisions.

In the wildest kind of weather they searched the rocky coast, trying to find the opening into the Strait of Magellan, but were unable to do so. Provisions ran low, and many times they feared actual starvation little less than destruction by storms and hidden rocks. Most of them were sick, and all were discouraged. At last they abandoned the idea of going through the straits, and sailed south around Tierra del Fuego through rain and fogs and frost.

About the middle of November they were able to turn their course to the north, and from that time we find them working steadily forward, till, on the twenty-eighth of January, they sighted the island of Barbados. Here they were told that peace was declared between Spain and England, but as they saw one of the British men-of-war lying at anchor, they did not dare to put into the harbor, fearing they would be seized as pirates, for throughout their whole expedition they had had no commission. Still they were overjoyed to see some of their countrymen again and to talk with them, as they did with the mariners on some of the small vessels that were putting out from the island.

They set free at this place a negro who had

served them as shoemaker, giving him his liberty
because he had worked so faithfully. Besides
this, they presented Captain Sharp with a
mulatto body servant as a mark of the respect
and admiration they had for his skill in conduct-
ing them through so many dangerous adventures.
Then they divided the last of their prize money
and started a fund for the celebration of their
return. As a nucleus, there were a hundred
pieces of eight, prize money which they could
not divide satisfactorily. To this they added
the price of a little Spanish dog which they had
found on one of their prizes, and which they had
fed and cared for to the present time. Captain
Sharp bought the dog, paying forty pieces of
eight for him, with the understanding that the
money should go into the "jollification fund."

On the thirtieth of January they sighted the
island of Antigua, and sent a canoe on shore to
get tobacco and find out whether the governor
would permit them to come into port. They
found everybody excepting the governor willing
and anxious to see them, but the latter flatly
denied them entry. Accordingly, the ship was
given to those of the pirates who had lost all their
money at play, while the remainder separated
themselves into two groups and took passage for
England.

Ringrose and thirteen of his companions
reached England on the twenty-sixth of March.
There they were tried for piracy in the South
Seas, at the instigation of the Spanish ambassa-
dor, but were not convicted. On the most seri-

ous charge they were released on the plea of self-defense, as it was claimed that the Spaniards had fired first upon them. Three of Sharp's crew were tried at Jamaica. One pleaded guilty and was hanged, but the other two fought their cases in court and were finally acquitted for lack of evidence.

DAVID CROCKETT

UNIQUE among the characters in American history and one of the most interesting men of pioneer days was David Crockett, who was born on the 17th of August, 1786, in the backwoods district of what has since become the State of Tennessee. His father, who was of Irish parentage, during his youth lived with his parents in Pennsylvania, but afterwards moved to North Carolina and thence into the Tennessee country. David's grandparents were both murdered in their own house by the Creek Indians. At the same time, one uncle of David's was badly wounded, and a second, a younger one, who was deaf and dumb, was captured by the Creeks and kept in captivity for seventeen years, when he was met and recognized by an elder brother, who purchased him from the Indians that held him. Hearing of such atrocities must have affected the young David, and undoubtedly accounts for some of the fierce hatred which the backwoodsman felt for the Creeks, and the callous way in which he looked upon their sufferings when later he fought against them with the militia from his neighborhood.

David had five brothers and three sisters; his father was a poor man who tried farming and other pioneer occupations, who built a mill and lost it in a freshet just as it was completed, and who finally established a little roadhouse or tavern on one of the Tennessee trails. So poor were they that much schooling was impossible for the children, yet David was sent at the proper time, and applied himself diligently for a few days to his letters. However, he was so unfortunate as to quarrel with one of his older companions, who little realized the savage nature of the newcomer. That night Davy lay in wait for the larger boy and set upon him so fiercely and beat him so unmercifully that he was soon ready to cry for quarter. On the way home Davy persuaded his brothers to say nothing about the fight, and the next morning instead of going to school, he ran off into the woods, where he stayed until the children returned at night. He kept this up for several days, fearing to return to school and take the whipping he knew he must get from his teacher. In the end his father heard that he was playing truant, and tried to force the boy back to school. Davy refused to go, and when his father tried to punish him, ran away from home and engaged himself to a drover. He was fifteen years old before he returned to his home, and then he had changed so much that his parents did not recognize him, and it was some time before one of his sisters discovered who he really was. They received him joyfully, and thereafter, until he reached his majority, he worked faithfully for his father, paying off the latter's indebtedness and assisting the family in every possible way.

His life during this time was that of a backwoods boy, working hard and finding his recreation in hunting, fishing and the sports of the
border. It was during this time that he acquired
the overpowering taste for hunting in the woods,
that lasted all his life. During these years, too,
he developed that sturdy manhood which carried
him through many trying ordeals. Though he
never had schooling, and his conversation and
writings were lacking in grammar, yet his speech
was full of a sharp, rude wit, and his ideas were
characterized by shrewd common sense.

Davy's motto, adopted early in life, was, "Be
sure you are right, then go ahead,"—words that
his own career made famous.

When the Creek War broke out, Crockett
volunteered, and he served as soldier and spy till
peace was declared. His experiences there we
will let him tell himself, as he wrote them in his
autobiography. (See page 380.)

After his return from the Creek War, he was
elected to Congress in 1826 and in 1828. He
was defeated in 1830 and reëlected in 1832.
When he was first elected he knew very little
about the government, and was totally ignorant
of his duties as a member of Congress, but here
again his good common sense and bright mind
came to his aid; and although he worked under
great disadvantages, yet he won respect and
admiration from the other lawmakers. He was
always a curious and noticeable figure in Wash-
ington, both on account of his dress, which was
similar to that of his backwoods companions, and

because of his manner, which was as strange as
his clothes. Such a man could not help being
noticed, and on a trip which he made to Philadelphia, New York and Boston, he was received
everywhere kindly and added not a little to his
fame. In fact, he was often mentioned as a
logical candidate for the presidency.

He was defeated at the close of his third term
in Congress, and being stirred by the exciting
news that came from Texas, he left his home in
Tennessee and went West to join those men who
were fighting the Mexicans in an endeavor to
make Texas really a free and independent state.

He kept a journal during this trip, and in it he
describes very entertainingly his companions and
their experiences. Among them were three
curious characters: a bee hunter, who was well
known through Texas and who left his wife
Kate at Nacogdoches; a fierce old man, who had
been a pirate and had abandoned the sea for
more exciting events on shore; and a quaint
gambler, whom Crockett picked up near the
Mississippi and persuaded to abandon the petty
shell game by which he was getting small sums
from the people he met on the way. The real
name of this man Crockett never told, but as-
signed to him the nickname "Thimblerig."

We have told of the fall of the Alamo in another place (Vol. IX, page 23), but Crockett's
connection with it is so intimate that we must
borrow a little from his diary.

We find him writing at San Antonio on the
nineteenth of February in high spirits, although

he confesses to a shortage of provisions, but hopes to satisfy his appetite with fighting if in no other way. On the twenty-third the enemy came in sight, and the little garrison resolved to defend the Alamo to the last extremity. They made a large national flag of thirteen stripes, red and white alternately on a blue ground, with a large white star in the center, and between the points the word "Texas." When the flag was raised, the bee hunter sang in his wonderfully mellow voice the following patriotic song, that roused the enthusiasm of his hearers to the highest pitch:

"Up with your banner, Freedom,
   The champions cling to thee;
They'll follow where'er you lead 'em,
   To death, or victory;—
Up with your banner, Freedom.

Tyrants and slaves are rushing
   To tread thee in the dust;
Their blood will soon be gushing,
   And stain our knives with rust;—
But not thy banner, Freedom.

While stars and stripes are flying,
   Our blood we'll freely shed;
No groan will 'scape the dying,
   Seeing thee o'er his head;—
Up with your banner, Freedom."

For the next nine days, Crockett gives an account of their privations and sufferings, their brave and successful defense, and the marked execution they were able to make among the Mexicans who showed themselves within range. On the third of March they had given up all hopes of receiving assistance from without, and had promised to fight to the last extremity, and in dying kill as many of their foes as possible.

His entry for the fourth of March is substantially as follows: "Shells have been falling into the fort like hail during the day, but without effect. About dusk this evening we saw a man running toward the fort pursued by about a dozen Mexican cavalry. The bee hunter immediately recognized him as the old pirate who had gone to Goliad for assistance, and calling to two others, the bee hunter sallied out of the fort to the relief of the old man, I following close after. Before we reached him the Mexicans were close upon his heels. He stopped suddenly, turned short upon his pursuers, discharged his rifle, and saw one of his enemies fall from his horse. After running a short distance again, the old pirate, finding that he would be taken and cut to pieces, turning fiercely, and to the amazement of the enemy clubbed his gun and dashed among them like a wounded tiger. By the time we reached him, his pursuers had fled like sparrows, and in the ardour of the moment we followed them some distance, not seeing that our retreat was cut off by another detachment of cavalry. Nothing was to be done but to fight our way through. We were all of the same mind. They were about twenty in number and stood their ground while we dashed among them, and for about five minutes a bloody conflict ensued. Then a detachment was seen coming from the fort to our relief, and the Mexicans scampered away, leaving eight of their men dead upon the fields. We did not escape unscathed, for both the pirate and the bee hunter were mortally wounded, and I received a saber cut across the forehead.

"The old man died without speaking as soon as we entered the fort. We bore my young friend to his bed, dressed his wounds, and I watched beside him. He lay without complaint or manifesting pain, until about midnight, when he spoke. I asked him what he wanted. 'Nothing,' he replied with a sigh that seemed to rend his heart, and his eyes filled with tears as he continued his 'Poor Kate of Nacogdoches; her words were prophetic, Colonel.' Then he sang in a low voice,—

'But toom' cam' the saddle, all bluidy to see, And hame cam' the steed, but hame never cam' he.'

"He spoke no more, and a few minutes afterward died. Poor Kate, who will tell this to thee?"

The last entry in Crockett's diary bears date March fifth. It is as follows:

"Pop, pop, pop! Bom, bom, bom! throughout the day.——No time for memorandums now.——Go ahead!——Liberty and independence forever!"

Before daybreak the next morning, the final assault was made on the Alamo, and when Santa Ana entered in person, after the terrible butchery, only six men, among whom was Colonel Crockett, were found alive. The Colonel stood alone in an angle of the fort, the barrel of his broken rifle in his right hand, and in his left a huge Bowie knife dripping blood. Across his forehead was a terrible gash, while around him lay a barrier of dead Mexicans who had fallen at his hands. At his feet lay the body of his friend Thimblerig with his knife driven to the hilt in the throat of a Mexican, and his left hand clenched in his hair.

"General Castrillon was brave and not cruel, and disposed to save the prisoners. He marched them up to that part of the fort where stood Santa Ana and his murderous crew. The steady, fearless step and undaunted tread of Colonel Crockett, on this occasion, together with the bold demeanour of the hardy veteran, had a powerful effect on all present. Nothing daunted, he marched up boldly in front of Santa Ana, and looked him sternly in the face, while Castrillon addressed 'his Excellency,'—'Sir, here are six prisoners I have taken alive; how shall I dispose of them?' Santa Ana looked at Castrillon fiercely, flew into a violent rage, and replied, 'Have I not told you before how to dispose of them? Why do you bring them to me?' At the same time his brave officers plunged their swords into the bosoms of their defenceless prisoners. Colonel Crockett, seeing the act of treachery, instantly sprung like a tiger at the ruffian chief, but before he could reach him a dozen swords were sheathed in his indomitable heart; and he fell, and died without a groan, a frown on his brow, and a smile of scorn and defiance on his lips. Castrillon rushed from the scene, apparently horrorstruck, sought his quarters, and did not leave them for several days, and hardly spoke to Santa Ana after."

It is only fair to say that the account which we have quoted above is denied by some authorities, who say that Crockett was killed before ever Santa Ana entered the Alamo.

DAVID CROCKETT IN THE CREEK WAR

ABRIDGED FROM HIS AUTOBIOGRAPHY.

I WAS living ten miles below Winchester when the Creek warriors commenced their open hostilities by a most bloody butchery at Fort Mimms. There had been no war among us for so long that but few who were not too old to bear arms knew anything about the business. I for one had often thought about war and had often heard it described, and I did verily believe in my own mind that I couldn't fight at all; but my after-experience convinced me that this was all a notion, for when I heard of the mischief which was done at the fort, I instantly felt like going, and I had none of the dread of dying that I expected to feel.

In a few days a general meeting of the militia was called for the purpose of raising volunteers; and when the day arrived for that meeting, my wife, who had heard me say I meant to go to war, began to beg me not to turn out. It was mighty hard to go against her arguments, but my countrymen had been murdered, and I knew that the next thing would be that the Indians would be scalping the women and children all about there if we didn't put a stop to it. I reasoned the case with her as well as I could, and told her that if every man would wait till his wife

I SAID FAREWELL TO MY WIFE AND TWO LITTLE BOYS

got willing to let him go to war, there would be
no fighting done until we would all be killed in
our houses; that I was as able to go as any man
in the world; and that I believed it was a duty I
owed to my country.   Whether she was satisfied
with this reasoning or not, she didn't tell me;
but seeing I was bent on it, all she did was to cry

a little and to turn about to her work. The truth is my dander was up and nothing but war should bring it right again.

I went to Winchester where a muster was to be. When the men were paraded, a lawyer by the name of Jones addressed us; informing us he wished to raise a company, and that then the men should meet and elect their officers. I believe I was about the second or third man that stepped out; but on marching up and down the regiment a few times we found we had a large company.

We volunteered for sixty days, as it was supposed our services would not be longer needed. A day or two after this we met and elected Mr. Jones our Captain, and also elected our other officers. We then received orders to start on the next Monday week; the time arrived, I took a parting farewell of my wife and two little boys, mounted my horse and set sail to join my company. Expecting only to be gone a short time, I took no more clothing with me than I supposed would be necessary; so that if I got into an Indian battle, I might not be pestered with any unnecessary plunder to prevent my having a fair chance with them. We all met and went ahead till we passed Huntsville and camped at a large spring called Beaty's Spring. Here we stayed several days, in which time the troops began to collect from all quarters. At last we mustered about thirteen hundred strong; all mounted volunteers and all determined to fight, judging from myself, for I felt wolfish all over.

I verily believe the whole army was of the real grit.

While we remained at the spring, a Major Gibson came and wanted some volunteers to go with him across the Tennessee River and into the Creek nation to find out the movements of the Indians. He came to my Captain and asked for two of his best woodsmen and such as were best with the rifle. The Captain pointed me out to him, and said he would be security that I would go as far as the major would himself, or any other man.

I willingly engaged to go with him, and asked him to let me choose my own mate to go with me, which he said he would let me do. I chose a young man by the name of George Russell, son of old Major Russell of Tennessee. I called him out, but Major Gibson said he thought he hadn't beard enough to please him—he wanted men, not boys. I must confess I was a little wrathy with this, for I know'd George Russell and I know'd there was no mistake in him and I didn't think that courage ought to be measured by the beard; for here a goat would have the preference over a man. I told the major he was on the wrong scent; that Russell could go as far as he could, and I must have him along. He saw I was a little wrathy and said I had the best chance of knowing, and agreed it should be as I wanted it.

We took our camp equipage and mounted our horses; and thirteen in number, including the major, we cut out. We crossed the Tennessee

River and then traveled about seven miles further, and took up camp for the night. The next morning, Major Gibson and myself concluded we should separate and take different directions to see what discoveries we could make; so he took six of the men and I five. We were to meet that evening where the roads came together, fifteen miles the other side of the house of a Cherokee Indian named Dick Brown.

I and my men then started and went on to the place of meeting, but Major Gibson was not there. We waited till almost dark, but still he didn't come. We left the Indian trail a little distance and turning into the head of a hollow, we struck up camp. We stayed next morning till after breakfast; but in vain, for the major didn't still come.

We started ahead and went about twenty miles to the house of a man by the name of Radcliff. He was a white man, but had married a Creek woman, and lived just in the edge of a Creek nation. He had two sons, large, likely fellows; and a great deal of potatoes and corn; so we fed our horses and got dinner with him. But he was bad scared all the time; he told us that there had been ten painted warriors at his house only an hour before, and if we were discovered there, they would kill us, and his family with us. I replied to him, that my business was to hunt for just such fellows as he had described, and I was determined not to go back until I had done it.

Our dinner being over we saddled up our horses and made ready to start; but some of my small company I found were disposed to return.

I told them if we were to go back we should never hear the last of it; and I was determined to go ahead. I know'd some of them would go with me and that the rest were afraid to go back by themselves; and so we pushed on to the camp of some friendly Creeks, which was distant about eight miles. The moon was about at the full, and the night was clear; we therefore had the benefit of her light from night to morning, and I knew if we were placed in such danger as to make retreat necessary, we could travel by night as well as in the daytime. It was after dark when we got to the camp, where we found about forty men, women and children.

They had bows and arrows, and I turned to shooting with their bows by the pine light. In this way we amused ourselves very well for a while, but at last a negro, who had been talking to the Indians, came to me and told me they were very much alarmed, for the *Red Sticks*, as they called the war party of the Creeks, would come and find us there; and if so, we should all be killed. I directed him to tell them that I would watch, and if one would come that night, I should carry the skin of his head home to make me a moccasin. When he made this communication, the Indians laughed aloud.

At about ten o'clock that night, we all concluded to try to sleep a little, but that our horses might be ready for use, we tied them up with their saddles on them and put everything in readiness in case in the night our quarters should get uncomfortable. We laid down with our guns in our arms, and I had just gotten into a dozing sleep when I heard the sharpest scream that ever escaped the throat of a human creature. It was more like a wrathy painter[1] than anything else. The negro understood, and he sprang to me, for though I heard the noise well enough, yet I wasn't wide awake enough to get up; so the negro caught me and said the Red Sticks was coming. I arose quickly then and asked what was the matter. Our negro talked with the Indian, who had just fetched the scream, and learned from him that he had come into camp as a runner, and said that the war party had been crossing the Coosa River all day at the Ten Islands and was going then to meet Jackson. This news very much alarmed the friendly Indians, who were in the camp, and they were all off in ten minutes.

I felt bound to make this intelligence known as soon as possible to the army which we had left; and so we all mounted our horses and put out in a long lope to make our way back to that place. We were about sixty-five miles off. We went on to the Cherokee town we had visited on our way out, having called at Radcliff's, who was off with his family. At the town we found large fires burning, but not a single Indian was to be seen. They were all gone, and it appeared we must be in great danger. We therefore stayed only a short time in the light of the fires about the town, preferring the light of the moon and the shade of the woods.

1. The name *painter* is a corruption of *panther*, and is applied in the United States to the cougar or American lion.

We pushed on till we got again to old Mr.
Brown's, which was still about thirty miles from
where we had left the main army. When we
got there, the chickens were just at the first
crowing for day. We fed our horses, got a
morsel to eat ourselves, and again cut out.

About ten o'clock in the morning we reached
the camp, and I reported to Colonel Coffee the
news. He didn't seem to mind my report a bit,
and this raised my dander higher than ever; but
I know'd I had to be on my best behavior, and
so I kept it all to myself; though I was so mad
that I was burning inside like a tar-kiln, and I
wonder that the smoke hadn't been pouring out
of me at all points. Major Gibson hadn't yet
returned, and we all began to think he was killed.

The next day, though, the major got in, and
brought a worse tale than I had, though he
stated the same facts as far as I went. This
seemed to put our colonel all into a fidget; and
it convinced me clearly of one of the hateful ways
of the world. When I made my report, it
wasn't believed because I was no officer: I was
no great man, but just a poor soldier; but when
the same thing was reported by Major Gibson!
why, then it was all as true as preaching, and the
Colonel believed it, every word.

He therefore ordered breastworks to be thrown
up nearly a quarter of a mile along; and sent an
express to General Jackson, requesting him to
push on like the very mischief, for fear we should
all be cooked up to a cracklin before they could
get there. "Old Hickory-face" made a forced

march on getting the news, and on the next day
he and his men got into camp with their feet all
blistered from the effects of their swift journey.
The volunteers therefore stood guard all together
to let them rest.

About eight hundred of the volunteers, and
of that number I was one, were sent on through
Huntsville so as to get on the Indians in another
direction.   After we passed Huntsville, we struck
the Tennessee River at Melton's Bluff.   The
river is here about two miles wide, and has so
rough a bottom in many places as to be dangerous.   At this place we left some of the horses
with their feet held fast in the crevices of the
rocks; their riders went on foot.

We pushed on till we got to what was called
the Black Warrior's town, which stood near the
very spot where Tuscaloosa now stands.   This
Indian town was a large one, but when we
arrived we found the Indians had all left it,
scared off no doubt by our arrival.   There was
a large field of corn standing out with a pretty
good supply in some cribs.   Without delay we
secured the corn as well as a fine quantity of
dried beans, which were very acceptable to us.
Then we burned the town and left the place.

The next day we were entirely out of meat.   I
went to Colonel Coffee, who was then in command of us, and asked his leave to hunt when
we marched.   He gave me leave, but told me
to take mighty good care of myself.   I turned
aside to hunt, and had not gone far when I found
a deer that had just been killed, for his flesh

FOUND A DEER THAT HAD JUST BEEN KILLED

was still warm and smoking. From this I was
sure that the Indian who had killed it had been
gone only a few minutes, and though I was never
much in favor of one hunter stealing from
another, yet meat was so scarce in camp, I just
took up the deer on my horse before me and
carried it on till night.

I could have sold it for almost any price I would have asked, but this wasn't my rule either in peace or war. Whenever I had anything and saw a fellow-being suffering, I was more anxious to relieve him than to benefit myself; and this is one of the true secrets of my being a poor man to this day. I gave all my deer away except a small part I kept for myself and just sufficient to make a good supper for my mess. We had to live mostly on parched corn.

The next night I told my mess I would again try for some meat; so I took my rifle and cut out, but hadn't gone far when I discovered a large gang of hogs. I shot one of them down in his tracks, and the rest broke directly toward the camp. In a few minutes the guns began to roar as bad as if the whole army had been in an Indian battle, and the hogs to squeal as bad as the pig did when the devil turned barber. I shouldered my hog and went on to camp, and when I got there I found they had killed a good many hogs and a fine fat cow into the bargain. The next morning we marched on to a Cherokee town and gave the inhabitants an order on Uncle Sam for the cow and the hogs we had killed.

The next day we met the main army and all went on to Radcliff's. There we found he had hid all his provisions, and learned that, when I was out as a spy, he had sent a runner to the Indian camp with the news that the Red Sticks were crossing at Ten Islands in order to scare me and my men away with a false alarm. To

make some atonement for this, we took the old
scoundrel's two big sons with us, and made them
serve through the war.

We marched to the Ten Islands on the Coosa
River, where we established a fort and sent out
spy companies. They soon made prisoners of
Bob Catala and his warriors, and in a few days
brought news of some Indians in a town about
eight miles off. So we mounted our horses, and
put out for that town under the direction of two
friendly Creeks.

When we got near the town, we divided, one
of our pilots going with each division. Thus we
passed on each side of the town, keeping near
to it until our lines met at both sides. We then
closed up at both ends so as to surround it
completely, and sent Captain Hammond to
bring on the affray. When he came near the
town, the Indians saw him, raised a yell and
came running at him like so many red devils.
The main army was now formed in a hollow
square around the town, to which Hammond
retreated till the Indians came within reach. We
then gave them a fire and they returned it, after
which they ran back into their town, when we
began to close on it. The Indians soon saw
they were on our property, and wanted us to
take them prisoners. Their squaws and children
would run and take hold of us as they could, and
give themselves up. I saw seven squaws at a
time holding on to the hunting-shirt of one man.
We took all prisoners that came out to us in this
way. I saw some warriors, however, run into

a house until I counted forty-six of them. We pursued them until we got near the house, when we saw a squaw sitting in the door. She placed her feet against the bow she had in her hand, took an arrow, raised her feet, drew with all her might and let the arrow fly at us, killing Lieutenant Moore, I believe. His death so enraged us all that she was fired on, and at least twenty balls were blown through her. This was the first man I ever saw killed with a bow and arrow. We now shot them down like dogs, and then set the house on fire, burning it with the forty-six warriors inside.

I remember seeing an Indian boy, who was shot down near the house. His arm and thigh were broken, and he was so near the burning house that his flesh was fairly cooking. In this situation he was still trying to crawl along, but not a murmur escaped him, though he was only twelve years old. When an Indian's dander is up, he would sooner die than make a noise, or ask for quarter.

The number that we took prisoners being added to the number we killed amounted to one hundred and eighty-six, while five of our men were killed. We then returned to our fort, but no provisions had yet reached us, and we had been for some time on half rations. For several days we remained there almost starving, as all our beef was gone. Then we commenced eating beef hides, and consumed every scrap we could lay our hands on, before we received orders for marching.

PILOTED BY FRIENDLY INDIANS

We crossed the Coosa River, and when we had come near to Fort Taladega, we met eleven hundred painted warriors, the very choice of the Creek nation, who had shut up the friendly Indians in the fort, and threatened that if they did not come out and fight against the whites, they would lose their fort, ammunition and provisions. The friendly Indians had asked three days to consider their answers, and had immediately started a runner to Captain Jackson, and it was the receipt of this message that had caused us to come over.

The Creeks from their spies had discovered us coming, and told the friendly Indians that we had a great many fine horses and blankets and guns and everything else, and if they would come out and help whip Captain Jackson, they should share the plunder. This they promised to do.

About an hour after sunrise in the morning, piloted by some friendly Indians, we came near the fort and divided as we had done in our former battle; so as to form around the Indians, as before, a hollow square. This time we sent Major Russell and Captain Evans with their companies to bring on the battle.

When they got near the fort, they saw that the top of it was lined with friendly Indians crying out as loud as they could roar—"How-de-do, brothers! How-de-do!" They kept this up till Major Russell had passed by the fort and was moving on toward the besiegers.

The Creeks had concealed themselves under the bank of a branch that run partly around the fort, in the manner of a half moon. They were all painted as red as scarlet, and were just as naked as they were born. Russell could not see them, and was going right into their circle; although the friendly Indians on the top of the fort were trying every plan to show him his danger. He could not understand them, but at last two of them jumped from the fort, ran and took his horse by the bridle, and pointing, told him there were thousands of Creeks lying under the bank. This brought his company to a halt.

At the same moment the Creeks fired on them and came rushing forth from their hiding place like a cloud of Egyptian locusts, and screaming like all the young devils had been turned loose with the old devil at their head. Russell's company jumped from their horses and hurried into the fort, while their horses ran up to our line, which by this time was come into full view.

The warriors came yelling on until they were within shot of us, when we fired and killed considerable of them. They then broke like a gang of steers, and ran across to the other line, where they were again fired on. And so we kept them running from one line to the other, constantly under a heavy fire, until we had killed upwards of four hundred of them. They fought with guns and also with their bows and arrows, but at length they made their escape through a part of our line, which was made up of drafted militia. We lost fifteen of our men, as brave fellows as ever lived or died. We buried them all in one grave, and started back to our fort, but before we got there two more of our men died with wounds they had received.

We now remained at the fort a few days, but as no provisions came, we were all liable to perish. The weather also began to get very cold, our clothes were nearly worn out, and our

horses getting very feeble and poor; so we proposed to General Jackson to let us return home,
get fresh horses and fresh clothing, and so be
prepared for another campaign. The sixty days
for which we had enlisted had long gone out.
The General, however, issued his orders against
it. Nevertheless, we began to fix for a start
home, but the General placed his cannon on a
bridge we had to cross, and ordered out his
regulars and drafted men to keep us from passing. But when the militia started to guard the
bridge, they would shout back to us to bring
their knapsacks along when we came, for they
wanted to go as bad as we did. We moved on
till we reached the bridge, where the general's
men were all strung along on both sides, but we
all had our flints ready picked, and our guns
ready, so that if we were fired upon, we might
fight our way through or all die together. When
we came still nearer the bridge, we heard the
guards cocking their guns, and we did the same;
but not a gun was fired nor a life lost. When
we had passed the bridge, no further attempt
was made to stop us. The general said we were
the worst volunteers he had ever seen in his life.
That we would volunteer and go out and fight,
and then that we would volunteer and go home
again in spite of the devil.

After we had procured fresh horses and a
more suitable supply of clothing, a few of us
pushed on to the army again. I joined Major
Russell's company of spies and overtook General
Jackson, where we established Fort Williams.

Then we pushed on to the Horseshoe bend of the Tallapoosa River, where we began to find Indian signs in plenty.

Here we struck up camp for the night; but about two hours before day we heard our guard firing and were all up in little or no time. We mended up our camp fires and then fell back into the dark, expecting to see the Indians pouring in, and intending, when they should do so, to shoot them by the light of our own fires. It so happened, however, that the Indians did not rush in as we expected, but commenced a fire on us as we were. This we returned and continued to shoot as well as we could in the dark, guided only by the flash of the Indian's guns. When day broke, the Indians disappeared, but they had killed four of our men and wounded several. Whether we killed any of the Indians or not, we could not tell, for it is their custom to carry off their dead whenever they can. We buried ours all in one grave and laid logs over them and set them afire, so that the savages might not find them when they returned, as we knew they would do, to scalp the slain.

We made some horse-litters for our wounded, and took up our retreat. We had to cross a large creek, and when about half our men were over, the Indians commenced firing and kept it up very warmly. They hid themselves behind a large log and could kill one of our men, who were in open ground and exposed, with almost every shot. At this trying moment two of our

colonels left their men, and by a *forced march*
crossed the creek out of the reach of the fire.
Here Governor Carroll distinguished himself by
a greater bravery than I ever saw in any other
man.   In truth, I believe that if it hadn't been
for Carroll, we should all have been genteelly
licked that time; with part of our men on one
side of the creek and part on the other, and the
Indians all the time pouring it in on us as hot as
fresh mustard is to sore skin.   I know I was
mighty glad when the savages quit us, for I
began to think there was one behind every tree
in the woods.

Soon after this, an army was raised to go to
Pensacola, and I determined to go again with
them, for I wanted a small taste of British fighting and supposed I would find it there.   I joined
old Major Russell again and followed on after
the main army with about a hundred and
thirty men in our company.   We crossed the
river near where I had crossed when I first went
out; then we passed through the Choctaw and
Chickasaw nations to what is called the Cut-off
at the junction of the Tom Bigby with the
Alabama River.

This place is near the old Fort Mimms where
the Indians committed the great butchery at the
commencement of the war.   The fort was built
right in the middle of a large old field; and
before the massacre the people had been there so
long and lived so quietly that they didn't apprehend any danger at all, and had therefore become
quite careless.   A small negro boy, whose

business it was to bring up the calves at milking time, had been out for that purpose, and on coming back he said he saw a great many Indians. At this the inhabitants took alarm, closed their gates and put out guards who continued to watch for a few days. Finding that no attack was made, they concluded the little negro had lied, and again threw their gates open and sent out their hands to work their fields. The same boy set out again on the same errand, and returned in great haste and alarm, and informed them he had seen the Indians as thick as trees in the woods. He was not believed, but was tied up to receive a flogging for the supposed lie. In fact he was actually getting badly licked at the very moment when the Indians came in a troop. They were loaded with rails with which they stopped all the portholes of the fort on one side, and then they fell to cutting down the picketing. Those inside the fort had only the bastion to shoot from, and as fast as one Indian would fall, another would catch up his ax and chop away until they succeeded in cutting down enough of the picketing to permit them to enter. Then they rushed through and immediately commenced scalping without regard to age or sex. Having forced the inhabitants up to one side of the fort, they carried on the work as a butcher would in a slaughter pen.

This scene was partly described to me by a young man who was in the fort when it happened. He said that he saw his father and mother, his

WHEN ONE INDIAN WOULD FALL, ANOTHER WOULD CATCH UP HIS AX

four sisters and the same number of brothers all butchered in the most shocking manner, and that he made his escape by running over the heads of the crowd to the top of the fort, and then jumped off and ran into the woods. He was closely pursued by several Indians until he came to a small bayou, across which there was a log. He knew the log was hollow on the under side, so he slipped off and hid himself. He said he heard the Indians walk over him, back and forward several times. Nevertheless he remained quiet there until night, when he came out and finished his escape.

We left our horses at the Cut-off and hurried on foot over the eighty miles to Pensacola, where our arrival was hailed with great applause; though we were a little after the feast, for they had taken the town and fort before we got there. The next morning we started back toward old Fort Mimms, where we remained two or three days until General Jackson and the main army set out for New Orleans; while we under the command of Major Russell turned south to attack the Indians on the Scamby River.

At Fort Montgomery, about a mile and a half from old Fort Mimms, we remained for some days, where we supplied ourselves pretty well with beef by killing wild cattle, which had formerly belonged to the people who had perished in the fort. At last we moved out on the Scamby River, near which we camped a thousand men, of whom about two hundred were Chickasaw and Choctaw Indians. The Indians had all along proposed to cross the river, and thinking it might be well for them to do so, Major Russell and I with fifteen other men went with them, and early the next morning set out from the river bank. We soon came to a place where the whole country was covered with water, and it looked like a sea. We didn't stop for this, but just put in like so many spaniels and waded on, sometimes up to our armpits, until we reached the pine hills about a mile and a half away. Here we struck up a fire to warm ourselves, for it was cold and we were chilled through. Again we moved on, keeping our spies out; two to our left near the bank of the river, two straight before us, and five others on our right.

We had gone in this way about six miles up the river, when our spies on the left came to us, leaping about like so many old bucks, and informed us that they had discovered a camp of Creek Indians and that we must kill them. Here we paused for a few minutes, and the prophets pow-wowed over their men awhile and then got out their paint and painted them all according to their custom when going into battle. Then they brought their paint to old Major Russell and said to him, that as he was an officer he must be painted too. He agreed, and they painted him just as themselves. We let the Indians understand that we white men would first fire on the camp and then fall back so as to give the Indians a chance to rush on them and scalp them. The Chickasaws marched on our left hand and the Choctaws on our right, and thus we moved on till we came in hearing of the camp. On nearer approach we found they were on an island, and we could not get to them.

While we were chatting about this matter we heard some guns fired, and in a very short time after a keen whoop. With that we all broke like quarter-horses for the firing. There we met

our two front spies, who said they had met two
Creeks who were out hunting their horses, and
as there was a large cluster of green bay bushes
exactly between them, they were within a few
feet of meeting before either was discovered.
Our spies, speaking in the Shawnee tongue,
said they were escaping from General Jackson,
who was at Pensacola, and that they wanted to
know where they could get something to eat.
The Creeks told them that nine miles up the
Conaker River was a large camp of Creeks where
they had cattle and plenty to eat; and that their
own camp was on an island about a mile off, just
below the mouth of the Conaker. Then the four
struck up a fire, smoked together, shook hands
and parted. One of the Creeks had a gun, but
the other had none. As soon as they had parted,
our Choctaws turned around and shot down
the one that had the gun. When the other
started to run off, they snapped at him several
times, but as the gun missed fire, they ran after
him and one of them clubbed him to death with
the gun. In doing so they broke the gun, but
they fired off the one the Creek had had, and
raised a whoop of victory. When we reached
them they had cut off the heads of both the
Indians and stood ready to scalp them.

Moving on, we came to where a Spaniard,
together with a woman whom we supposed to
be his wife, and four children, had all been
killed and scalped. It was now late evening,
and we came down to the river bank opposite
the Indian camp, where some friendly Creeks

who were with us said they would decoy the Indians from the island. Although they could not call the Indians over, they did succeed in learning that a canoe belonging to the Indians was on our side of the river. Soon we found it, and forty of our warriors crossed over to take the camp. When they arrived they found only one man in the camp, and he escaped; but they captured two squaws and ten children.

For some time after this we marched about, and had several skirmishes with the Indians, in which we killed several of them. We suffered most from lack of food, and were very hard put to it to keep soul and body together; but by hunting a great deal, we managed to live till we met some East Tennessee troops who were on the road to Mobile, and my youngest brother was with them. They had plenty of corn and provisions, and I remained with them until next morning.

Nothing more that is worthy of the reader's attention transpired till I was safely landed at home once more with my wife and children. I found them, however, doing well, and though I was only a rough sort of a backwoodsman, they seemed mighty glad to see me, however little the quality folks might suppose it. For I do reckon we love as hard in the backwoods country as any people in creation.

AMERICA

SAMUEL FRANCIS SMITH

NOTE,—This poem, which is now considered by many to be the great national hymn of the United States, was sung first at a Fourth of July celebration for children in the Park Street Church, Boston.

The author was born in Boston in 1808, and graduated from Harvard University in the same class with Oliver Wendell Holmes. When Smith wrote *America* he was a student in the Andover Theological Seminary. Many years after they had left college, Dr. Holmes at a re-union of his class read his famous poem *The Boys*. In it he alludes to Samuel Francis Smith as follows:

"He chanted a song for the brave and the
     free;
Just read on his medal 'My country, of
     thee.'"

———————

My country, 'tis of thee,
Sweet land of liberty,
  Of thee I sing;
Land where my fathers died,
Land of the pilgrims' pride,
From every mountain side
  Let freedom ring.

My native country, thee—
Land of the noble free—
  Thy name I love;
I love thy rocks and rills,
Thy woods and templed hills,
My heart with rapture thrills
  Like that above.

Let music swell the breeze,
And ring from all the trees
  Sweet freedom's song;
Let mortal tongues awake;
Let all that breathe partake;
Let rocks their silence break—
  The sound prolong.

Our fathers' God, to thee,
Author of liberty,
  To thee we sing:
Long may our land be bright,
With freedom's holy light;
Protect us by thy might,
  Great God, our King.

Perhaps few who know *America* and who sing it well understand it thoroughly.

There are a few historical allusions in it. Who were the pilgrims? Why did the pilgrims take pride in the land? Does the author mean Puritans when he says pilgrims?

The first stanza turned into prose might read something as follows: I sing of thee, my own country, the sweet land of liberty. Let all the people who live in this land where our fathers died, in this land which was the pilgrims' pride, sing songs of freedom till they ring from every mountain side.

In the second stanza the poet in his religious fervor thinks of the hills as being like temples. He calls America the land of the noble free meaning the noble freemen. Sometimes this line is printed with a comma after the word *noble*. Then the line means land of the noble man, the free man. The stanza as a whole might be rendered into prose after this manner: I love thee, my country, thou land of the noble free, and I love thy name; I love, too, thy rocks, rills, woods and templed hills, and my heart thrills with rapture like that which is felt by the angels above.

The meaning of the third stanza is clearer if we put it into prose as follows: Let music swell grandly on the breeze, and let the sweet song of freedom ring from all the trees; let every human being sing the song; let all living things join in the chorus. Let even the rocks break the silence and prolong the music with their echoes.

The last stanza means this: O Thou great God, who protected our fathers in the wilderness and who created for them and their descendants the liberty we enjoy, to Thee we offer this devout song and prayer: "Through all the coming centuries may our land be free, and do Thou, great God our King, protect us by Thy far-reaching power."

We should learn to think of a song like this as a unit, a perfect whole, and the following summary will aid us in so doing:

First stanza.—I sing this song about my country, and may such songs of freedom ring everywhere within it.

Second stanza.—I love my country and every good thing in it devotedly.

Third stanza.—Let every one join in songs of freedom.

Fourth stanza.—We sing praises to God, and ask Him to protect us, and keep freedom forever ours.

THE RETREAT OF CORTES

WILLIAM H. PRESCOTT

NOTE,—Hernando Cortés, the conqueror of Mexico, sailed from Cuba, which he had assisted in subduing, for the mainland, where he landed in the spring of 1519. After tarrying on the coast for a time, and founding the city of Vera Cruz, he started inland, passing first through the country of the Tlascalans, who were easily induced to submit to him, and who became his most faithful native allies. By November 1519, the Spaniards had reached the city of Mexico, the capital of the Aztecs, and here they established themselves.

The chief of the Aztecs, Montezuma, determined not to offer serious opposition to the Spaniards, but Cortés was distrustful of the Aztecs, and managed to secure possession of Montezuma, whom he kept as a hostage. Called from the city of Mexico by an expedition which had been sent against him from Cuba, Cortés returned as soon as possible, only to find that the Aztecs had adopted a more aggressive policy. His men were surrounded and attacked as soon as they entered the city, and the attacks were kept up from day to day. Finally, when Montezuma died, it became clear to Cortés that a longer stay in the city would be impossible. The following extract from Prescott's *The Conquest of Mexico* tells the story of the retreat.

HERE was no longer any question as to the expediency of evacuating the capital. The only doubt was as to the time of doing so, and the route. The Spanish commander called a council of officers to deliberate on these matters. It was his purpose to retreat on Tlascala, and in that capital to decide according to circumstances on his future operations. After some discussion, they agreed on the causeway of Tlacopan as the avenue by which to leave the city. It would, indeed, take them back by a circuitous route, considerably longer than either of those by which they had approached the capital. But, for that reason, it would be less likely to be guarded, as least suspected; and the causeway itself, being shorter than either of the other entrances, would sooner place the army in comparative security on the mainland.

There was some difference of opinion in respect to the hour of departure. The daytime, it was argued by some, would be preferable, since it would enable them to see the nature and extent of their danger, and to provide against it. Darkness would be much more likely to embarrass their own movements than those of the enemy, who were familiar with the ground. A thousand impediments would occur in the night, which might prevent them acting in concert, or obeying, or even ascertaining, the orders of the commander. But, on the other hand, it was urged that the night presented many obvious advantages in dealing with a foe who rarely carried his hostilities beyond the day. The late active operations of the Spaniards had thrown the Mexicans off their guard, and it was improbable they would anticipate so speedy a departure of their enemies. With celerity and caution, they might succeed, therefore, in making their escape from the town, possibly over the causeway, before their retreat should be discovered; and, could they once get beyond that pass of peril, they felt little apprehension for the rest.

The general had already superintended the construction of a portable bridge to be laid over the open canals in the causeway. This was given in charge to an officer named Magarino, with forty soldiers under his orders, all pledged to defend the bridge to the last extremity. The bridge was to be taken up when the entire army had crossed one of the breaches, and transported to the next. There were three of these openings in the causeway, and most fortunate would it have been for the expedition, if the foresight of the commander had provided the same number of bridges. But the labor would have been great, and the time was short.

At midnight the troops were under arms, in readiness for the march. Mass was performed by Father Olmedo, who invoked the protection of the Almighty through the awful perils of the night. The gates were thrown open, and, on the first of July, 1520, the Spaniards for the last time sallied forth from the walls of the ancient

THE GATES WERE THROWN OPEN

fortress, the scene of so much suffering and such indomitable courage.

The night was cloudy, and a drizzling rain, which fell without intermission, added to the obscurity. The great square before the palace was deserted, as, indeed, it had been since the fall of Montezuma. Steadily, and as noiselessly as possible, the Spaniards held their way along the great street of Tlacopan, which so lately had resounded to the tumult of battle. All was now hushed in silence; and they were only reminded of the past by the occasional presence of some solitary corpse, or a dark heap of the slain, which too plainly told where the strife had been hottest. As they passed along the lanes and alleys which opened into the great street, or looked down the canals, whose polished surface gleamed with a sort of ebon lustre through the obscurity of the night, they easily fancied they discerned the shadowy forms of their foe lurking in ambush, and ready to spring on them. But it was only fancy; and the city slept undisturbed even by the prolonged echoes of the tramp of horses, and the hoarse rumbling of the artillery and baggage trains. At length, a lighter space beyond the dusky line of buildings showed the van of the army that it was emerging on the open causeway. They might well have congratulated themselves on having thus escaped the dangers of assault in the city itself, and that a brief time would place them in comparative safety on the opposite shore. But the Mexicans were not all asleep.

As the Spaniards drew near the spot where the street opened on the causeway, and were preparing to lay the portable bridge across the uncovered breach which now met their eyes, several Indian sentinels, who had been stationed at this, as at the other approaches to the city, took alarm and fled, rousing their countrymen by

their cries. The priests, keeping their night
watch on the summit of the *teocallis*, instantly
caught the tidings and sounded their shells, while
the huge drum in the desolate temple of the
war-god sent forth those solemn tones, which,
heard only in seasons of calamity, vibrated
through every corner of the capital. The
Spaniards saw that no time was to be lost. The
bridge was brought forward and fitted with all
possible expedition. Sandoval was the first to
try its strength, and, riding across, was followed
by his little body of cavalry, his infantry, and
Tlascalan allies, who formed the first division
of the army. Then came Cortés and his squad-
rons, with the baggage, ammunition wagons, and
a part of the artillery. But before they had
time to defile across the narrow passage, a
gathering sound was heard, like that of a mighty
forest agitated by the winds. It grew louder
and louder, while on the dark waters of the lake
was heard a plashing noise, as of many oars.
Then came a few stones and arrows striking at
random among the troops. They fell every
moment faster and more furious, till they
thickened into a terrible tempest, while the very
heavens were rent with the yells and war cries of
myriads of combatants, who seemed all at once
to be swarming over land and lake!

The Spaniards pushed steadily on through
this arrowy sleet, though the barbarians, dashing
their canoes against the sides of the causeway,
clambered up and broke in upon their ranks.
But the Christians, anxious only to make their

escape, declined all combat except for self-preservation. The cavaliers, spurring forward their steeds, shook off their assailants, and rode over their prostrate bodies, while the men on foot with their good swords or the butts of their pieces drove them headlong again down the sides of the dike.

But the advance of several thousand men, marching, probably, on a front of not more than fifteen or twenty abreast, necessarily required much time, and the leading files had already reached the second breach in the causeway before those in the rear had entirely traversed the first. Here they halted, as they had no means of effecting a passage, smarting all the while under unintermitting volleys from the enemy, who were clustered thick on the waters around this second opening. Sorely distressed, the vanguard sent repeated messages to the rear to demand the portable bridge. At length the last of the army had crossed, and Magarino and his sturdy followers endeavoured to raise the ponderous frame-work. But it stuck fast in the sides of the dike. In vain they strained every nerve. The weight of so many men and horses, and above all of the heavy artillery, had wedged the timbers so firmly in the stones and earth, that it was beyond their power to dislodge them. Still they labored amidst a torrent of missiles, until, many of them slain, and all wounded, they were obliged to abandon the attempt.

The tidings soon spread from man to man, and no sooner was their dreadful import comprehended, than a cry of despair arose, which for a moment drowned all the noise of conflict. All means of retreat were cut off. Scarcely hope was left. The only hope was in such desperate exertions as each could make for himself. Order and subordination were at an end. Intense danger produced intense selfishness. Each thought only of his own life. Pressing forward, he trampled down the weak and the wounded, heedless whether it were friend or foe. The leading files, urged on by the rear, were crowded on the brink of the gulf. Sandoval, Ordaz, and the other cavaliers dashed into the water. Some succeeded in swimming their horses across. Others failed, and some, who reached the opposite bank, being overturned in the ascent, rolled headlong with their steeds into the lake. The infantry followed pellmell, heaped promiscuously on one another, frequently pierced by the shafts, or struck down by the war clubs of the Aztecs; while many an unfortunate victim was dragged half-stunned on board their canoes, to be reserved for a protracted, but more dreadful death.

The carnage raged fearfully along the length of the causeway. Its shadowy bulk presented a mark of sufficient distinctness for the enemy's missiles, which often prostrated their own countrymen in the blind fury of the tempest. Those nearest the dike, running their canoes alongside, with a force that shattered them to pieces, leaped on the land, and grappled with the Christians, until both came rolling down the

side of the causeway together. But the Aztec
fell among his friends, while his antagonist was
borne away in triumph to the sacrifice. The
struggle was long and deadly. The Mexicans
were recognized by their white cotton tunics,
which showed faint through the darkness.
Above the combatants rose a wild and discordant
clamor, in which horrid shouts of vengeance
were mingled with groans of agony, with invo-
cations of the saints and the Blessed Virgin, and
with the screams of women; for there were
several women, both natives and Spaniards, who
had accompanied the Christian camp. Among
these, one named Maria de Estrada is particularly noticed for the courage she displayed,
battling with broadsword and target like the
stanchest of the warriors.

The opening in the causeway, meanwhile, was
filled up with the wreck of matter which had
been forced into it, ammunition wagons, heavy
guns, bales of rich stuffs scattered over the waters,
chests of solid ingots, and bodies of men and
horses, till over this dismal ruin a passage
was gradually formed, by which those in the
rear were enabled to clamber to the other side.
Cortés, it is said, found a place that was fordable,
where, halting, with the water up to his saddle
girths, he endeavored to check the confusion,
and lead his followers by a safer path to the
opposite bank. But his voice was lost in the
wild uproar, and finally, hurrying on with the
tide, he pressed forward with a few trusty
cavaliers, who remained near his person, to the

van; but not before he had seen his favorite
page, Juan de Salazar, struck down, a corpse,
by his side.   Here he found Sandoval and his
companions, halting before the third and last
breach, endeavouring to cheer on their followers
to surmount it.   But their resolution faltered.
It was wide and deep; though the passage was
not so closely beset by the enemy as the preceding
ones.   The cavaliers again set the example by
plunging into the water.   Horse and foot followed as they could, some swimming, others
with dying grasp clinging to the manes and tails
of the struggling animals.   Those fared best, as
the general had predicted, who traveled lightest;
and many were the unfortunate wretches, who,
weighed down by the fatal gold which they loved
so well, were buried with it in the salt floods of
the lake.   Cortés, with his gallant comrades,
Olid, Morla, Sandoval, and some few others,
still kept in the advance, leading his broken
remnant off the fatal causeway.   The din of
battle lessened in the distance; when the rumor
reached them, that the rearguard would be
wholly overwhelmed without speedy relief.   It
seemed almost an act of desperation; but the
generous hearts of the Spanish cavaliers did not
stop to calculate danger, when the cry for
succour reached them.   Turning their horses'
bridles, they galloped back to the theatre of
action, worked their way through the press,
swam the canal, and placed themselves in the
thick of the mêlée on the opposite bank.

The first grey of the morning was now coming

over the waters.   It showed the hideous confusion of the scene which had been shrouded in the
obscurity of night.   The dark masses of combatants, stretching along the dike, were seen
struggling for mastery, until the very causeway
on which they stood appeared to tremble, and
reel to and fro, as if shaken by an earthquake;
while the bosom of the lake, as far as the eye
could reach, was darkened by canoes crowded
with warriors, whose spears and bludgeons,
armed with blades of "volcanic glass," gleamed
in the morning light.

The cavaliers found Alvarado unhorsed, and
defending himself with a poor handful of followers against an overwhelming tide of the enemy.
His good steed, which had borne him through
many a hard fight, had fallen under him.   He
was himself wounded in several places, and was
striving in vain to rally his scattered column,
which was driven to the verge of the canal by the
fury of the enemy, then in possession of the
whole rear of the causeway, where they were re-
inforced every hour by fresh combatants from
the city.   The artillery in the earlier part of the
engagement had not been idle, and its iron
shower, sweeping along the dike, had mowed
down the assailants by hundreds.   But nothing
could resist their impetuosity.   The front ranks,
pushed on by those behind, were at length forced
up to the pieces, and, pouring over them like a
torrent, overthrew men and guns in one general
ruin.   The resolute charge of the Spanish cavaliers, who had now arrived, created a temporary

check, and gave time for their countrymen to
make a feeble rally. But they were speedily
borne down by the returning flood. Cortés and
his companions were compelled to plunge again
into the lake, though all did not escape. Alvarado stood on the brink for a moment, hesitating what to do. Unhorsed as he was, to throw
himself into the water, in the face of the hostile
canoes that now swarmed around the opening,
afforded but a desperate chance of safety. He
had but a second for thought. He was a man
of powerful frame, and despair gave him unnatural energy. Setting his long lance firmly on
the wreck which strewed the bottom of the lake,
he sprung forward with all his might, and cleared
the wide gap at a leap! Aztecs and Tlascalans
gazed in stupid amazement, exclaiming, as they
beheld the incredible feat, "This is truly the
Tonatiuh,—the child of the Sun!"—The breadth
of the opening is not given. But it was so great,
that the valorous Captain Diaz, who well remembered the place, says the leap was impossible to
any man. Other contemporaries, however, do
not discredit the story. It was, beyond doubt,
a matter of popular belief at the time; it is to this
day familiarly known to every inhabitant of the
capital; and the name of the *Salto de Alvarado*,
"Alvarado's Leap," given to the spot, still com-
memorates an exploit which rivaled those of the
demi-gods of Grecian fable.

Cortés and his companions now rode forward
to the front, where the troops, in a loose, dis-
orderly manner, were marching off the fatal

THE COMMANDER GAZED MOURNFULLY AT THE BROKEN FILES

causeway. A few only of the enemy hung on
their rear, or annoyed them by occasional flights
of arrows from the lake. The attention of the
Aztecs was diverted by the rich spoil that strewed
the battle-ground; fortunately for the Spaniards,
who, had their enemy pursued with the same

ferocity with which he had fought, would, in their crippled condition, have been cut off, probably, to a man.   But little molested, therefore, they were allowed to defile through the adjacent village, or suburbs, it might be called, of Popotla.

The Spanish commander there dismounted from his jaded steed, and, sitting down on the steps of an Indian temple, gazed mournfully on the broken files as they passed before him.   What a spectacle did they present!   The cavalry, most of them dismounted, were mingled with the infantry, who dragged their feeble limbs along with difficulty; their shattered mail and tattered garments dripping with the salt ooze, showing through their rents many a bruise and ghastly wound; their bright arms soiled, their proud crests and banners gone, the baggage, artillery, all, in short, that constitutes the pride and panoply of glorious war, forever lost.   Cortés, as he looked wistfully on their thinned and disordered ranks, sought in vain for many a familiar face, and missed more than one dear companion who had stood side by side with him through all the perils of the Conquest.   Though accustomed to control his emotions, or, at least, to conceal them, the sight was too much for him.   He covered his face with his hands, and the tears which trickled down revealed too plainly the anguish of his soul.

BATTLE OF IVRY

LORD MACAULAY

NOTE,—When Henry of Navarre became king of France as Henry IV, he found that a part of his subjects, under the duke of Mayenne, refused to submit to him. On March 14, 1590, he won over his enemies a splendid victory at Ivry. In his speech to his soldiers before the battle he called upon them to rally to his white plume, if at any time they lost sight of the standard.

NOW glory to the Lord of Hosts,
    from whom all glories are!
And glory to our Sovereign Liege,
    King Henry of Navarre!
Now let there be the merry
    sound of music and the dance,
Through thy cornfields green
and sunny vines, oh! pleasant land of France.
And thou, Rochelle, our own Rochelle, proud
    city of the waters,
Again let rapture light the eyes of all thy mourn-
    ing daughters.
As thou wert constant in our ills, be joyous in our joy,
For cold, and stiff, and still are they who wrought
    thy walls annoy.
Hurrah! hurrah! a single field hath turned the
    chance of war;
Hurrah! hurrah! for Ivry and King Henry of
    Navarre.

WE SAW THE ARMY OF THE LEAGUE

Oh! how our hearts were beating, when, at the
    dawn of day,
We saw the army of the League drawn out in
    long array;
With all its priest-led citizens, and all its rebel
    peers,
And Appenzel's stout infantry, and Egmont's
    Flemish spears,

There rode the brood of false Lorraine, the curses
    of our land,
And dark Mayenne was in the midst, a truncheon
    in his hand;
And as we looked on them, we thought of Seine's
    empurpled flood,
And good Coligni's hoary hair all dabbled with
    his blood;
And we cried unto the living God, who rules the
    fate of war,
To fight for his own holy name and Henry of
    Navarre.

The King is come to marshal us, in all his armor
    drest,
And he has bound a snow-white plume upon his
    gallant crest;
He looked upon his people, and a tear was in his
    eye,
He looked upon the traitors, and his glance was
    stern and high.
Right graciously he smiled on us, as rolled from
    wing to wing,
Down all our line, in deafening shout, "God
    save our lord, the King."
"And if my standard-bearer fall, as fall full well
    he may—
For never saw I promise yet of such a bloody
    fray—
Press where ye see my white plume shine, amidst
    the ranks of war,
And be your oriflamme to-day the helmet of
    Navarre."

Hurrah! the foes are moving. Hark to the
    mingled din
Of fife, and steed, and trump, and drum, and
    roaring culverin!
The fiery Duke is pricking fast across St. Andre's
    plain,
With all the hireling chivalry of Guelders and
    Almayne.
Now by the lips of those ye love, fair gentlemen
    of France,
Charge for the golden lilies now, upon them
    with the lance!
A thousand spurs are striking deep, a thousand
    spears in rest,
A thousand knights are pressing close behind the
    snow-white crest;
And in they burst, and on they rushed, while,
    like a guiding star,
Amidst the thickest carnage blazed the helmet
    of Navarre.

Now, God be praised, the day is ours! Mayenne
    hath turned his rein,
D'Aumale hath cried for quarter, the Flemish
    Count is slain,
Their ranks are breaking like thin clouds before
    a Biscay gale;
The field is heaped with bleeding steeds, and flags
    and cloven mail;
And then we thought on vengeance, and all along
    our van,
"Remember St. Bartholomew," was passed from
    man to man;

But out spake gentle Henry then, "No French-
man is my foe;
Down, down with every foreigner, but let your
brethren go."
Oh! was there ever such a knight in friendship
or in war,
As our sovereign lord, King Henry, the soldier
of Navarre.

Ho! maidens of Vienna,—ho! matrons of Lu-
zerne,
Weep, weep, and rend your hair for those who
never shall return.
Ho! Philip, send for charity, thy Mexican pis-
toles,
That Antwerp monks may sing a mass for thy
poor spearmen's souls.
Ho! gallant nobles of the League, look that your
arms be bright;
Ho! burghers of St. Généviève, keep watch and
ward to-night;
For our God hath crushed the tyrant, our God
hath raised the slave,
And mocked the counsel of the wise and the
valor of the brave.
Then glory to his holy name from whom all
glories are;
And glory to our sovereign lord, King Henry of
Navarre.

THE "REVENGE"

A BALLAD OF THE FLEET

ALFRED TENNYSON

NOTE,—In 1591, a fleet of six British ships under the command of Lord Thomas Howard was sent to intercept and capture the treasure ships of Spain. While the British were cruising near the Azores, they learned that a powerful armada of fifty-three Spanish ships was approaching. This splendid ballad of Tennyson's tells the story of the encounter between the *Revenge*, the ship under the command of Lord Howard's lieutenant, Grenville, and the Spanish fleet. The poet did not find it necessary to add any striking or dramatic elements to the story.

I

AT Flores in the Azores Sir Richard Grenville lay,
    And a pinnace, like a flutter'd bird, came flying from far away:
    "Spanish ships of war at sea! we have sighted fifty-three!"
Then sware Lord Thomas Howard: "'Fore God I am no coward;
But I can not meet them here, for my ships are out of gear,

ALFRED TENNYSON

And the half my men are sick.   I must fly, but
    follow quick.
We are six ships of the line; can we fight with
    fifty-three?"

II

Then spake Sir Richard Grenville: "I know you
    are no coward;
You fly them for a moment to fight with them
    again.
But I've ninety men and more that are lying sick
    ashore.
I should count myself the coward if I left them,
    my Lord Howard,
To these Inquisition dogs and the devildoms of
    Spain."

III

So Lord Howard past away with five ships of war
    that day,
Till he melted like a cloud in the silent summer
    heaven;
But Sir Richard bore in hand all his sick men
    from the land
Very carefully and slow,
Men of Bideford in Devon,
And we laid them on the ballast down below;
For we brought them all aboard,
And they blest him in their pain, that they were
    not left to Spain,
To the thumbscrew and the stake, for the glory
    of the Lord.

IV

He had only a hundred seamen to work the ship
     and to fight,
And he sailed away from Flores till the Spaniard
     came in sight,
With his huge sea-castles heaving upon the weath-
     er bow.
"Shall we fight or shall we fly?
Good Sir Richard, tell us now,
For to fight is but to die!
There'll be little of us left by the time this sun
     be set."
And Sir Richard said again: "We be all good
     English men.
Let us bang these dogs of Seville, the children of
     the devil,
For I never turn'd my back upon Don or devil
     yet."

V

Sir Richard spoke and he laugh'd, and we roar'd
     a hurrah, and so
The little "Revenge" ran on sheer into the heart
     of the foe,
With her hundred fighters on deck, and her
     ninety sick below;
For half of their fleet to the right and half to the
     left were seen,
And the little "Revenge" ran on thro' the long
     sea-lane between.

VI

Thousands of their soldiers look'd down from
    their decks and laugh'd,
Thousands of their seamen made mock at the
    mad little craft
Running on and on, till delay'd
By their mountain-like "San Philip" that, of
    fifteen hundred tons,
And up-shadowing high above us with her yawn-
    ing tiers of guns,
Took the breath from our sails, and we stay'd.

VII

And while now the great "San Philip" hung
    above us like a cloud
Whence the thunderbolt will fall
Long and loud,
Four galleons drew away
From the Spanish fleet that day,
And two upon the larboard and two upon the
    starboard lay,
And the battle-thunder broke from them all.

VIII

But anon the great "San Philip," she bethought
    herself and went,
Having that within her womb that had left her
    ill content;
And the rest they came aboard us, and they
    fought us hand to hand,

SHIP AFTER SHIP, THE WHOLE NIGHT LONG

For a dozen times they came with their pikes and
    musketeers,
And a dozen times we shook 'em off as a dog that
    shakes his ears
When he leaps from the water to the land.

IX

And the sun went down, and the stars came out
 far over the summer sea,
But never a moment ceased the fight of the one
 and the fifty-three.
Ship after ship, the whole night long, their high-
 built galleons came,
Ship after ship, the whole night long, with her
 battle-thunder and flame;
Ship after ship, the whole night long, drew back
 with her dead and her shame.
For some were sunk and many were shatter'd,
 and so could fight us no more—
God of battles, was ever a battle like this in the
 world before?

X

For he said "Fight on! fight on!"
Tho' his vessel was all but a wreck;
And it chanced that, when half of the short sum-
 mer night was gone,
With a grisly wound to be drest he had left the
 deck,
But a bullet struck him that was dressing it sud-
 denly dead,
And himself he was wounded again in the side
 and the head,
And he said "Fight on! fight on!"

XI

And the night went down, and the sun smiled
 out far over the summer sea,

And the Spanish fleet with broken sides lay
    round us all in a ring;
But they dared not touch us again, for they fear'd
    that we still could sting,
So they watch'd what the end would be.
And we had not fought them in vain,
But in perilous plight were we,
Seeing forty of our poor hundred were slain,
And half of the rest of us maim'd for life
In the crash of the cannonades and the desperate
    strife;
And the sick men down in the hold were most of
    them stark and cold,
And the pikes were all broken or bent, and the
    powder was all of it spent;
And the masts and the rigging were lying over
    the side;
But Sir Richard cried in his English pride,
"We have fought such a fight for a day and a
    night
As may never be fought again!
We have won great glory, my men!
And a day less or more
At sea or ashore,
We die—does it matter when?
Sink me the ship, Master Gunner—sink her,
    split her in twain!
Fall into the hands of God, not into the hands,
    of Spain!"

XII

And the gunner said "Ay, ay," but the seamen
    made reply:

"We have children, we have wives,
And the Lord hath spared our lives.
We will make the Spaniards promise, if we yield,
   to let us go;
We shall live to fight again and to strike another
   blow."
And the lion there lay dying, and they yielded
   to the foe.

XIII

And the stately Spanish men to their flagship
   bore him then,
Where they laid him by the mast, old Sir Richard
   caught at last,
And they praised him to his face with their
   courtly foreign grace;
But he rose upon their decks, and he cried:
"I have fought for Queen and Faith like a val-
   iant man and true;
I have only done my duty as a man is bound
   to do:
With a joyful spirit I, Sir Richard Grenville,
   die!"
And he fell upon their decks, and he died.

XIV

And they stared at the dead that had been so
   valiant and true,
And had holden the power and glory of Spain so
   cheap
That he dared her with one little ship and his
   English few;

Was he devil or man? He was devil for aught
    they knew,
But they sank his body with honor down into the
    deep,
And they mann'd the "Revenge" with a swarth-
    ier alien crew,
And away she sail'd with her loss and long'd for
    her own;
When a wind from the lands they had ruin'd
    awoke from sleep,
And the water began to heave and the weather to
    moan,
And or ever that evening ended a great gale blew,
And a wave like the wave that is raised by an
    earthquake grew,
Till it smote on their hulls and their sails and
    their masts and their flags,
And the whole sea plunged and fell on the shot-
    shatter'd navy of Spain,
And the little "Revenge" herself went down by
    the island crags
To be lost evermore in the main.

THE BATTLE OF THERMOPYLAE

OR some time the Greeks had known that danger was threatening them, and in 480 B. C. they learned that it was well-nigh at their gates. Xerxes, the "Great King," whose heralds when announcing a decree began with the words, "All people and nations and languages," whose resources both of men and of treasures were more than could be estimated, was gathering his forces to proceed against Greece; and many were the rumors as to the size of his army.

"There were twelve hundred and seven great ships; and in each ship there were two hundred rowers and thirty fighting men. Also he had of smaller ships, having fifty oars or under, three thousand, and in each of these, taking one with another, there were eighty men. Therefore the whole number of the men that served on the ships was five hundred and seventeen thousand and six hundred. Of foot soldiers there were seventeen hundred thousand, and of horsemen eighty thousand, and of Arabs riding on camels and of Libyans that fought from chariots twenty thousand. There were also one hundred and twenty ships of Greeks that dwelt in Thrace and in the islands thereof, and in these twenty and four thousand men. To these must be added foot soldiers of the Thracians, the Pæonians, the

Macedonians, and others. And the sum of the whole was two million six hundred and forty-one thousand six hundred and ten. And of all this great host there was none fitter to be the ruler for beauty and great stature than King Xerxes himself. Of those that followed the camp, and of the crews of the provision ships and other vessels of transport, the number was more rather than less than the number of the fighting men. As for the women that ground the corn, and others that came with the army, and the horses, and the beasts of burden, and the dogs, their number can not be told."

What could the Greeks do against so many? And yet when the envoys of King Xerxes came to the Greek states, demanding from each earth and water, as a sign that Xerxes was lord of land and sea, all the states but Thessaly, which Xerxes would enter first, refused. The Greek states were not always on friendly terms one with another; but the great danger that threatened them now united them in one common object—to repel the Persian invader and to save their temples and their idols from desecration. A council, at which were present deputies from all the Greek states, was held on the Isthmus of Corinth, and plans for defense were considered.

There were two narrow passes through which Xerxes would have to come before he should find himself in Greece proper, and it was evident that it was at such places as these that the few Greeks could best withstand the numerous Persians. To Tempe, therefore, the northernmost of these passes, a body of troops was hastily despatched, but they soon returned declaring that the defense of the pass was out of the question. All agreed then that the best plan would be to guard Thermopylae, which led from Thessaly into Locris. To-day a swampy plain almost three miles broad lies between Mount Œta and the Maliac Gulf, but in ancient times there was but a stretch of sand not more than fifty feet wide at its broadest part, and in some places so narrow that a single wagon could scarce pass along it. The Greek fleet was posted off the coast to prevent the Persians from landing men beyond the pass, and a company was at once gathered for the defense of Thermopylae and put under the command of Leonidas, King of Sparta.

"Now, the Greeks that abode the coming of the Persians in this place were these—three hundred Spartans, heavy-armed men; and men of Tegea and Matinea a thousand, from each five hundred, and from Orchomenus one hundred and twenty, and from the rest of Arcadia a thousand. From Corinth there came four hundred, and from Phlius two hundred, and from Mycenae eighty. So many came from the Peloponnesus; of the Bœotians there came seven hundred from Thespiae and four hundred from Thebes. Besides these there had come at the summons the Locrians of Opus with all the men that they had, and a thousand Phocians."

All of the Greeks knew that they were setting out on a dangerous enterprise, but to the Spartans it meant more than that. Leonidas himself felt that he was going to his death, for the oracle at Delphi had foretold that Sparta should be saved if one of her kings should perish, and Leonidas was more than willing to make this sacrifice for his state. His three hundred followers, trained from childhood to look upon death as infinitely preferable to defeat, had, with that courage which has made their name an epithet indicating the highest sort of bravery, celebrated their funeral games before setting out. When they came to the pass of Thermopylae, they found a new cause for fear. This was the path which led over the mountains, and which made possible a descent of the enemy to the rear of those stationed in the pass. However, Leonidas was assured that this mountain track was practically unknown, and that the entrance to it was very difficult to find; so when he had sent a band of Phocians to guard it, he thought little more about it. Many of the soldiers, however, felt that they were being subjected to danger unnecessarily, and insisted that they be allowed to retreat to the Isthmus of Corinth. As this would have guarded only the Peloponnesus and have left the other states at the mercy of the Persians, Leonidas determined that they should remain where they were and await the onset of the enemy.

While they lay encamped in the pass, a scout sent by Xerxes rode up to see how strong the enemy were, and how they were employing their time. In front of and on the walls were a number of the Greeks engaging in games and combing out their long hair. Surprised to see so few men, and to see those few busying themselves in such an apparently unnecessary way, the scout rode back and made his report to the Persian king. Now there was in the camp of Xerxes one Demaratus, who had formerly been King of Sparta, but who had been driven out and had joined himself to the Persian court. Xerxes sent for him and, describing to him what he considered the foolishness of the Greeks, asked what it might mean. In reply Demaratus said, "Thou hast heard from me, O King, the truth concerning these men before this, even when we were first beginning this war; but when thou heardest it thou didst laugh at me, though I told thee that which I knew would surely come to pass. For indeed, O King, I strive always with my whole heart to tell thee the truth. Hear, therefore, yet again what I say. These men are come hither to contend with us for the pass; and this they now prepare to do; and they have this custom among them, that when they are about to put their lives in peril they adorn their heads with exceeding care. Know, also, O King, that if thou canst subdue these men, and such others of their nation as have been left behind in Sparta, there is no nation upon the earth that will abide thy coming or lift up a hand against thee; for this city that thou now fightest against is the most honorable in all Greece, and these men are the bravest."

Incredulously Xerxes asked, "In what manner will these men, being so few, as we know them to be, fight with my great army?"

Demaratus replied, "O King, deal with me as with a liar if everything fall not out even as I have said."

After this, Xerxes allowed four days to pass, thinking that perhaps the Greeks would come to their senses and flee. "But on the fifth day, seeing that they were not departed, but, as it seemed to him, were full of impudence and folly, he grew angry, and sent against them the Medes and the Cissians, giving them a command that they should take these Greeks alive and bring them before him. But when these men came up and fell upon the Greeks, many of them were slain. Then others came up into their places and ceased not from fighting, though indeed they suffered a very grievous slaughter, so that it was manifest to all men, and more especially to the King, that though he had very many that bore arms, yet had he but few men of war. And this battle endured throughout the whole day."

For two days the troops of Xerxes, even his great Ten Thousand, who were known as the Immortals, hurled themselves upon the Greeks, but they accomplished nothing, for they fought in a narrow place, where their greater numbers were of no help to them; and their spears were shorter than those of the Greeks, so that they were easily thrust through before they could come close enough to harm an enemy. Three times, it is said, while his troops were being driven backward, did Xerxes spring in despair from his throne at the sight of the peril of his army.

But on the evening of the second day there came to the camp of the Persian King a man named Ephialtes. On being ushered into the presence of Xerxes, this man admitted that he was a Greek, and proposed that for a great reward he should lead the Persian army over the hidden mountain path, and bring them to the rear of the Greek defenders. Of course Xerxes accepted the offer, and sent off one of his generals with a detachment to follow Ephialtes over the mountain path. In the morning the Phocians who had been set to guard this path were awakened by the sound of rustling in the underbrush and rushed from their camp only to see a detachment of Persian soldiers close upon them. Resolving to sell their lives dearly, they fled to the top of the mountain, where they thought that they might have the advantage of position over their enemies; but the Persians, paying no attention to them, passed on down the mountain to fall upon the brave defenders of Thermopylae.

The Greeks in the pass knew when morning dawned of the danger that awaited them, for Megistias the soothsayer told of it, and certain messengers running before the Persians confirmed his prophecy. "Then the Greeks held a council, considering what they should do; and they were divided; for some would not leave the post where they had been set, and others were very eager to depart. And when the council was broken up, some departed, going each to

their own cities, and others made ready to abide
in the pass with Leonidas. Some say, indeed,
that Leonidas sent away them that departed,
having a care for their safety; but it did not become him and the Spartans that were with him,
he said, to leave their post that they had come to
keep at the first. And indeed it seems fit to be
believed that Leonidas, seeing that the others
were faint-hearted and would not willingly abide
the peril, bade them go, but that he himself held
it to be a shameful thing to depart. For he
knew that he should get for himself great glory
by abiding at his post, and that the prosperity
of Sparta should not be destroyed."

The allies, therefore, with the exception of the
Thespians and the Thebans, departed, and the
brave remainder prepared themselves for their
death. Hitherto, Leonidas had stood on the
defensive in order to spare the lives of his men,
but now, knowing that death must come, he desired only to work as great havoc among the
Persians as possible, and he therefore marched
his men out before the wall and fell upon the
vanguard of the Persian army. It does not seem
strange that the hired soldiers should have feared
to meet this little band of Greeks, and indeed it
is told that the Persian captains were obliged to
go behind their troops and with whips scourge
them to the fight. Many of the Persians were
forced into the sea and so died; some were trodden under foot, and thousands fell by the hands
of the Greeks. But it was not only the Persians
who fell in this fierce struggle; Leonidas was one

THE LAST ENCOUNTER

of the first who was slain, and many other Spartans fell with him.

But the death of their leader did not demoralize the Greeks—it only made them more reckless and more desperate. At length they saw that the end was close at hand; the "Immortals," who had come in the night over the mountain, had arrived, and were ready to fall upon their rear. Closely pressed by the Persians, they drew back to the narrowest part of the pass, where they had fought on the preceding days, and there made their last stand. Their spears were broken, their swords were dulled; but even had their weapons been still of the best, it would have availed them little, for the Persians, all too well acquainted now with the Greek daring, refused to close with their enemies. In their wellnigh useless armour, which had been hacked from their limbs during their earlier encounters, the Greeks stood on a little hillock and braved the shower of Persian arrows and javelins. By the time the sun went down there remained not one of all the Grecian band, but before their death they had succeeded in slaying twenty thousand of the enemy.

Xerxes inquired of Demaratus, in whose word he had come to have more confidence since witnessing the events of the last three days, whether there were many more men at Sparta like these; and when he was told that there were thousands, he realized that perhaps even his mighty army might not be a match for them. That all Greeks were not like the Spartans who had fallen at Thermopylae; that all Greek leaders were not as brave and as devoted as Leonidas—these facts Xerxes did not realize. The struggle which had proved fatal to so many of his men had shown him that he was not irresistible, and had thereby done much for the Greeks.

Where the Greeks fell they were buried, and in after years pillars were set up to commemorate their bravery. One, in honor of those who fell before the allies were sent away, bore the words,

"Four times a thousand men from Pelops' land
Three thousand times a thousand did withstand."

While over the Spartans by themselves there stood another column which bore the words,

"Go tell the Spartans, thou that passeth by,
That here, obedient to their laws, we lie."

MARCO BOZZARIS

FITZ-GREENE HALLECK

NOTE,—Marco Bozzaris, a Greek patriot of
Suli, threw himself heart and soul into the Greek
struggle for freedom. On August 20, 1823, he
led a night attack against the Turks, who were
encamped on the site of ancient Platæa. The
Greek army was but a handful in comparison
with that of the Turks, but the Turks were
thrown into utter confusion, and the attacking
party won a complete victory. Bozzaris, however, was killed in the final attack.

At midnight, in his guarded tent,
　The Turk was dreaming of the hour
When Greece, her knee in suppliance bent,
　Should tremble at his power.
In dreams, through camp and court, he bore
The trophies of a conqueror;
　In dreams his song of triumph heard;
Then wore his monarch's signet-ring,
Then pressed that monarch's throne—a king;
As wild his thoughts, and gay of wing,
　As Eden's garden bird.

At midnight, in the forest shades,
　Bozzaris ranged his Suliote band,—
True as the steel of their tried blades,
　Heroes in heart and hand.
There had the Persian's thousands stood,

THE TURK AWOKE

There had the glad earth drunk their blood,
   On old Platæa's day;
And now there breathed that haunted air
The sons of sires who conquered there,
With arms to strike, and soul to dare,
   As quick, as far, as they.

An hour passed on, the Turk awoke:
  That bright dream was his last;
He woke—to hear his sentries shriek,
"To arms! they come! the Greek! the Greek!"
He woke—to die midst flame, and smoke,
And shout and groan, and sabre-stroke,
  And death-shots falling thick and fast
As lightning from the mountain-cloud;
And heard, with voice as trumpet loud,
  Bozzaris cheer his band:
"Strike—till the last armed foe expires;
Strike—for your altars and your fires;
Strike—for the green graves of your sires,
  God, and your native land!"

They fought—like brave men, long and well;
  They piled that ground with Moslem slain:
They conquered—but Bozzaris fell,
  Bleeding at every vein.
His few surviving comrades saw
His smile when rang their proud hurrah,
  And the red field was won;
Then saw in death his eyelids close
Calmly, as to a night's repose,
  Like flowers at set of sun.

Come to the bridal chamber, death,
  Come to the mother's, when she feels,
For the first time, her first-born's breath;
  Come when the blessed seals
That close the pestilence are broke,
And crowded cities wail its stroke;
Come in consumption's ghastly form,

The earthquake shock, the ocean storm;
Come when the heart beats high and warm,
With banquet song and dance and wine,—
And thou art terrible; the tear,
The groan, the knell, the pall, the bier,
And all we know, or dream, or fear
 Of agony, are thine.

But to the hero, when his sword
 Has won the battle for the free,
Thy voice sounds like a prophet's word,
And in its hollow tones are heard
 The thanks of millions yet to be.
Come when his task of fame is wrought;
Come with her laurel-leaf, blood-bought;
 Come in her crowning hour,—and then
Thy sunken eye's unearthly light
To him is welcome as the sight
 Of sky and stars to prisoned men;
Thy grasp is welcome as the hand
Of brother in a foreign land;
Thy summons welcome as the cry
That told the Indian isles were nigh
 To the world-seeking Genoese,
When the land-wind, from woods of palm,
And orange-groves, and fields of balm,
 Blew o'er the Haytian seas.

Bozzaris! with the storied brave
 Greece nurtured in her glory's time,
Rest thee; there is no prouder grave,
 Even in her own proud clime.
She wore no funeral weeds for thee,

Nor bade the dark hearse wave its plume,
Like torn branch from death's leafless tree,
In sorrow's pomp and pageantry,
    The heartless luxury of the tomb.
But she remembers thee as one
Long loved, and for a season gone.
For thee her poet's lyre is wreathed,
Her marble wrought, her music breathed;
For thee she rings the birthday bells;
Of thee her babes' first lisping tells;
For thine her evening prayer is said
At palace couch and cottage bed.
Her soldier, closing with the foe,
Gives for thy sake a deadlier blow;
His plighted maiden, when she fears
For him, the joy of her young years,
Thinks of thy fate, and checks her tears.
    And she, the mother of thy boys,
Though in her eye and faded cheek
Is read the grief she will not speak,
    The memory of her buried joys,—
And even she who gave thee birth,—
Will, by her pilgrim-circled hearth,
    Talk of thy doom without a sigh;
For thou art freedom's now, and fame's,—
One of the few, the immortal names
    That were not born to die.

A DESCENT INTO THE MAELSTROM

EDGAR ALLAN POE

WE had now reached the summit of the loftiest crag. For some minutes the old man seemed too much exhausted to speak.

"Not long ago," said he at length, "and I could have guided you on this route as well as the youngest of my sons; but, about three years past, there happened to me an event such as never happened before to mortal man—or at least such as no man ever survived to tell of—and the six hours of deadly terror which I then endured have broken me up body and soul. You suppose me a *very* old man—but I am not. It took less than a single day to change these hairs from a jetty black to white, to weaken my limbs, and to unstring my nerves, so that I tremble at the least exertion, and am frightened at a shadow. Do you know I can scarcely look over this little cliff without getting giddy?"

The "little cliff," upon whose edge he had so carelessly thrown himself down to rest that the weightier portion of his body hung over it, while he was only kept from falling by the tenure of his elbow on its extreme and slippery edge—this "little cliff" arose, a sheer, unobstructed precipice of black shining rock, some fifteen or sixteen hundred feet from the world of crags beneath us.

Nothing would have tempted me to within half a dozen yards of its brink. In truth, so deeply was I excited by the perilous position of my companion, that I fell at full length upon the ground, clung to the shrubs around me, and dared not even glance upward at the sky—while I struggled in vain to divest myself of the idea that the very foundations of the mountain were in danger from the fury of the winds. It was long before I could reason myself into sufficient courage to sit up and look out into the distance.

"You must get over these fancies," said the guide, "for I have brought you here that you might have the best possible view of the scene of that event I mentioned—and to tell you the whole story with the spot just under your eye.

"We are now," he continued in that particularizing manner which distinguished him—"we are now close upon the Norwegian coast—in the sixty-eighth degree of latitude—in the great province of Nordland—and in the dreary district of Lofoden. The mountain upon whose top we sit is Helseggen, the Cloudy. Now raise yourself up a little higher—hold on to the grass if you feel giddy—so—and look out, beyond the belt of vapor beneath us, into the sea."

I looked dizzily, and beheld a wide expanse of ocean, whose waters wore so inky a hue as to bring at once to my mind the Nubian geographer's account of the *Mare Tenebrarum*. A panorama more deplorably desolate no human imagination can conceive. To the right and left, as far as the eye could reach, there lay outstretched, like ramparts of the world, lines of horridly black and beetling cliff, whose character of gloom was but the more forcibly illustrated by the surf which reared high up against it its white and ghastly crest, howling and shrieking forever. Just opposite the promontory upon whose apex we were placed, and at a distance of some five or six miles out at sea, there was visible a small, bleak-looking island; or, more properly, its position was discernible through the wilderness of surge in which it was enveloped. About two miles nearer the land arose another of smaller size, hideously craggy and barren and encompassed at various intervals by a cluster of dark rocks.

The appearance of the ocean, in the space between the more distant island and the shore, had something very unusual about it. Although at the time so strong a gale was blowing landward that a brig in the remote offing lay to under a double-reefed trysail, and constantly plunged her whole hull out of sight, still there was here nothing like a regular swell, but only a short, quick, angry cross dashing of water in every direction—as well in the teeth of the wind as otherwise. Of foam there was little except in the immediate vicinity of the rocks.

"The island in the distance," resumed the old man, "is called by the Norwegians Vurrgh. The one midway is Moskoe. That a mile to the northward is Ambaaren. Yonder are Islesen, Hotholm, Keildhelm, Suarven, and Buckholm. Farther off—between Moskoe and Vurrgh—are

Otterholm, Flimen, Sandflesen, and Stockholm.
These are the true names of the places—but
why it has been thought necessary to name
them at all, is more than either you or I can
understand. Do you hear anything? Do you
see any change in the water?"

We had now been about ten minutes upon
the top of Helseggen, to which we had ascended
from the interior of Lofoden, so that we had
caught no glimpse of the sea until it had burst
upon us from the summit. As the old man
spoke, I became aware of a loud and gradually
increasing sound, like the moaning of a vast
herd of buffaloes upon an American prairie; and
at the same moment I perceived that what seamen term the *chopping* character of the ocean
beneath us, was rapidly changing into a current
which set to the eastward. Even while I gazed
this current acquired a monstrous velocity. Each
moment added to its speed—to its headlong
impetuosity. In five minutes the whole sea as
far as Vurrgh was lashed into ungovernable
fury; but it was between Moskoe and the coast
that the main uproar held its sway. Here the
vast bed of the waters, seamed and scarred into a
thousand conflicting channels, burst suddenly
into frenzied convulsion—heaving, boiling, hiss-
ing—gyrating in gigantic and innumerable vortices, and all whirling and plunging on to the
eastward with a rapidity which water never
elsewhere assumes except in precipitous descents.

In a few minutes more, there came over the
scene another radical alteration. The general

surface grew somewhat more smooth, and the
whirlpools one by one disappeared, while prodigious streaks of foam became apparent where
none had been seen before. These streaks, at
length, spreading out to a great distance, and
entering into combination, took unto themselves
the gyratory motion of the subsided vortices, and
seemed to form the germ of another more vast.
Suddenly—very suddenly—this assumed a distinct and definite existence in a circle of more
than a mile in diameter. The edge of the
whirl was represented by a broad belt of gleaming
spray; but no particle of this slipped into the
mouth of the terrific funnel, whose interior, as
far as the eye could fathom it, was a smooth,
shining and jet-black wall of water, inclined to
the horizon at an angle of some forty-five degrees,
speeding dizzily round and round with a swaying
and sweltering motion, and sending forth to the
wind an appalling voice, half-shriek, half-roar,
such as not even the mighty cataract of Niagara
ever lifts up in its agony to Heaven.

The mountain trembled to its very base, and
the rock rocked. I threw myself upon my face,
and clung to the scant herbage in an excess of
nervous agitation.

"This," said I at length, to the old man—
"this *can* be nothing else than the great whirlpool
of the Maelstrom."

"So it is sometimes termed," said he. "We
Norwegians call it the Moskoe-strom, from the
island of Moskoe in the midway."

The ordinary accounts of this vortex had by

no means prepared me for what I saw. That of
Jonas Ramus, which is perhaps the most circumstantial of any, cannot impart the faintest
conception of either the magnificence, or of the
horror of the scene—or of the wild, bewildering
sense of *the novel* which confounds the beholder.
I am not sure from what point of view the writer in
question surveyed it, nor at what time; but it
could neither have been from the summit of
Helseggen, nor during a storm. There are
some passages of this description, nevertheless,
which may be quoted for their details, although
their effect is exceedingly feeble in conveying an
impression of the spectacle.

"Between Lofoden and Moskoe," he says,
"the depth of the water is between thirty-five
and forty fathoms; but on the other side, toward
Ver (Vurrgh) this depth decreases so as not to
afford a convenient passage for a vessel, without
the risk of splitting on the rocks, which happens
even in the calmest weather. When it is flood,
the stream runs up the country between Lofoden
and Moskoe with a boisterous rapidity, but the
roar of its impetuous ebb to the sea is scarce
equaled by the loudest and most dreadful
cataracts—the noise being heard several leagues
off, and the vortices or pits are of such an extent
and depth, that if a ship comes within its attraction it is inevitably absorbed and carried down
to the bottom and there beat to pieces against
the rocks, and when the water relaxes the fragments thereof are thrown up again. But these
intervals of tranquillity are only at the turn of

the ebb and flood, and in calm weather, and last but a quarter of an hour, its violence gradually returning. When the stream is most boisterous, and its fury heightened by a storm, it is dangerous to come within a Norway mile of it. Boats, yachts, and ships have been carried away by not guarding against it before they were within its reach. It likewise happens frequently that whales come too near the stream, and are overpowered by its violence, and then it is impossible to describe their howlings and bellowings in their fruitless struggles to disengage themselves. A bear once, attempting to swim from Lofoden to Moskoe, was caught by the stream and borne down, while he roared terribly, so as to be heard on shore. Large stocks of firs and pine trees, after being absorbed by the current, rise again broken and torn to such a degree as if bristles grew upon them. This plainly shows the bottom to consist of craggy rocks, among which they are whirled to and fro. This stream is regulated by the flux and reflux of the sea—it being constantly high and low water every six hours. In the year 1645, early in the morning of Sexagesima Sunday, it raged with such noise and impetuosity that the very stones of the houses on the coast fell to the ground."

In regard to the depth of the water, I could not see how this could have been ascertained at all in the immediate vicinity of the vortex. The "forty fathoms" must have reference only to portions of the channel close upon the shore either of Moskoe or Lofoden. The depth in

the center of the Moskoe-strom must be im-
measurably greater; and no better proof of
this fact is necessary than can be obtained from
even the sidelong glance into the abyss of the
whirl which may be had from the highest crag
of Helseggen.   Looking down from this pinnacle
upon the howling Phlegethon below, I could not
help smiling at the simplicity with which the
honest Jonas Ramus records, as a matter difficult
of belief, the anecdotes of the whales and the
bears; for it appeared to me, in fact, a self-evident
thing that the largest ship of the line in existence
coming within the influence of that deadly
attraction could resist it as little as a feather the
hurricane, and must disappear bodily and at
once.

The attempts to account for the phenomenon—
some of which I remember seemed to me sufficiently plausible in perusal—now wore a very
different and unsatisfactory aspect.   The idea
generally received is that this, as well as three
smaller vortices among the Ferroe Islands, "have
no other cause than the collision of waves rising
and falling at flux and reflux against a ridge
of rocks and shelves, which confines the water
so that it precipitates itself like a cataract; and
thus the higher the flood rises the deeper must
the fall be, and the natural result of all is a whirlpool or vortex, the prodigious suction of which
is sufficiently known by lesser experiments."
These are the words of the Encyclopædia
Britannica.   Kircher and others imagine that
in the center of the channel of the Maelstrom is

an abyss penetrating the globe, and issuing in some very remote part—the Gulf of Bothnia being somewhat decidedly named in one instance. This opinion, idle in itself, was the one to which, as I gazed, my imagination most readily assented; and, mentioning it to the guide, I was rather surprised to hear him say that, although it was the view almost universally entertained of the subject by the Norwegians, it nevertheless was not his own. As to the former notion, he confessed his inability to comprehend it; and here I agreed with him—for, however conclusive on paper, it becomes altogether unintelligible, and even absurd, amid the thunder of the abyss.

"You have had a good look at the whirl now," said the old man, "and if you will creep round this crag so as to get in its lee, and deaden the roar of the water, I will tell you a story that will convince you I ought to know something of the Moskoe-strom."

I placed myself as desired, and he proceeded.

"Myself and my two brothers once owned a schooner-rigged smack of about seventy tons burthen, with which we were in the habit of fishing among the islands beyond Moskoe, nearly to Vurrgh. In all violent eddies at sea there is good fishing at proper opportunities if one has only the courage to attempt it, but among the whole of the Lofoden coastmen, we three were the only ones who made a regular business of going out to the islands, as I tell you. The usual grounds are a great way lower down to the southward. There fish can be got at all hours, without much risk, and therefore these places are preferred. The choice spots over here among the rocks, however, not only yield the finest variety, but in far greater abundance, so that we often got in a single day what the more timid of the craft could not scrape together in a week. In fact, we made it a matter of desperate speculation—the risk of life standing instead of labor, and courage answering for capital.

"We kept the smack in a cove about five miles higher up the coast than this; and it was our practice, in fine weather, to take advantage of the fifteen minutes' slack to push across the main channel of the Moskoe-strom, far above the pool, and then drop down upon anchorage somewhere near Otterholm, or Sandflesen, where the eddies are not so violent as elsewhere. Here we used to remain until nearly time for slack water again, when we weighed and made for home. We never set out upon this expedition without a steady side wind for going and coming—one that we felt sure would not fail us before our return—and we seldom made a miscalculation upon this point. Twice during six years we were forced to stay all night at anchor on account of a dead calm, which is a rare thing indeed just about here; and once we had to remain on the grounds nearly a week, starving to death, owing to a gale which blew up shortly after our arrival, and made the channel too boisterous to be thought of. Upon this occasion we should have been driven out to sea in spite of everything (for the whirlpools threw us round and round so violently that at length we fouled our anchor and dragged it) if it had not been that we drifted into one of the innumerable cross currents—here to-day and gone to-morrow—which drove us under the lee of Flimen, where, by good luck, we brought up.

"I could not tell you the twentieth part of the difficulties we encountered 'on the grounds'—it is a bad spot to be in, even in good weather—but we made shift always to run the gauntlet of the Moskoe-strom itself without accident; although at times my heart has been in my mouth when we happened to be a minute or so behind or before the slack. The wind sometimes was not as strong as we thought it at starting, and then we made rather less way than we could wish, while the current rendered the smack unmanageable. My eldest brother had a son eighteen years old, and I had two stout boys of my own. These would have been of great assistance at such times in using the sweeps, as well as afterward in fishing, but somehow, although we ran the risk ourselves, we had not the heart to let the young ones get into the danger—for, after all is said and done, it *was* a horrible danger, and that is the truth.

"It is now within a few days of three years since what I am going to tell you occurred. It was on the tenth day of July, 18—, a day which the people of this part of the world will never forget—for it was one in which blew the most terrible hurricane that ever came out of the heavens;

and yet all the morning, and indeed until late in the afternoon, there was a gentle and steady breeze from the southwest, while the sun shone brightly, so that the oldest seaman among us could not have foreseen what was to follow.

"The three of us—my two brothers and myself—had crossed over to the islands about 2 o'clock p. m., and had soon nearly loaded the smack with fine fish, which, we all remarked, were more plentiful that day than we had ever known them. It was just seven *by my watch* when we weighed and started for home, so as to make the worst of the Strom at slack water, which we knew would be at eight.

"We set out with a fresh wind on our starboard quarter, and for some time spanked along at a great rate, never dreaming of danger, for indeed we saw not the slightest reason to apprehend it. All at once we were taken aback by a breeze from over Helseggen. This was most unusual—something that had never happened to us before—and I began to feel a little uneasy without exactly knowing why. We put the boat on the wind, but could make no headway at all for the eddies, and I was put upon the point of proposing to return to the anchorage, when, looking astern, we saw the whole horizon covered with a singular copper-colored cloud that rose with the most amazing velocity.

"In the meantime the breeze that had headed us off fell away, and we were dead becalmed, drifting about in every direction. This state of things, however, did not last long enough to give

us time to think about it.   In less than a minute
the storm was upon us—in less than two the sky
was entirely overcast—and what with this and
the driving spray it became suddenly so dark
that we could not see each other in the smack.

"Such a hurricane as then blew it is folly to
attempt describing.   The oldest seaman in Norway never experienced anything like it.   We had
let our sails go by the run before it cleverly took
us; but, at the first puff, both our masts went by
the board as if they had been sawed off—the
mainmast taking with it my youngest brother,
who had lashed himself to it for safety.

"Our boat was the lightest feather of a thing
that ever sat upon water.   It had a complete
flush deck, with only a small hatch near the bow,
and this hatch it had always been our custom to
batten down when about to cross the Strom, by
way of precaution against the chopping seas.
But for this circumstance we should have
foundered at once—for we lay entirely buried
for some moments. How my elder brother
escaped destruction I cannot say, for I never had
an opportunity of ascertaining.   For my part, as
soon as I had let the foresail run, I threw myself
flat on deck, with my feet against the narrow
gunwale of the bow, and with my hands grasping
a ring-bolt near the foot of the fore-mast.   It
was mere instinct that prompted me to do this—
which was undoubtedly the very best thing I
could have done—for I was too much flurried
to think.

"For some moments we were completely

deluged, as I say, and all this time I held my breath, and clung to the bolt. When I could stand it no longer I raised myself upon my knees, still keeping hold with my hands, and thus got my head clear. Presently our litttle boat gave herself a shake, just as a dog does in coming out of the water, and thus rid herself in some measure of the seas. I was now trying to get the better of the stupor that had come over me, and to collect my senses so as to see what was to be done, when I felt somebody grasp my arm. It was my elder brother, and my heart leaped for joy, for I had made sure that he was overboard—but the next moment all this joy was turned into horror—for he put his mouth close to my ear, and screamed out the word '*Moskoe-strom!*'

"No one will ever know what my feelings were at that moment. I shook from head to foot, as if I had had the most violent fit of the ague. I knew what he meant by that one word well enough—I knew what he wished to make me understand. With the wind that now drove us on we were bound for the whirl of the Strom, and nothing could save us!

"You perceive that in crossing the Strom *channel*, we always went a long way up above the whirl, even in the calmest weather, and then had to wait and watch carefully for the slack—but now we were driving right upon the pool itself, and in such a hurricane as this! 'To be sure,' I thought, 'we shall get there just about the slack—there is some little hope in that'—but in the next moment I cursed myself for being so great a fool as to dream of hope at all. I knew very well that we were doomed had we been ten times a ninety-gun ship.

"By this time the first fury of the tempest had spent itself, or perhaps we did not feel it so much as we scudded before it, but at all events the seas, which at first had been kept down by the wind and lay flat and frothing, now got up into absolute mountains. A singular change, too, had come over the heavens. Around in every direction it was still as black as pitch, but nearly overhead there burst out, all at once, a circular rift of clear sky—as clear as I ever saw, and of a deep bright blue—and through it there blazed forth the full moon with a luster that I never before knew her to wear. She lit up everything about us with the greatest distinctness—but, O God, what a scene it was to light up!

"I now made one or two attempts to speak to my brother—but, in some manner which I could not understand, the din had so increased that I could not make him hear a single word, although I screamed at the top of my voice in his ear. Presently he shook his head, looking as pale as death, and held up one of his fingers as if to say '*listen!*'

"At first I could not make out what he meant— but soon a hideous thought flashed upon me. I dragged my watch from its fob. It was not going. I glanced at its face by the moonlight, and then burst into tears as I flung it far away into the ocean. *It had run down at seven*

o'clock!　We were behind the time of the slack,
and the whirl of the Strom was in full fury!

"When a boat is well built, properly trimmed,
and not deep laden, the waves in a strong gale,
when she is going large, seem always to slip from
beneath her—which appears very strange to a
landsman—and this is what is called *riding*, in
sea-phrase. Well, so far we had ridden the
swells very cleverly, but presently a gigantic sea
happened to take us right under the counter,
and bore us with it as it rose—up—up—as if into
the sky. I would not have believed that any
wave could rise so high. And then down we
came with a sweep, a slide, and a plunge, that
made me feel sick and dizzy, as if I was falling
from some lofty mountain-top in a dream. But
while we were up I had thrown a quick glance
around—and that one glance was all sufficient.
I saw our exact position in an instant. The
Moskoe-strom whirlpool was about a quarter of
a mile dead ahead—but no more like the everyday Moskoe-strom, than the whirl as you now
see it is like a mill-race. If I had not known
where we were, and what we had to expect, I
should not have recognized the place at all. As
it was, I involuntarily closed my eyes in horror.
The lids clenched themselves together as if in a
spasm.

"It could not have been more than two
minutes afterward until we suddenly felt the
waves subside, and were enveloped in foam.
The boat made a sharp half turn to larboard,
and then shot off in its new direction like a

thunderbolt. At the same moment the roaring noise of the water was completely drowned in a kind of shrill shriek—such a sound as you might imagine given out by the waste-pipes of many thousand steam-vessels letting off their steam all together. We were now in the belt of surf that always surrounds the whirl; and I thought of course that another moment would plunge us into the abyss—down which we could only see indistinctly on account of the amazing velocity with which we were borne along. The boat did not seem to sink into the water at all, but to skim like an air-bubble upon the surface of the surge. Her starboard side was next the whirl, and on the larboard arose the world of ocean we had left. It stood like a huge writhing wall between us and the horizon.

"It may appear strange, but now, when we were in the very jaws of the gulf, I felt more composed than when we were only approaching it. Having made up my mind to hope no more, I got rid of a great deal of that terror which unmanned me at first. I suppose it was despair that strung my nerves.

"It may look like boasting—but what I tell you is truth—I began to reflect how magnificent a thing it was to die in such a manner, and how foolish it was in me to think of so paltry a consideration as my own individual life in view of so wonderful a manifestation of God's power. I do believe that I blushed with shame when this idea crossed my mind. After a little while I became possessed with the keenest curiosity

about the whirl itself. I positively felt a *wish*
to explore its depths, even at the sacrifice I was
going to make; and my principal grief was that I
should never be able to tell my old companions
on shore about the mysteries I should see.
These, no doubt, were singular fancies to occupy
a man's mind in such extremity, and I have
often thought since that the revolutions of the
boat around the pool might have rendered me a
little light-headed.

"There was another circumstance which
tended to restore my self-possession, and this
was the cessation of the wind, which could not
reach us in our present situation—for, as you
saw yourself, the belt of surf is considerably
lower than the general bed of the ocean, and
this latter now towered above us, a high, black,
mountainous ridge. If you have never been at
sea in a heavy gale you can form no idea of the
confusion of mind occasioned by the wind and
spray together. They blind, deafen, and strangle
you, and take away all power of action or
reflection. But we were now, in a great measure, rid of these annoyances—just as death-
condemned felons in prison are allowed petty
indulgences, forbidden them while their doom
is yet uncertain.

"How often we made the circuit of the belt
it is impossible to say. We careered round and
round for perhaps an hour, flying rather than
floating, getting gradually more and more into
the middle of the surge, and then nearer and
nearer to its horrible inner edge. All this time

I had never let go of the ring-bolt. My brother was at the stern, holding on to a small empty water-cask which had been securely lashed under the coop of the counter, and was the only thing on deck that had not been swept overboard when the gale first took us. As we approached the brink of the pit he let go his hold upon this, and made for the ring, from which, in the agony of his terror, he endeavored so force my hands, as it was not large enough to afford us both a secure grasp. I never felt deeper grief than when I saw him attempt this act—although I knew he was a madman when he did it—a raving maniac through sheer fright. I did not care, however, to contest the point with him. I knew it could make no difference whether either of us held on at all, so I let him have the bolt, and went astern to the cask. This there was no great difficulty in doing, for the smack flew round steadily enough, and upon an even keel, only swaying to and fro with the immense sweeps and swelters of the whirl. Scarcely had I secured myself in my new position when we gave a wild lurch to starboard, and rushed headlong into the abyss. I muttered a hurried prayer to God, and thought all was over.

"As I felt the sickening sweep of the descent I had instinctively tightened my hold upon the barrel, and closed my eyes. For some seconds I dared not open them, while I expected instant destruction, and wondered that I was not already in my death-struggles with the water. But moment after moment elapsed. I still lived.

The sense of falling had ceased; and the motion of the vessel seemed much as it had been before while in the belt of foam, with the exception that she now lay more along. I took courage, and looked once again upon the scene.

"Never shall I forget the sensations of awe, horror, and admiration with which I gazed about me. The boat appeared to be hanging, as if by magic, midway down, upon the interior surface of a funnel vast in circumference, prodigious in depth, and whose perfectly smooth sides might have been mistaken for ebony but for the bewildering rapidity with which they spun around, and for the gleaming and ghastly radiance they shot forth, as the rays of the full moon, from that circular rift amid the clouds which I have already described, streamed in a flood of golden glory along the black walls, and far away down into the inmost recesses of the abyss.

"At first I was too much confused to observe anything accurately. The general burst of terrific grandeur was all that I beheld. When I recovered myself a little, however, my gaze fell instinctively downward. In this direction I was able to obtain an unobstructed view from the manner in which the smack hung on the inclined surface of the pool. She was quite upon an even keel—that is to say, her deck lay in a plane parallel with that of the water—but this latter sloped at an angle of more than forty-five degrees, so that we seemed to be lying upon our beam-ends. I could not help observing, nevertheless, that I had scarcely more difficulty in maintaining my hold and footing in this situation than if we had been upon a dead level, and this, I suppose, was owing to the speed at which we revolved.

"The rays of the moon seemed to search the very bottom of the profound gulf; but still I could make out nothing distinctly, on account of a thick mist in which everything there was enveloped, and over which there hung a magnificent rainbow, like that narrow and tottering bridge which Musselmen say is the only pathway between Time and Eternity. This mist or spray was no doubt occasioned by the clashing of the great walls of the funnel as they all met together at the bottom, but the yell that went up to the heavens from out of that mist I dare not attempt to describe.

"Our first slide into the abyss itself, from the belt of foam above, had carried us a great distance down the slope, but our farther descent was by no means proportionate. Round and round we swept—not with any uniform movement—but in dizzying swings and jerks, that sent us sometimes only a few hundred yards— sometimes nearly the complete circuit of the whirl. Our progress downward at each revolution was slow but very perceptible.

"Looking about me upon the wide waste of liquid ebony on which we were thus borne, I perceived that our boat was not the only object in the embrace of the whirl. Both above and below us were visible fragments of vessels, large masses of building timber and trunks of trees, with many smaller articles, such as pieces of

house furniture, broken boxes, barrels, and
staves. I have already described the unnatural
curiosity which had taken the place of my
original terrors. It appeared to grow upon me
as I drew nearer and nearer to my dreadful
doom. I now began to watch, with a strange
interest, the numerous things that floated in our
company. I *must* have been delirious, for I even
sought *amusement* in speculating upon the
relative velocities of their several descents toward
the foam below. 'This fir tree,' I found myself
at one time saying, 'will certainly be the next
thing that takes the awful plunge and dis-
appears'—and then I was disappointed to find
that the wreck of a Dutch merchant ship overtook it and went down before. At length, after
making several guesses of this nature, and being
deceived in all, this fact—the fact of my in-
variable miscalculation—set me upon a train
of reflection that made my limbs again tremble,
and my heart beat heavily once more.

"It was not a new terror that thus affected
me, but the dawn of a more exciting *hope*. This
hope arose partly from memory, and partly from
present observation. I called to mind the great
variety of buoyant matter that strewed the coast
of Lofoden, having been absorbed and then
thrown forth by the Moskoe-strom. By far the
greater number of the articles were shattered in
the most extraordinary way—so chafed and
roughened as to have the appearance of being
stuck full of splinters—but then I distinctly
recollected that there were *some* of them which

were not disfigured at all. Now I could not
account for this difference except by supposing
that the roughened fragments were the only ones
which had been *completely absorbed*—that the
others had entered the whirl at so late a period
of the tide, or, for some reason, had descended
so slowly after entering, that they did not reach
the bottom before the turn of the flood came, or
of the ebb, as the case might be. I conceived it
possible, in either instance, that they might thus
be whirled up again to the level of the ocean,
without undergoing the fate of those which had
been drawn in more early, or absorbed more
rapidly. I made also three important observations. The first was that, as a general rule, the
larger the bodies were, the more rapid their
descent; the second, that, between two masses
of equal extent, the one spherical and the other
of any other shape, the superiority in speed of
descent was with the sphere; the third, that
between two masses of equal size, the one
cylindrical and the other of any other shape, the
cylinder was absorbed the more slowly. Since
my escape I have had several conversations on
this subject with an old schoolmaster of the
district, and it was from him that I learned the
use of the words 'cylinder' and 'sphere.' He
explained to me—although I have forgotten the
explanation—how what I observed was in fact
the natural consequence of the forms of the
floating fragments, and showed me how it
happened that a cylinder swimming in a vortex
offered more resistance to its suction, and was

drawn in with greater difficulty than an equally bulky body of any form whatever.

"There was one startling circumstance which went a great way in enforcing these observations and rendering me anxious to turn them to account, and this was that at every revolution we passed something like a barrel, or else the yard or the mast of a vessel, while many of these things which had been on our level when I first opened my eyes upon the wonders of the whirlpool were now high up above us, and seemed to have moved but little from their original station.

"I no longer hesitated what to do. I resolved to lash myself securely to the water-cask upon which I now held, to cut it loose from the counter, and to throw myself with it into the water. I attracted my brother's attention by signs, pointed to the floating barrels that came near us, and did everything in my power to make him understand what I was about to do. I thought at length that he comprehended my design, but, whether this was the case or not, he shook his head despairingly, and refused to move from his station by the ring-bolt. It was impossible to reach him, the emergency admitted of no delay, and so, with a bitter struggle, I resigned him to his fate, fastened myself to the cask by means of the lashings which secured it to the counter, and precipitated myself with it into the sea without another moment's hesitation.

"The result was precisely what I had hoped it might be. As it is myself who now tell you this tale—as you see that I *did* escape—and as

you are already in possession of the mode in
which this escape was effected, and must therefore anticipate all that I have further to say,
I will bring my story quickly to conclusion. It
might have been an hour or thereabout after my
quitting the smack, when, having descended to
a vast distance beneath me, it made three or four
wild gyrations in rapid succession, and, bearing
my loved brother with it, plunged headlong at
once and forever into the chaos of foam below.
The barrel to which I was attached sunk very
little farther than half the distance between the
bottom of the gulf and the spot at which I leaped
overboard, before a great change took place in
the character of the whirlpool. The slope of
the sides of the vast funnel became momently
less and less steep. The gyrations of the whirl
grew gradually less and less violent. By degrees
the froth and the rainbow disappeared, and the
bottom of the gulf seemed slowly to uprise. The
sky was clear, the winds had gone down, and
the full moon was setting radiantly in the west,
when I found myself on the surface of the ocean,
in full view of the shores of Lofoden, and above
the spot where the pool of the Moskoe-strom
had been. It was the hour of the slack—but the
sea still heaved in mountainous waves from the
effects of the hurricane. I was borne violently
into the channel of the Strom, and in a few
minutes was hurried down the coast into the
'grounds' of the fishermen. A boat picked me
up, exhausted from fatigue and (now that the
danger was removed) speechless from the mem-

ory of its horror. Those who drew me on board
were my old mates and daily companions, but
they knew me no more than they would have
known a traveler from the spirit-land. My
hair, which had been raven-black the day before,
was as white as you see it now. They say, too,
that the whole expression of my countenance
had changed. I told them my story—they did
not believe it. I now tell it to *you*, and I can
scarcely expect you to put more faith in it than
did the merry fishermen of Lofoden."

A Descent into the Maelstrom is a remarkable example of forcible description as well as of
artistic skill in the setting.

I. The first third of the story is an introduction
to the main tale. The story itself might seem to
be sufficiently exciting, but it would have much
less power if it began where the old man com-
mences to tell the tale. Notice what Poe throws
into his introduction:

1. He represents the tale as told to himself by
an old man with white hair, weakened limbs and
unstrung nerves that tremble at the least exertion. The old man claims to be frightened at a
shadow, yet he is able to throw himself down to
rest with the weightier portion of his body
hanging over a precipice and held back from
the slippery edge of the cliff of black shining
rock, some sixteen hundred feet high, merely by
the power of his elbows thrust into the earth.
The position is so perilous that the hearer throws
himself at full length upon the ground, clinging

to the shrubs around him and scarcely daring to glance upward at the sky. Besides the precarious position in which the men are placed, fierce winds that seem to shake the very foundations of the mountain cause thrills of terror to the onlooker.

2. The guide points out the scene of his terrible experience.

3. The author describes the sea, the islands and the location of the whirlpool.

4. Then follows a description of the water in the conflicting channels.

5. Suddenly the circular whirlpool appears, and from the awful height the observers are able to look down into the mouth of the terrific funnel.

6. More description follows, showing what happens to objects caught within the fierce grasp of the revolving waters.

7. Reference is made to ancient accounts of the whirlpool.

8. He makes some effort to explain the causes which would produce such fearful currents so furiously in action, but finds himself unable to arrive at a satisfactory explanation.

Such sights, such a discussion, such a perilous position in which to listen, make the hearer susceptible to the slightest impression.

II. The story proper is told in the most convincing, matter-of-fact way, yet we are conscious all the time that the language of the old man is rather that of a trained writer than of an ignorant fisherman, and here Poe sacrifices the personality of his hero to vividness of incident. What he wishes to accomplish is to impress us with a terrible experience. He does not care to make us see the narrator as a man, yet the story is not devoid of touches of strong human interest; if it were it would be less powerful. The fisherman and his brothers will not take with them their sons on their perilous fishing trip. The youngest brother is carried away in the first blast of the tempest with the mainmast to which he had bound himself. The oldest brother selfishly drives our hero from the ring in the deck.

There are remarkable touches of realism in the story. It was just seven by the old man's watch when they started for home; later, when the tempest is upon them, it is discovered that the watch had run down at seven o'clock, and they are behind the time of the slack water in the whirlpool.

III. Vividly descriptive phrases abound in the narration, and figures of speech give powerful interest to the imagination.

"We came with a sweep, a slide, and a plunge, that made me feel sick and dizzy, as if I was falling from some lofty mountain-top in a dream."

"The roaring noise of the water was completely drowned in a kind of shrill shriek—such a sound as you might imagine given out by the waste-pipes of many thousand steam-vessels letting off their steam all together."

"How foolish it was in me to think of so paltry a consideration as my own individual life in view of so wonderful a manifestation of God's power."

"We were now, in a great measure, rid of these annoyances—just as death-condemned felons in prison are allowed petty indulgences, forbidden them while their doom is yet uncertain."

IV. It is meant that our interest should center in the story itself. Accordingly, when the narrator has finished his tale the story is finished. We are not further interested in the listener, or in the old man.

V. It is almost unnecessary to say that the tale is pure fiction, and an example of brilliant exaggeration. As a matter of fact the maelstrom is a whirlpool lying where Poe places it, and it has been made noted by many other accounts than this of Poe, most of which are exaggerated, but none of them so brilliant in execution as Poe's. The difference between high tide and low tide in this vicinity is very great, and every twelve hours vast masses of water must be moved into the fiord and out again through narrow channels and rough rocks. The currents resulting are dangerous to navigation, and there are numerous whirlpools and eddies besides the great maelstrom itself. Ordinarily, however, ships traverse the passage without danger; but when in conjunction with high tide the winds blow fiercely, the sea for miles around becomes highly perilous to small vessels.

PRONUNCIATION OF PROPER NAMES

Note,—The pronunciation of difficult words
is indicated by respelling them phonetically.
N is used to indicate the French nasal sound;
K the sound of *ch* in German; *ü* the sound of the
German *ü* and French *u*; *ö* the sound of *ö* in
foreign languages.

Achilles, *a kil' leez*
Actæon, *ak tee' on*
Æneas Sylvius, *ee nee' as sil' vy us*
Æschylus, *es' ky lus*
Alvarado, *ahl vah rah' do*
Amadis, *am' a dis*
Antigua, *an tee' gwa*
Arica, *a ree' ka*
Babieca, *ba be ay' ka*
Benoit, *ben wah'*
Bose, *bo' zeh*
Briareus, *bri a' re us*
Bucephalus, *bu sef' a lus*
Casa Guidi, *kah' sa gwee' dee*
Cervantes Saavedra, Miguel de, *sur van'-*
    teez sah ved' ra, mee gayl' day
Christiern, *kris' tee urn*
Clavileño, *klah ve lay' nyo*
Coligni, *ko" leen" yee', or ko leen' yee*
D'Aumale, *do mahl'*
Demaratus, *de mar' a tus*
Diaz, *dee' ahs, or dee' ath*

DON QUIXOTE, *don kwiks' oat,* (Sp.) *don" kee-ho' tay*

DU CHAILLU, *dü shay" yü'*

EPHIALTES, *ef y al' teez*

HERNANDO CORTÉS, *her nahn' do kor tays'*

HOTEL DES INVALIDES, *o" tel' day zaN" va"-leed'*

IVRY, *eev ree'*

JAEL, *jay' el*

LEONIDAS, *lee on' y das*

MAELSTROM, *mayl' strum*

MAMBRINO, *mam bree' no*

MARCO BOZZARIS, *mahr' ko bo' tsa rees,* popularly *bo zar' is*

MARTINO, *mar tee' no*

MAYENNE, *mi en'*

MIGUEL, *mee gayl'*

MEGISTIAS, *me gis' ty as*

MICHAEL AROUT, *mee shel' ah roo'*

MYCENÆ, *mi see' nee*

NACOGDOCHES, *nak o do' chez*

NGOBI, *ngo' bi*

NAVARRE, *nah vahr'*

ŒTA, *ee' ta*

OLAUS MAGNUS, *o lay' us mag' nus*

OLMEDO, *ol may' do*

ORAN, *o rahn'*

ORCHOMENUS, *or kom' ee nus*

ORDAZ, *or dath'*

ORPHEON, *or fay oN'*

PARÁ, *pah rah'*

PARACELSUS, *par a sel' sus*

PATROCLUS, *pa tro' klus*

Peloponnesus, *pel″ o pon nee′ sus*

Phaethon, *fay′ eh thon*

Phlegethon, *fleg′ eh thon*

Pisa, *pee′ za*

Platæa, *pla tee′ a*

Pleiades, *plee′ ya deez*

Potamochœrus, *pot ah mo kee′ rus*

Potosi, *po to see′*

Ptolemy, *tol′ e my*

Puebla Nueva, *pweb′ lah nway′ va*

Quesada, *kee sah′ da*

Rocinante (Rosinante), *ro″ see nahn′ tay*

St. Généviève, *saN zhen″ vyayv′*

St. Germain, *saN zher″ maN′*

Salto de Alvarado, *sahl′ to day ahl vah-rah′ do*

Sancho Panza, *sang′ ko pan′ za,* (Sp.) *sahn′-cho pahn′ tha*

Sandoval, *sahn do vahl′*

Seine, *sayn*

Sexagesima, *seks″ a jes′ y ma*

Sisera, *sis′ ee ra*

Souvestre, Emile, *soo″ vestr′, ay″ meel′*

Taladega, *tah lah day′ ga*

Tegea, *tee′ jee a*

Thermopylæ, *thur mop′ y lee*

Thoreau, *tho′ ro,* or *tho ro′*

Tlascalans, *tlahs kah′ lahnz*

Versailles, *vur saylz′*

Willamette, *wil ah′ met*

Xerxes, *zurks′ eez*

Journeys
Through
Bookland